W9-CMD-770

Weapons Technology and Arms Control

W. F. Biddle

The Praeger Special Studies program—utilizing the most modern and efficient book production techniques and a selective worldwide distribution network—makes available to the academic, government, and business communities significant, timely research in U.S. and international economic, social, and political development.

Weapons Technology and Arms Control

PRAEGER SPECIAL STUDIES IN INTERNATIONAL POLITICS AND PUBLIC AFFAIRS

Praeger Publishers New York Washington London

PRAEGER PUBLISHERS
111 Fourth Avenue, New York, N.Y. 10003, U.S.A.
5, Cromwell Place, London S.W.7, England

Published in the United States of America in 1972
by Praeger Publishers, Inc.

Library of Congress Catalog Card Number: 74-189301

Printed in the United States of America

CONTENTS

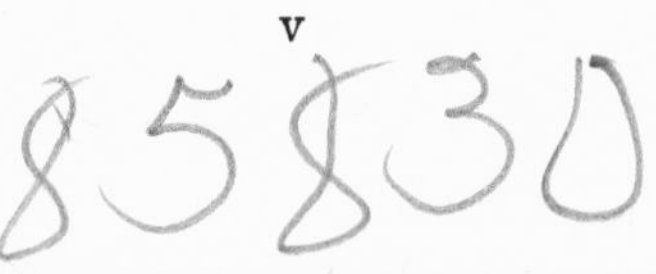

Chapter Page

Chapter Page

LIST OF TABLES

LIST OF FIGURES

Weapons Technology and Arms Control

CHAPTER 1
INTRODUCTION

The rapid advances in military technology during this century are now such that the existence of man as a species would be threatened if a large-scale war should break out. Avoiding the catastrophe of a general war between the superpowers and the prevention of escalation to the global scale of such conflicts as do occur are the most important immediate objectives. Until these tasks are fulfilled, longer-term and more insidious dangers are of lesser significance.

Disarmament is, of course, the panacea; but there are practical difficulties in achieving it in a world of nation-states with conflicting ideologies, vastly different levels of economic development and access to raw materials, and contrasting cultures and values. Thus disarmament, however desirable as a long-term achievement, seems to be beyond our present capabilities.

During the past few years arms control has come to be widely accepted as a way in which more certain, if more gradual, progress can be made. The interaction between military technology and arms control poses many problems and some opportunities for advancing toward a less dangerous world: the main object of this book is a discussion of this interaction.

This is not a technical study and does not deal in the kind of detail and at the level that would satisfy experts in the various related disciplines. Rather, it is an attempt to discuss the wide impact of science and technology on the problems of arms control. The intention is to try to bridge the gap that exists between the scientists and technologists who are involved in the design, procurement, and use of weapons, and the diplomats and other experts who are responsible for designing and negotiating agreements. There is a continuous interaction between advancing technology and the political, legal, diplomatic, and military facets of the relations between states. Development of a foreign and military policy—a national strategy—has as one component an attitude toward arms control; and this in turn is related to the existing military posture, including the current technical situation, and also to what is being planned for the future. This is not, of course, the first time that the effects of new weapons systems on international relations have been examined: there have been many such studies. But, as far as is known, this is the first time that a comprehensive study has been attempted. In doing so it has been inevitable that many important topics have been examined somewhat cursorily, but references are made in the notes to original sources that may be consulted. On the other hand, the knowledgeable reader may feel that he is already familiar with some weapons systems and that the discussion is unnecessarily detailed. It should be remembered, however, that the scope of this material is so wide that experts in one of the disciplines may not be conversant with other weapons systems. There is also, of course, the hidden trap that a long familiarity with a topic may conceal ignorance about some important feature.

A basic assumption, which it is beyond the scope of this book to explore in detail, is that a major preoccupation of the powers with substantial military resources is to avoid all-out nuclear war but, at the same time, to gain what advantages there may be from the possession and retention of military forces, including deterrence of attacks upon themselves. General and complete disarmament is therefore seen as unlikely in the present and any realistic foreseeable political contexts. What are of growing interest are the means for increasing stability and for decreasing the likelihood of large-scale war between the blocs around each of the superpowers. There are many processes that tend in the direction of increased stability—examples are interdependence in trade and the growth of international agencies—but without doubt the overwhelming factor is the fear of the effects of all-out war. Arms control is, however, quite directly and specifically aimed at increasing stability and decreasing the likelihood of war.

A few words of explanation are in order at this stage regarding the form of this study. It would have been possible to trace the changes in strategic postures of the major powers since the end of World War II and the arms control proposals and negotiations during this time. Such a course would have involved discussion of many factors other than the technical; this would have been the method of the historian. Instead, emphasis is on the technical aspects of weapons and arms control. One result of the decision to deal with the various topics in turn has been that there is a certain amount of repetition, since some of the data and arguments apply to more than one of the topics. Important cross-references are noted in the text.

Weapons may be divided roughly into strategic and tactical systems. Tactical weapons are those which are employed in the area of the battle joined between the military forces of the two sides; strategic weapons are those which could be used for a direct attack on the homeland of an opponent. This employment of the terms "strategic" and "tactical" is now common, but the older meanings "direction of the war" and "military operations when in contact with the enemy" are still used. It is difficult to draw firm lines between these different uses of the terms, or between operations that are strategic or tactical. Military operations that devastate large tracts of country, kill and wound large numbers of citizens, and disrupt the economy might be regarded as tactical operations by an invader or an ally but would certainly fall within the definition of strategic for the victims.

Nuclear weapons are the most important strategic weapons, and much of the text is concerned with them. The problems posed by arms control of nuclear weapons will be considered in two contexts: the control of the special materials of nuclear power, that is, generally fissile and some related materials, and, separately, the control of nuclear delivery vehicles. Control of materials will be examined in relation to the growing worldwide civilian nuclear power industry, and then in regard to the armories of the nuclear powers. Control of nuclear delivery vehicles can supplement control of fissile material.

In recent years defense against strategic nuclear weapons has become a possibility, and this technical innovation has been responsible for new problems in maintaining a convincing deterrent and in arms control. Methods for strategic surveillance have also improved within the last few years, particularly with the orbiting of satellites and the development of long-range radars; and these advances are intimately related to arms control of strategic nuclear delivery vehicles.

Chemical and biological weapons present particular problems from the point of view of classification, since they have a potential as strategic weapons and are generally discussed in these terms; but yet, insofar as the limited amount of information on present deployments goes, chemical weapons at least appear to be more suitable for a tactical role, while neither chemical nor biological weapons appear to compete seriously with nuclear weapons for strategic purposes. A special problem arises with chemical and biological warfare agents because there is widespread moral objection to their use. Particular attention is paid in this study to the possibility of special agreements relating to biological weapons alone.

Tactical weapons include nuclear weapons in the kiloton range of yields; these are deployed in large numbers and have important interactions with what are usually described as conventional weapons. The greatest concentration of tactical weapons is in Europe, which therefore merits special consideration.

The final chapter deals with the future problems of arms control and policies.

The arrangement outlined above was adopted for this study in order to attempt to present a coherent account of a complex and what at times may seem almost chaotic subject. However, as was indicated earlier, a quite false logic is imposed on the material that in practice constantly interacts. Scientific method, with its urge to classify and relate, has been notably less successful in the human sciences than in the physical sciences. In the case of the scientific aspects of arms control, the separation of certain main themes may help in the search for technical solutions to some of the problems.

One of the objectives in carrying out this study was to trace and accumulate as many of the relevant sources as possible and to correlate them to particular aspects of the subject as a basis for further, more detailed study. The appended bibliography is therefore rather more extensive than might otherwise be justified.

So far only one book has been published that is specifically devoted to the technical aspects of disarmament and arms control—and it appeared in 1931.* The book is valuable in that it attempts to draw out some general principles for disarmament. However, these do not now have the force they had forty years ago, and a rather different emphasis now applies to the problems of arms control between the superpowers.

The most detailed public records available on current negotiations are in the daily transcripts of the Eighteen Nations Disarmament

---

*Victor Lefebure, Scientific Disarmament (London: Mundanus, 1931).

Conference, reconstituted as the Conference of the Committee on Disarmament; the most comprehensive source of current information on arms control is the Yearbook of World Armaments and Disarmament, published annually by the International Peace Research Institute. This gives an account of current and recent negotiations and provides data on nuclear testing, arms sales, conflicts, etc.

Two indispensable sources of technical information are the journals Aviation Week and Space Technology and Space/Aeronautics. The latter often carries full and up-to-date surveys and reviews of the state of the art in particular areas; the former provides a guide to debate in the U.S. Congress and official circles and on the status of particular weapons systems. Journals specifically devoted to arms control and disarmament tend to have a limited life, but some with a rather wider coverage are Survival (of the International Institute for Strategic Studies), Bulletin of the Atomic Scientists, Journal of Conflict Resolution, and Arms Control and National Security.

The bulk of the sources available, and quoted in the text of this book, are American in origin or relate to U.S. deployments. This largely reflects the fact that a much greater volume of relevant study has been done in the United States than elsewhere. The amount of published work in the Soviet Union appears to be less and more often describes the state of the art in the West than Soviet developments.

CHAPTER

2

DESIGN OF ARMS CONTROL AGREEMENTS

Arms control has been defined by several writers on strategy. U. Schwarz and R. Hadrik describe arms control as "the restraint internationally exercised upon armament policy, whether in respect of level of armaments, their characteristics, deployment, or use."[1] Herman Kahn and Anthony Weiner give as the aims of arms control:

> . . . to improve the inherent stability of the situation, decrease the occasions or the approximate causes of war within the system, and decrease the destructiveness and other disutilities of any wars that actually occur. One may also add to this last, 'decrease the cost of defence preparation', but we would argue that this would take a rather low priority to the first three objectives.[2]

For the purposes of this study arms control is taken to mean any agreement among two or more powers to regulate some aspects of their military capabilities or potential, which may apply to the location, amount, readiness or types of forces, weapons, or facilities or similar unilateral actions made with the intention of reducing the likelihood of war or the damage that would occur should war break out.

Arms control in this sense includes both the formal agreement and what is virtually an invitation to cooperate. We may describe this latter form as unilateral arms control. It can be cited to justify procurement of arms that are intended to improve the balance of forces and thus improve deterrence. But it is not intended to include decisions not to proceed with the procurement of arms for purely budgetary reasons, that is, when the cost of further capabilities has become excessive.

The fundamental axiom of arms control is that a state can be trusted to carry out its side of an agreement only if it is in its own interest to do so. Self-interest must be the dominant feature of arms control: how else, apart from coercion, can a state be drawn into an agreement except by reward? Arms control must satisfy the same need of self-interest as does the present system based on deterrence. To be acceptable, arms control must be seen not to weaken present inhibitions until assuredly more enduring ones can be substituted. Nevertheless, arms control does introduce new methods and techniques for dealing with problems and for supporting the stable deterrent system.

The intention of this book is to examine in some detail the technical problems of arms control. There exists an extensive literature on the political and diplomatic facets of arms control, and on the relation of arms control to disarmament, deterrence, and other aspects of international relations. Nevertheless, it is necessary to relate some of these problems to the theme of the study and to provide a setting in which the technical requirements of arms control may be evaluated. It is not the intention, however, to correlate each technical problem with the more general aspects of arms control: to do so would considerably extend the text at the risk of diluting the interest in the technical aspects.

Peace and stability between nations depends upon fear of the consequences of hostile action. The aim of deterrence is to persuade another state not to do something by threat of sanctions or the promise of reward. Because the relationship between the superpowers has tended to dominate international relations, deterrence is often regarded only in terms of nuclear deterrence: however, deterrence can operate at many levels—for example, by threat of a trade boycott or the withholding of economic aid. Hence deterrence, in its wider aspect, does not always depend upon military force, since allies, as well as enemies, may be deterred. It is important that arms control measures not impair the balance of deterrence between powers. It is because of such doubts that arms control agreements are so cautiously approached and why negotiation is often so prolonged.

For deterrence to be effective, the estimated balance of losses and gains for the alternative courses of action must be such that the most desirable outcome results from compliance with the wishes of the other party. Deterrence depends upon such psychological factors as perception of capabilities, understanding of messages, and appreciation of risks. Indeed, the deep psychological nature of deterrence can be seen when it is realized that a government can be deterred by its own ethical standards. The sheer unpredictability of war is, of course, itself a deterrent against becoming involved. Deterrence may even operate in war to prevent further escalation or to induce surrender. Nevertheless, overemphasis on deterrence may produce a reaction. Bernard Brodie has put it thus:

> Deterrence after all depends upon a subjective feeling which we are trying to create in the opponent's mind, a feeling compounded of respect and fear and we have to ask ourselves whether it is not possible to overshoot the mark. It is possible to make him fear us too much, especially if what we make him fear is our over-readiness to react, whether or not he translates it into clear evidence of our aggressive intent.[3]

Stability in the international system has come to depend increasingly on the maintenance of "surprise-free" deterrence—that is, on the limited rate at which technological advances can be incorporated into the armed forces in sufficient quantity to jeopardize the balance of deterrence as each nation strives to enhance its own security by building up its deterrent forces and, by doing so, increases the threat against which other nations must guard.

A cliché of our time is the rapid rate of technological advance; and undoubtedly, over the broad front, innovations are frequently introduced. This gives an appearance of instability to the military situation between the great powers that is not always justified by the facts. The rate of change in weapon systems is considerably less than it appears. Many systems that are invented and developed may not go into production when they are found to be too costly, too complex, or inadequate in some way. Hence those systems which reach the stage of full-scale deployment are a fraction of those considered. Another factor is the time scale from the initial scientific discovery to deployment and to eventual obsolescence. A period of around 15 years may be required before a new type of weapon reaches service: the same type of weapon, with periodic refits, may be in service for many years—as much as 40 years for an aircraft carrier and more than 20 years for some aircraft.

A third fact that enhances stability is the quantity and complexity of weapons required to upset the balance between the great powers, involving long production runs and the use of considerable national resources. The nonexpert may not make such an allowance for these factors and may be unduly impressed by claims for a breakthrough. Besides the initial discovery, many other positive factors are necessary before a weapon system or individual process can come to maturity. One of these factors is, of course, any perceived interaction with procurement policies of possible opponents, leading in some cases to an arms race. As an illustration, the effects of advances in nuclear weapons technology on strategy are shown in Tables 1 and 2.

Nevertheless, to guard against an opponent's securing the military advantage, a state will wish to know what options are available and which of these other nations are pursuing. The first need can be satisfied to some extent by a broadly based research and development (R&D) program. Hence the great powers consider it essential to maintain a military R&D capability not only in order to modernize their own forces but also to estimate possible improvements in those of the opponent. For this reason arms control agreements are unlikely to be reached that attempt to restrict R&D. Furthermore, it is difficult to differentiate between R&D carried out for military purposes and that carried out in support of the civil economy. Attempts to restrict the former are likely to lead to the same work's being carried out under the guise of the latter. There may be some instances where, because of special circumstances, the general rule that arms control should not attempt to constrain R&D does not apply. One of these is in the flight testing of intercontinental ballistic missiles, when it is

TABLE 1

General Effects of Nuclear Weapons Technology on Military Strategy

State of Technology	Opposing Strategy	Relationship
One-sided first strike	Massive reprisal/arms race	Unstable
Two-sided first strike	First strike/first strike	Very unstable
One-sided second strike	Deterrence/arms race	Unstable
Two-sided second strike	Mutual deterrence	Metastable[a]
One-sided effective BMD[b]	Deterrence/arms race	Unstable
Two-sided effective BMD	Limited war	Semistable

[a]This is intended to imply that the relationship is stable except to a fairly substantial change, such as the large-scale introduction of new weapons.

[b]BMD= Ballistic missile defense.

TABLE 2

Principal Developments in Superpowers' Strategies

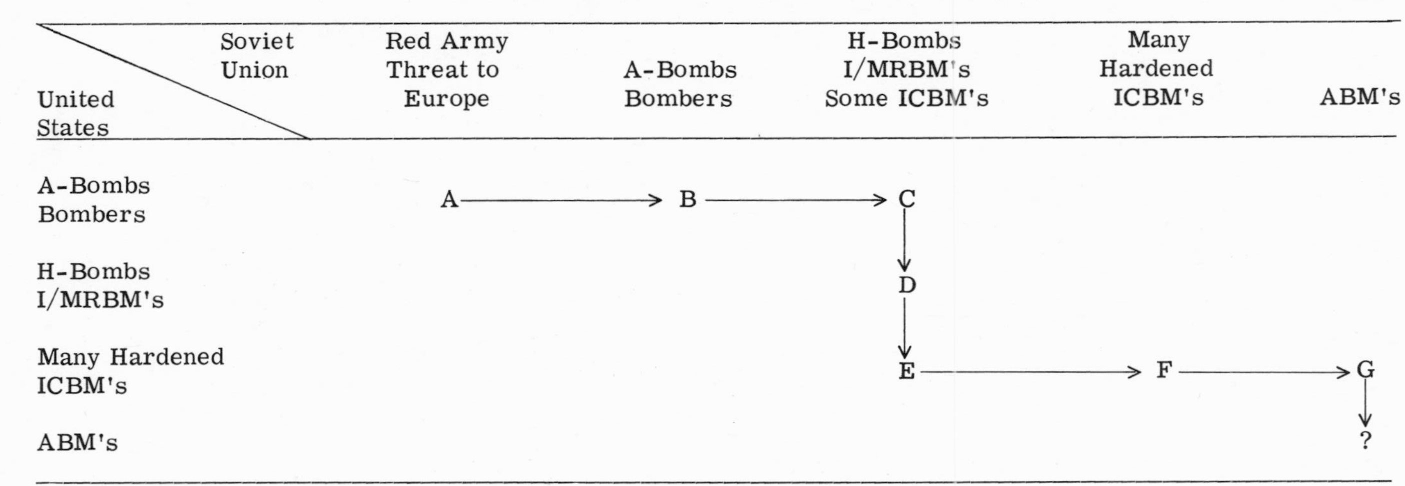

Soviet Union / United States	Red Army Threat to Europe	A-Bombs Bombers	H-Bombs I/MRBM's Some ICBM's	Many Hardened ICBM's	ABM's
A-Bombs Bombers	A	B	C		
H-Bombs I/MRBM's			D		
Many Hardened ICBM's			E	F	G
ABM's					?

impossible to disguise that a test has been carried out (although it could be claimed to be a space exploration mission). Another case is that of bacteriological weapons, where special ethical conditions apply. Both cases are considered later.

The second requirement to guard against technological surprise is some means of verification. Some arms control treaties have opportunities for inspection built into the agreement, while in others provision of facilities for inspection is the sole purpose of the treaty. However, it is unlikely that nations can be expected to depend for their security upon an inspection system, with its inevitable limitations. Intelligence has a wider function than inspection, in that the latter measures capabilities while intelligence also gauges intentions. It is to be expected that means will be found for a national intelligence organization to inform an inspectorate of suspected violations, although this might have to be done with care to avoid disclosure of sources and to avoid conveying the impression that the inspectorate had been infiltrated by intelligence agents.

The third requirement is an escape clause. In order that parties to a treaty shall not find themselves disadvantaged and their security threatened, a treaty will almost certainly have a withdrawal clause that requires giving notice of, and perhaps the reasons for, the intention. Threat of withdrawal would itself act as a sanction to ensure compliance with the terms of a treaty by another party and would also provide pressure for keeping the treaty up to date. The reason for withdrawal may not lie in the relationships of the signatories but in changes in power structures involving parties not bound by treaty.

Technological change may be an incentive for revision of treaties, since a fear of its destabilizing effects may be an inducement to obtain an agreement before matters get out of hand. However, since each nation depends upon its own particular mix of weapons, each will see introduction of new weapons in a different light and as causing new and different kinds of difficulties in control.

In seeking an agreement that has as its major aim the prevention of loss of security through technical advances, several questions are pertinent:

What effects will the agreement have on nonsignatories?

Is the review date commensurate with advance of technology?

Will the agreement accommodate advances in technology?

Will the technical means for verification be adequate?

Are improvements in verification techniques imminent?

An arms control agreement or some technical advance that reduces the threat from nuclear weapons could enhance the importance of less powerful weapons in deterring war. While some technical advances may jeopardize stability between powers, others may increase stability. Development of submarine-launched nuclear-armed missiles that are highly immune to attack has provided second-strike retaliatory forces that can reduce the fear of surprise attack. Development of long-range surveillance systems will also increase stability by reducing the chance for an effective first strike. Other changes in technology that will aid arms control come from the recent advances made in sensors, a variety of which have been developed for the detection of intruders, the detection of underground nuclear tests, the sampling of radioactive gases escaping from such tests, and the use of unmanned sensors to monitor the use of airfields, bridges, and so on.

In part because of past experience of the difficulties in imposing sanctions against a sovereign state violating an agreement, and in part because of the difficulty in distinguishing between and separating inspection and intelligence-gathering, the emphasis in recent years has tended to be on "self-policing" agreements—that is, agreements with which it is so obviously in a nation's interest to comply that it can be relied upon to ensure that its nationals do not attempt, through misguided loyalty or ignorance, to circumvent them.

Inspection agencies can be international, neutral, parties to the treaty, or adversaries. Each of these has advantages and disadvantages. For example, international inspection might be thought to have special authority in that its findings would be available to many nations and could affect the international standing of the country reported upon. Neutral inspection might also be considered to have the same advantages plus a certain element of detachment. Inspection by the signatories might have the advantage that disputes could be settled without publicity, while adversary inspection would appear to be the most stringent and would avoid disclosures of military information to third parties.

While the extent of formal inspection would be specified in an agreement, methods of unilateral verification would depend on evaluation of the nature and level of the threat. Intelligence can augment formal inspection and is likely to do so most effectively in the case of adversary inspection, when the sources of this additional information could best be safeguarded.

Attitudes toward inspection will vary. In an open society so much is published about military affairs that little will be gained by inspection: in a closed society secrecy itself may be considered a military asset. Evasions would be much easier to arrange in a closed society and more difficult in an open society. Thus an agreement that included close inspection would generally be favored by an open society and disfavored by a closed society.

It is often thought that inspection for arms control must be perfect. This is not so. In fact it would be impossible, and some lower but adequate level of effectiveness in inspection must be assured. Even quite a low probability of a detection could be enough to deter violations if the benefits of the agreement were valued. A low probability for observing a single event rapidly becomes a much higher probability for observing at least one in a number of such events; and for a serious violation it would be necessary in most cases to introduce many weapons to upset the military balance. Of importance is the estimate of the number of individual violations to secure military advantage, the difficulties of detection, and the time required for the advantage to build up. The probability for detection increases with the number of violations and the time over which the events take place. Violations are much more likely to be detected if they need much effort in preparation and execution. It is only when armaments are reduced to very low levels that introduction of a small number of powerful weapons could completely upset the military balance. At present this is a hypothetical problem in relation to the great powers (although it did produce a lot of interest at one time) but could be of importance in regard to the less heavily armed states—particularly the first deployment of a nuclear weapon that could immediately change a local balance.

A complete ban on a particular weapon is much more easily verified than a numerical ceiling, since in the former case a single sighting will betray a violation, while in the latter case a complete stocktaking may be necessary. When numbers are restricted, the work of an inspectorate can be much reduced if it is supplied with a formal specification of the inventory, so that inspection is reduced to checking stated facts and figures.

There has always been an enormous military advantage in mounting a surprise attack. Not only does the attacker have the psychological initiative in directing his attack where his opponent is weak or from an unexpected direction, but the victim may suffer from several practical disadvantages: his troops may not be mobilized and deployed to battle stations, stores and equipment may not be available, his defenses may be overwhelmed before they can be alerted, and the government and civil population may be unnerved by the speed and course of events. A first-strike surprise attack with nuclear weapons by one superpower against the other might completely or partly destroy the ability to retaliate and leave the populated cities of the victim as hostages for continued compliance with demands. Arms control should be designed at least to ensure that the possibility of a first strike is not increased and, if possible, that it is decreased.

A first strike could be made in order to prevent surprise attack by the other side. The incentive would be a reduction in casualties and damage that would be suffered in the anticipated attack. If there is no possibility of reducing these losses, the incentive for a preemptive attack is reduced. In defending against surprise attack a disarming first strike may be disallowed, either because it is considered unethical, or because it cannot be sufficiently effective, or because it might itself provoke an anticipatory counterblow. However, other means that in general do not pose such a threat to the opponent are available through early-warning systems, inspection, and surveillance. In this present context inspection may be considered as permitted ground patrols and observation posts, surveillance as observation by such long-range systems as satellites, radars, long-range aircraft, and electronic intelligence-gathering ships. Arms control agreements should be designed, as a minimum, not to interfere with early-warning verification and, if possible, to enhance its scope and performance—for example, by providing warning of troop movements, allowing inspection of maneuvers and garrisons, and permitting installation of unattended sensors.

The basic policy of each of the superpowers appears to be compounded of the following aims:

to deter the other from making an all-out nuclear attack

to deter lesser conflicts that could escalate into an all-out nuclear exchange

to employ military force in support of foreign policy objectives, in the event of an all-out nuclear war, in order to reduce damage and loss of life to themselves and to ensure that it is devastating to the opponent.

Arms control plainly can serve some of these aims, but the third item, if it continues to be pursued, will set limits on the extent of the application of arms control.

The parties to an agreement must concur in the following:

the scope and limitations of the agreement

verification procedures

sanctions against noncompliance.

These conditions may—indeed, will—affect the parties quite differently. Each of the parties must decide that, on balance, the conditions are such as to make it favor agreement. Each party will also have to take into account the present situation and compare it with the possible outcomes from the agreement, in the ways already discussed. Will it reduce the chance of war, the number of casualties, the cost of defense?

What has been called the "triptych" of disarmament and control involves definitions of three items:

The zone subject to agreement

The types of arms, equipment, and installations

The system of verification, inspection, and control.[4]

In many areas of potential conflict the overriding factor is the political tensions that encourage the local governments to purchase arms and other powers to supply them. The arms trade is obviously within the purview of the arms controller, as is prevention of local conflicts; and there are technical means available to help in controlling these problems. The main requirements, however, are restraint by the purchaser and supplier of arms, and the provision of troops from outside the area to observe for infringements or even to intervene. (The arms trade is not further discussed in this text.)

Arms control is not limited to the eventual attainment of an international agreement; it also embraces actions and restraints unilaterally undertaken for the purpose of reducing the risks of war. The state that aims to enhance its security by reassuring possible enemies of its peaceful intent may do so by public and private statements. Likewise, it may issue warnings intended to deter further action by another state. An important way in which such communications can be made is directly, between heads of government: other ways include the passing of messages through normal diplomatic channels and the attachment of liaison officers to military headquarters.

The state may also wish to demonstrate its intentions, for example, that a surprise attack is not being prepared. This can be done in several ways, according to the situation: by choice of weapon systems, providing opportunities of observation, avoiding provocative actions and statements, giving warning of troop movements, and supplying information on the rules that govern peacetime operations of forces.

Arms control thus embraces a wide range of complex problems. Traditionally these have been shared between different departments of state. For example, in Great Britain the Foreign Office would generally be responsible for the drafting of treaties and negotiations, the Ministry of Defense for advice on the technology and use of weapons. Other departments may become involved as some arms control agreements impinge on the civil industry.

These established methods of procedure are not always satisfactory. The gulf between the diplomat and the technical adviser tends to be rather wide, and in any case arms control is in neither case their main activity. Very prolonged technical negotiations in a narrow area are hardly the diplomat's ideal appointment; defense technologists have as their main concern and skill the development of new weapons; military officers may be concerned lest agreements impair the defense capabilities for which they are responsible. There appears to be a requirement for experts of various kinds, deeply skilled in their own disciplines but also aware of the wider implications and capable of working with others of quite different backgrounds.

But expert advisers alone will not be sufficient. What is also required is systematic studies not only on the technical problems of arms control but also on their political, diplomatic, historical, military, economic, social, and international relations aspects. What may be needed is a new interdisciplinary area in which systematic studies can be made to provide a basis for a scientific approach to arms control in all its aspects. There already exist organizations that could contribute to such studies—for example, government agencies specially charged with research into arms control, national and international academies, departments of universities, and some journals. However, compared with the vast efforts that continue to be expended on the design, procurement, and deployment of weapons, the number of efforts on arms control appears insufficient. In particular, technical problems are relatively inadequately investigated. This may be in part due to the fact that scientists and technologists engaged in the military area are involved with the procurement of weapons, but another factor is that those who have been responsible for arms control do not of necessity have a deep understanding of the contribution that science could make.

In the design of an agreement there are three significant parameters: concept, content, and timing. These interrelate to some degree, but it is valuable to attempt to separate them. The concept of what an agreement is expected to do is largely, but not solely, a political matter and, as such, not of direct concern in this study. The content—that is, the way the content is to be achieved—is largely technical and, as such, is the proper subject of study in this book. Timing of arms control agreements has been little studied: it involves both technical and political aspects. An attempt at agreement made too early may make matters seem not particularly urgent, will be doomed to failure, and may even prejudice later attempts; and attempt may be made too late to contain technological advances that bypass the agreement. Occasionally timely agreements are reached in which the political pressures coincide with the technical opportunities. No attempt has been made in this book to explore this interesting facet of arms control.

While, in theory, a fairly clear distinction can be made between political and technical aspects, in practice this is much more difficult. In general two kinds of difficulties may arise. The first is from an imprecise knowledge of the limits of participants' expertise: from familiarity nontechnical personnel may believe that they have a good understanding of technical matters, when in fact all that they know is some of the jargon. But the mistake of a technologist may be worse: he may assume that what has to be solved is a technical problem in the solution of which he is being thwarted by diplomats, administrators, and politicians. The truth, as has been indicated, is that arms control agreements are political, even if clothed in the language of technology. An illustration of this point lies in the treaties that have been negotiated to prevent deployment of nuclear weapons in different environments. Instead of spelling out specifications for nuclear weapons, the treaties refer to "weapons of mass destruction." Thus an incentive to circumvent the treaty by deploying weapons other than nuclear weapons is countered. Also there is a restraint on the development of weapons that might be construed as breaking the treaty, since to do so might drive the other countries to denounce the treaty.

An arms control agreement is thus a political event in which the means by which it is to be achieved and the scope are spelled out as technical definitions.

This study is intended to deal in a comprehensive manner with the technical problems that arise with arms control. This it does by concentrating in turn on specific areas of threat and examining the technology involved and the ways in which it can make difficult or can facilitate the intentions of an agreement. While any proposed agreement must be weighed by the standards discussed in this chapter—and this should be borne in mind in the following pages—little attempt has been made to analyze each of the technical proposals against the contents of this chapter. To do so would not only have meant an even lengthier discussion of the text but also would have impaired the emphasis on the often neglected technology of arms control.

NOTES

1. U. Schwarz and R. Hadrik, Strategic Terminology (London: Pall Mall Press, 1966), p. 33.

2. Herman Kahn and Anthony Weiner, "Technological Innovation and the Future of Strategic Warfare," Astronautics and Aeronautics (December 1967), p. 28.

3. Bernard Brodie, Strategy in the Missile Age (London: Oxford University Press, 1959), p. 397.

4. Conference of the Eighteen Nations Disarmament Committee, Verbatim Record PV 428 (August 14, 1969).

CHAPTER

3

CATEGORIES AND TYPES OF WEAPONS

For the purposes of arms control some scheme of classification of weapons systems will be required. In some circumstances the classification may have to be quite detailed, since a loosely worded agreement could well lead to considerable misunderstanding and disagreement afterward. Furthermore, with an imprecise schedule it might be possible deliberately to falsify records—for example, by counting into the original inventory large numbers of redundant and even unserviceable items and offering them for destruction instead of more modern weapons, and by using the boosted inventory for replacing these useless pieces with new and even more powerful items under a clause in the agreement that permits one-to-one modernizations.

A primary classification can be made on the lines of that proposed by Kenneth Hunt to divide arms into broad classes.* It will be appreciated that at some stage more detailed categories and specification will be necessary, and a broad categorization will merely indicate the problems to be met when arms control leaves generalities and becomes specific. Table 3 is expanded from that provided by Hunt.

For the purposes of this study even the relatively broad divisions indicated above are premature. The technical aspects of arms control have been examined more or less in relation to the following format:

---

*Kenneth Hunt, The Requirements of Military Technology in the 1970's (London: Pergamon Press, 1967).

TABLE 3

Categories of Weapons

Ground Forces
- Armored vehicles: tanks, personnel carriers, self-propelled guns
- Missiles: antitank, surface-to-air, surface-to-surface
- Artillery: field guns, mortars
- Target acquisition devices: radars
- Logistic backing: stores, dumps, transport, training establishments

Naval Forces
- Surface warships: aircraft carriers, cruisers, destroyers
- Submarines: nuclear-powered and other long range, coastal defense
- Missiles: ship-to-air, ship-to-surface, antisubmarine
- Light forces: hovercraft, patrol boats, hydrofoils, landing ships, transports
- Submarine detection equipment
- Logistic backing: ports, fleet tenders, onshore facilities and establishments

Tactical Air Forces
- Combat aircraft: light bombers, ground-attack, interceptors, V/STOL
- Helicopters
- Transport aircraft: long-range, medium-range, short-range,
- Missiles: air-to-surface, air-to-air
- Logistics and backing: airfields, spares, reserves, training echelons, warning systems

Strategic Weapons Systems
- Intercontinental ballistic missiles
- Intermediate-range and short-range ballistic missiles
- Submarine-launched ballistic missiles
- Submarine-launched cruise missiles
- Antiballistic missiles
- Atomic demolition munitions, atomic sea mines
- Chemical and biological warfare agents
- Manned bombers
- Strategic air-to-surface missiles
- Orbital satellite surveillance systems
- Long range radars and other early-warning devices

Source: Expanded version of Kenneth Hunt, The Requirements of Military Technology in the 1970's (London: The Institute for Strategic Studies, 1967), p. 4.

1. Strategic weapons, weapons of mass destruction
   Nuclear weapons
   Materials: uranium and plutonium
   Delivery Systems: long range missiles, strike fleets, ballistic missile submarines, space weapons
   Chemical and biological weapons
2. Tactical Weapons
   Tactical nuclear delivery systems
   Conventional weapons
3. Surveillance: long range radars, orbital satellites, offshore monitoring by aircraft and patrol ships

Another division, which tends to cut across the above, is in terms of environment:

1. Space
2. Air
3. Land
4. Sea: surface
   undersea
   seabed

Military forces are designed to be balanced, that is, to be self-supporting. This is so at the three levels: national forces, task forces, and even, to some extent, units. Reliance upon long range strategic nuclear weapons alone leads to a policy of "massive retaliation," that is, an all-or-nothing response that is plainly inappropriate to all but a threat to the existence of the nation. For lower levels of threat (which, in the case of the superpowers, would not necessarily be from the other superpower) other forces capable of violence at the same level are required. Depending upon the geopolitical situation, these lower-level forces, armed mainly with conventional weapons but perhaps with tactical nuclear weapons in reserve, may be projected forward, to engage the enemy as far from the homeland as possible, to defend allies, to engage in limited war, or to establish centers of power from which it would be difficult to dislodge these forces—and thus to influence other governments.

Balanced forces are also required in task forces or expeditionary forces. Naval task forces may consist of capital ships, such as battleships or aircraft carriers, supported by cruisers, destroyers, logistic ships, and other vessels. While the force as a whole would have both offensive and self-defensive capabilities, many naval vessels have both capabilities and can act independently.

Ground military forces are designed to be balanced in that they comprise weapons systems and manpower categories organized into units of different types that offer mutual support. Balanced ground forces would include units for reconnaissance, both on the ground and in the air, units for warning against air attack or the approach of surface forces, tanks, antiaircraft weapons, artillery, signals, infantry, transport for mobility, supply organizations, stores, and dumps. The smallest self-sufficient force having all or most of these arms is generally described as an army—in the British forces an army corps. Some of the units mentioned above can be capable of a degree of independent action—for example, long range penetration by tanks or small-unit operations by commandos—and have their own self-defense weapons.

Air forces have somewhat different functions. Their primary role in the superpowers is to provide part of the long range deterrent launcher vehicles. Another role is for deep penetration to attack the supply organization of the enemy with conventional ("iron") bombs and rockets. Air forces must attempt to secure combat superiority over the battle area so as to protect their own ground forces and airfields, to ensure freedom of action to attack enemy forces, and to carry out reconnaissance. Interceptor aircraft may be integrated with missiles and guns in air defense of the homeland, field forces, and naval forces. A function of increasing importance is to provide mobility for ground forces and subsequent replenishment and reinforcement, either in long range strategic operations or in tactical operations. Similar operations may be carried out in support of naval forces. Apart from strategic bombing and interception, air forces tend to cooperate and act in conjunction with one of the other services.

From this survey of the role of military units it is apparent that to retain balanced forces—that is, forces with the capability for acting in an integrated manner both offensively and defensively—would be difficult if particular arms were banned. To add to this difficulty, nations have adopted different mixes of arms in their balanced forces, according to the tasks that are anticipated. To ban a particular kind of weapon would only lead to some other attempt to solve the problem.

It might be argued that a ban specifically applied to offensive weapons would be advantageous. At the highest level—that is, of nuclear strategic weapons—it could be that a very much reduced threat would mean less restraint on war. At a lower level it could be considered that elimination of such weapons as tanks and bombers would do much to reduce the threat. Many military experts find it difficult to distinguish between offensive and defensive weapons, saying that it is the intention that counts, and that weapons can be used in either role—for example, that the best weapon to fight a tank is another tank. However, it is possible to say whether weapons are designed primarily for offense or defense. Comparatively little attention, in fact, has been paid to ideas for banning specific weapons other than nuclear, biological, and chemical agents.

In recent times the notion has gained ground that a better approach than piecemeal dismantling of forces lies in forms of reduction that preserve the balance between national forces. One of the simplest ways in which this might be done is by demobilizing whole army groups on each side. Some of the problems in control of conventional forces will be considered later.

In general this discussion has been about what are often called "teeth" units, that is, those which would make direct contact with the enemy. Military forces also include training units and bases for stores and repairs. At these strata a proportion of the personnel will be civilians, but the arrangements will differ from country to country. At an even earlier stage of support there is the industrial base, only part of which will be in specialized armament plants. In procurement of weapons there will be even earlier stages of development carried out by civilians and military; and there is also research in government, industrial, and educational laboratories.

There is thus a broadening out of military power into the national economy, with different national practices in the employment of military and civilian personnel. A precise demarcation of military potential becomes impossible. However, control of "teeth" units will undoubtedly determine the demand for control at the earlier stages.

CHAPTER

4

THE NUCLEAR POWER INDUSTRY

Nuclear energy was developed for military purposes before it was utilized for the production of electrical power, although much of the very earliest interest was in schemes for maritime propulsion; these were temporarily abandoned when the enormous potentialities for explosive purposes were realized. However, regardless of the historical order of events, in this study the manufacturing processes of the civil nuclear industry will be discussed first, since it is from the civil industry that nuclear materials may be diverted to nuclear weapons.

This chapter is intended as a brief introduction to various aspects of manufacture and control of nuclear materials. The problems of controlling the production processes for plutonium will be discussed in Chapter 5. After this the production processes for the enrichment of uranium will be described, and then methods for controlling fissile materials are considered. Control of nuclear warheads and of delivery vehicles will also be considered.

Nuclear power has completely changed the military situation and has introduced new problems of arms control, the most important of which are the following:

Preventing manufacture of nuclear weapons by the nonnuclear weapons powers

Limitation, reduction, and finally elimination of stocks of nuclear weapons held by the nuclear powers

Control of fissile material produced and used in the civil power industry throughout the world.

Control in the nuclear power industry is essentially the control of the fissile materials plutonium, uranium-235, and, in the future, uranium-233, any of which, under appropriate conditions, can release nuclear energy in a controlled manner in a nuclear reactor, or explosively, in a nuclear weapon or civil nuclear explosive.

When the first nuclear weapons were planned in the Manhatten Project, it was decided to attempt to manufacture both fissile materials—plutonium and uranium-235—in order to improve the chances of success, despite the high costs and the difficulties of the processes to be investigated and developed. Separation of quantities of both fissile materials was successfully accomplished: a uranium-235 bomb destroyed Hiroshima and a plutonium bomb destroyed Nagasaki. Plutonium could be produced by the irradiation of uranium in reactors, as was demonstrated in Chicago Pile No. 1; and the problem was essentially one of scaling up the size of the manufacturing units, although this was not without unexpected difficulties. The problem of obtaining quantities of uranium-235 lay in separating the 0.7 percent of it present in natural uranium from the remaining uranium, which consists mainly of the U-238 isotope with traces of other uranium isotopes. The different isotopes of uranium are chemically identical, ruling out processes that are relatively straightforward; and recourse had to be made to physical differences between the different isotopes. The physical processes were understood in principle but had not been employed on anything larger than the laboratory scale—and even then for materials considerably more amenable than uranium.

The methods of production and control of plutonium and uranium are considered separately, since the key processes at which control may be particularly essential are different and there are special technical features of each manufacturing process that may be employed to improve control. Some general requirements of the nuclear power industry itself that are common to processing of either fissile material can be used to enhance control.

Full control of processing for production of nuclear weapons involves a number of interlocking agreements: those which apply to the nonnuclear powers are intended to prevent them from acquiring the materials and know-how to produce nuclear weapons and to reduce the incentive and the intention to do so; those agreements which apply to the nuclear powers are intended first to freeze present production and stocks of both fissile materials and nuclear delivery vehicles, and then to reduce them to some agreed level and eventually to eliminate them entirely. Table 4 lists the requirements that would have to be considered in a general and comprehensive scheme of control.

TABLE 4

General Requirements for Control of Fissile Materials and Nuclear Weapons

Applying to Nuclear Powers	Applying to Nonnuclear Powers
Prevention of growth of stockpiles of nuclear materials: the "cutoff"	Prohibition of nuclear weapons in particular areas: "Latin American Treaty"
Disassembly of nuclear warheads	Prohibition of manufacture of nuclear weapons: "Nonproliferation Treaty"
Reduction of stocks of nuclear materials and transfer to civil uses: the "cutback"	Nonacceptance of know-how
Guarantees of support to nonnuclear powers: the "nuclear umbrella"	Prevention of diversion of fissile material from civil nuclear installations
Agreement on nonuse of nuclear weapons: "nonfirst use"	Safeguarding of fissile material purchased from abroad
Reduction of danger to populations and degradation of the environment through weapons testing: "Moscow Treaty"	Search for clandestine facilities
Limiting further development of nuclear warheads: "comprehensive nuclear test ban"	Prohibition on production of NDV
Verification of shutdown of fissile material plant	Control of R&D
Nontransfer of weapons know-how	
Supervision of peaceful nuclear explosions	
Freeze on further production of NDV*	
Destruction of NDV: "the bomber bonfire"	
Verification of NDV: "minimum deterrent"	
Control of permitted production of NDV	
Restriction of deployment of NDV: "Antarctic and Outer Space Treaties"	
Control of R&D (if possible or desirable)	
Restriction of damage in war: limitation on stocks of warheads and nuclear delivery vehicles	
Restraints on transporting nuclear weapons outside national boundaries	
Reduction of first-strike option: hardening of silos, dispersal of airfields, reliable warning, survival of command and control	
Hot-line communications between national leaders	

*NDV = Nuclear delivery vehicles.

FIGURE 1

Flow Chart for Fissile Materials

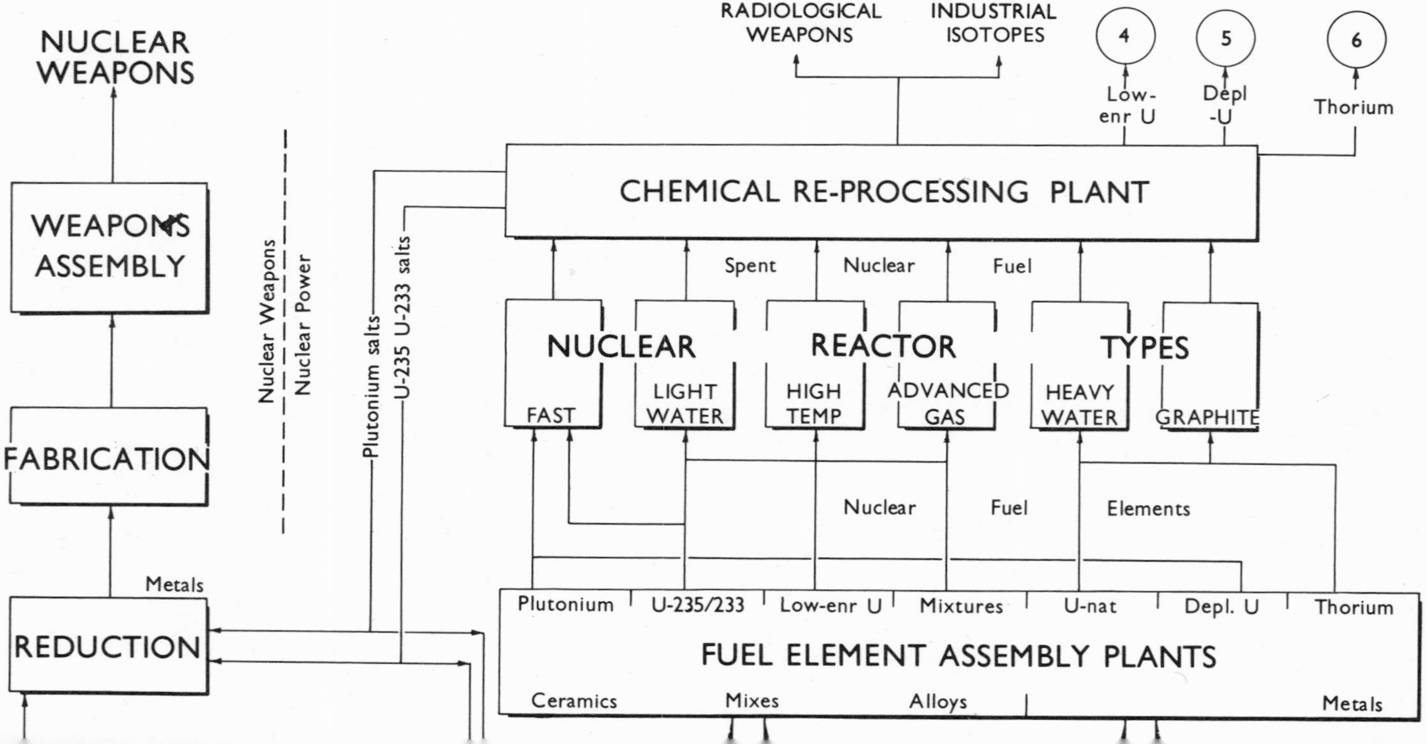

NUCLEAR WEAPONS
WEAPONS ASSEMBLY
FABRICATION
Metals
REDUCTION
Nuclear Weapons
Nuclear Power
Plutonium salts
U-235 U-233 salts
RADIOLOGICAL WEAPONS
INDUSTRIAL ISOTOPES
4
5
6
Low-enr U
Depl -U
Thorium
CHEMICAL RE-PROCESSING PLANT
Spent Nuclear Fuel
NUCLEAR REACTOR TYPES
FAST
LIGHT WATER
HIGH TEMP
ADVANCED GAS
HEAVY WATER
GRAPHITE
Nuclear Fuel Elements
Plutonium
U-235/233
Low-enr U
Mixtures
U-nat
Depl. U
Thorium
FUEL ELEMENT ASSEMBLY PLANTS
Ceramics
Mixes
Alloys
Metals

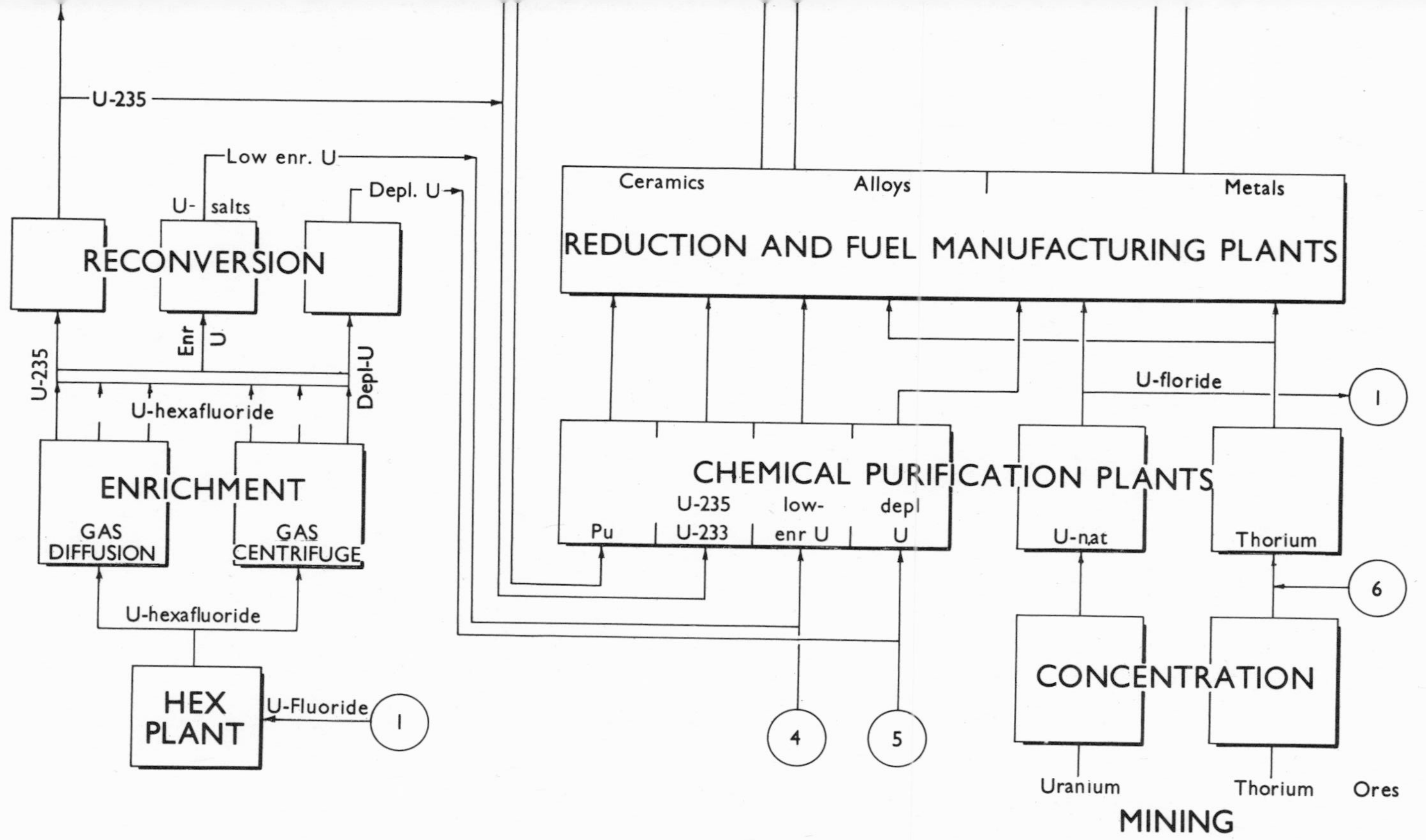

U-235
Low enr. U
Depl. U
U- salts
RECONVERSION
U-235
Enr U
Depl-U
U-hexafluoride
ENRICHMENT
GAS DIFFUSION
GAS CENTRIFUGE
U-hexafluoride
HEX PLANT
U-Fluoride
1
Ceramics
Alloys
Metals
REDUCTION AND FUEL MANUFACTURING PLANTS
U-floride
1
CHEMICAL PURIFICATION PLANTS
Pu
U-235
U-233
low-
enr U
depl
U
U-nat
Thorium
6
4
5
CONCENTRATION
Uranium
Thorium
Ores
MINING

A flow chart for fissile materials in a civil and military nuclear power industry is shown in Figure 1. A brief discussion of this chart will serve to introduce the possibilities of control. Nuclear power industries in individual countries would almost certainly be far less complicated than the chart would indicate, since not all of the reactor types shown would be constructed. It is likely that the nuclear power economy in most countries would eventually include fast reactors and one other type, selected to complete an integrated system and to suit the local power requirements. All of the other processing plants would be needed unless some operations could be carried out abroad under contract.

Manufacture of nuclear weapons, starting at the reduction process at the top left of the chart, is seen as an offshoot from the civil power industry. If this is not so, then the costs of nuclear weapons are inflated by the costs of providing all of the other plants, including reactors required for plutonium manufacture.

The most important conclusions that can be drawn from examination of the chart are the following:

Weapons-grade—that is, pure—plutonium and uranium-233 first appear as outputs from the chemical reprocessing plant

Pure uranium-235 appears first as the output of the enrichment process

Even at these stages the fissile materials are in the form of chemical compounds, so that diversion for clandestine weapons manufacture would require several secret plants to manufacture and assemble metallic weapons components.

These points will be examined in much greater detail in subsequent chapters.

Leonard Beaton has emphasized that nuclear power is not economically competitive in the small installations that would be required in less densely populated areas of the world but considers that over-optimistic scientists have been a pressure group in favor of installation of reactors in many such countries, thus unwittingly conferring a nuclear weapons option. *

---

*Leonard Beaton, book review in Nature (September 20, 1969).

Those aspects of the nuclear industry which are of greatest concern in respect to arms control are the likely spread of nuclear reactors to many countries, with the possibilities of extracting plutonium for weapons; the control, reduction in number, and eventual elimination of nuclear weapons in the hands of the nuclear powers; and the general control of fissile material throughout the world. The technical problems that interpenetrate these objectives are the details of the process of manufacture of plutonium in nuclear reactors and the associated chemical operation and refining processes, the various processes for enrichment—that is, for the extraction of U-235 from natural uranium—and the organization for the management and control of nuclear materials. Each of these problems concerns both the nuclear and the nonnuclear powers. Control of nuclear warheads and delivery systems is of concern to the present nuclear powers, to possible future nuclear powers, and to the nonnuclear powers, since all would be affected in a nuclear war.

Development of nuclear weapons by each of the present nuclear powers (except possibly China) has followed a similar path—development of kiloton-range fission weapons based on plutonium, with delivery by aircraft, followed by development of megaton fission weapons with a uranium trigger, with delivery by missile. With the introduction of long-range missiles of high accuracy that are able to deliver several warheads, the dependence upon uranium for very destructive weapons may not be so very important. This should be borne in mind when assessing the effect of the spread of nuclear weapons.

While from the arms control point of view it might have been better for the U.S. (and British) governments to encourage the alternative use of fossil fuel, continued and increasing use of the latter contaminates the atmosphere with finely divided solid dust, sulfur dioxide, and excess carbon dioxide. The first two are directly injurious to plant and animal life (including humans), while the latter may be responsible for changes in the rates at which solar energy is absorbed, and thus for climatic changes that could, if unchecked, in the end be disastrous. While nuclear energy has potentially dangerous by-products and effluents, because of close scientific control and restrictive legislation there appears to be less contamination of the environment than from conventional fuels.*

There has, of course, been considerable concern about possible injurious effects from fallout of radioactive debris following tests of nuclear weapons. This matter will be returned to in Chapter 8.

---

*S. G. Lawrence, letter to New Society (July 17, 1969).

CHAPTER

5

PLUTONIUM MANUFACTURE AND CONTROLS

THE MANUFACTURE OF PLUTONIUM

In this chapter the processes used in the manufacture of plutonium and the controls that might be applied are described. In Chapter 7 more general methods of control applicable to fissile materials will be discussed; thus there will be some repetition in these arguments.

A nuclear reactor is essentially a device in which neutrons released by the fission of a fissile material (often uranium-235) will cause the fission of further fissile material in a self-perpetuating but controlled chain reaction:

$$\underline{n} + \text{U-235} \longrightarrow 2\underline{FP} + 2 \text{ or } 3\underline{n} + \text{energy.}$$

This reaction represents a neutron, $\underline{n}$, combining with an atom of uranium-235 to form an unstable atom that almost immediately splits into fission products ($\underline{FP}$), of which, in most cases, there are two. At the same time there is the release of two or three neutrons and atomic binding energy. The neutrons are ejected at high speeds and may interact with other atoms, including more U-235, thus perpetuating the chain reaction. In addition to the prompt neutrons released at the instant of fission, other neutrons may be released from fractions of a second up to minutes after the event: by absorbing more or less of these delayed neutrons in control rods, a reactor may be controlled and prevented from running away.

Some of the neutrons that are released may be captured by any U-238 present, which is converted to plutonium in a series of nuclear reactions:

$$n + U\text{-}238 \longrightarrow U\text{-}239$$

$$U\text{-}239 \longrightarrow Np\text{-}239 + \beta$$

$$Np\text{-}239 \longrightarrow Pu\text{-}239 + \beta.$$

The amount of plutonium produced depends mainly on the neutron flux, the neutron energy, and the amount of U-238 present. These parameters vary not only with the size of the reactor but also with the design. In Great Britain attention has been concentrated on reactors fueled with natural uranium and cooled with gas: these reactors are most economical when very large and used for base-load generation of electricity. In the United States enriched fuel containing more U-235 than is present in natural uranium has been combined with water cooling, and the optimum size of the plant is rather smaller.

British "Magnox"*-type civil reactors fueled with natural uranium yield as a by-product about 0.5 kg of plutonium per megawatt-year (electrical) of output; American water-cooled reactors fueled with enriched uranium (higher in U-235 and therefore lower in U-238) produce about 0.2 kg per megawatt-year (electrical).

While these two types represent the mainstreams of reactor development, in the future other kinds of reactors are likely to be in service, including fast reactors and high-temperature gas reactors. Fast reactors will be fueled either with plutonium or with highly enriched uranium (i.e., almost pure U-235). The particular value of the fast reactor (so called because it operates with fast neutrons, rather than with thermal neutrons that have been slowed by collision with moderator material in the reactor core), which is shared to a limited extent with some other reactors, in that it is a breeder. That is, it has such a high neutron flux that there is an excess that can be absorbed in a blanket of natural or depleted uranium (from which some of the U-235 has been removed) surrounding the core; and some of the U-238 in the blanket is converted to plutonium. In a breeder reactor the rate at which new fissile material is created is in excess of the rate at which fissile material is being consumed, so that there is a net increase in the fissile material investment. In nonbreeder

---

*"Magnox" is the name given to a series of magnesium alloys used as canning materials to protect the uranium against corrosion and burning in a reactor.

reactors, although plutonium may be created, the total amount of fissile material decreases. To put the matter briefly, in a nuclear reactor fueled with U-235 and also containing U-238, during operation there is a change in the composition of the fuel. As U-235 is burned, some plutonium is created and some of this also is burned. In fast reactors the amount of fissile material produced exceeds the amount of that destroyed, so that there is a net gain. The fuel deteriorates over time; and when the fuel is removed for reprocessing, the excess fissile material can be recovered for fueling new reactor systems.

PRESENT PRODUCTION FACILITIES

The nuclear powers—the United States, Great Britain, the Soviet Union, France, and China—have each built secret reactor facilities for the production of plutonium for weapons. The output from these facilities has not been revealed, although estimates have been made. The two first British reactors for producing plutonium for military purposes at Windscale were shut down in the mid-1950's. A second generation of military producing reactors was designed to yield electricity as a byproduct. The operating parameters of these reactors have since been reoptimized with production of electricity for the national grid as a primary aim; but, on the other hand, one of the first generation of reactors built specifically for the production of electricity was so designed that it could be used to produce weapons-grade plutonium if increased production was required. The main difference in operating reactors to produce weapons-grade plutonium is more rapid throughput of fuel, so that the plutonium-239 is not too heavily contaminated with nonfissile Pu-240.

The foregoing illustrates that there is a limited flexibility in the way that reactors can be operated, to maximize the production either of electricity or of plutonium. The range of performance can be enhanced at the design stage, albeit at some not inconsiderable cost in the provision of extra fuel-handling equipment and perhaps decreased onload availability for production of electricity.

In addition to the large reactor installations of the nuclear powers, many countries have nuclear research reactors of varying sizes, some of which could produce significant quantities of plutonium. In a few countries power reactors have been built under contract by one or other of the nuclear powers; and these reactors too produce plutonium that, despite any safeguards, might be diverted to weapons manufacture.

Potential outputs in 1970 from planned civil reactors have been estimated in the open literature as the following:

Country	Output	Country	Output
Belgium	2 kg	Netherlands	10 kg
Canada	650	Pakistan	60
Czechoslovakia	75	Soviet Union	110
Germany	235	Spain	120
Great Britain	1,250	Sweden	120
India	190	Switzerland	70
Israel	5	United States	1,250
Italy	160		
Japan	300		

Omitted from this list are the quantities of plutonium that are manufactured for military purposes by the present nuclear powers. Many other countries would be reluctant to expose their facilities to inspection unless some form of control were placed on the much greater stocks and annual productions of the nuclear powers.

If international control could be effectively imposed on each of the present plutonium-producing countries, this control could be extended as each new reactor is installed.

PRESENT SAFEGUARDS

Safeguards on Uranium Supplies

One form of control of the production of plutonium is that on the supplies of uranium minerals from the mines. This form of control already exists as an informal suppliers' group, consisting of the United States, Canada, South Africa, Sweden, and some lesser producers. While the suppliers' group can control bulk quantities of nuclear fuel that would be needed for a civil electrical power program, production in the Communist countries is not so controlled, and there are other possibilities for acquiring uranium. The widespread distribution of uranium and thorium ores means that many countries would be able to extract small quantities of uranium from indigenous ores, even if this were at high cost: alternatively, they could obtain their requirements from friendly uncontrolled sources. Taking into account the likely development of breeder reactors, control by suppliers would be of only limited value in the long run.

For an inspectorate effectively to control the mining and subsequent movement of uranium ore would be too great a burden, since the number of personnel and the costs would be excessive for the reliability of control that could be achieved. This is not to suggest that no control or observation be kept on the trade in uranium and thorium minerals but, rather, that this should be accepted as a secondary control only, possibly limited to scrutiny of records and supplemented by spot checks on actual shipments.

Safeguards on Nuclear Fuel Manufacture

Uranium ores are subjected to elaborate physical and chemical processing to extract the uranium from the mineral, to refine it to an exceptionally high degree of purity, to convert it to metal or oxide, and to fabricate finished fuel elements.

Checks are possible on the flow of material through the manufacturing plant and are, of course, carried out as part of the normal management. It should be possible to verify plant records by weighing and other measurements at particular stages. However, an elaborate inspection operation is not justified at this stage of manufacture of fuel; a more limited control should operate, perhaps by sampling the records maintained for normal manufacturing purposes.

Safeguards on Reactors

The kinds of control that might operate in the nuclear weapons states will be considered later. This chapter is concerned with the control that exists when a nuclear research or power reactor has been built by foreigners. Control may be exercised by a bilateral agreement between the parties or by international agreement.

Present safeguards are essentially of two kinds, both of which may be included in an agreement: the first type specifies the terms under which reactors are constructed under contract, and the second specifies the conditions under which plutonium is separated from spent fuel. The agreement may stipulate that the reactor will be inspected to prevent diversion of plutonium and that irradiated fuel must be returned to the original supplier or to some other nominated operator for the extraction of plutonium that is retained and paid for. Critics have noted that there has been a noticeable preference for bilateral agreements rather than IAEA safeguards and for buying from smaller manufacturing countries less able to exert strong pressures in favor of inspection; it is possible that in some cases there is already scope for diversion of fissile materials. The main international system providing inspection to prevent diversion is the

IAEA, but in the opinion of critics this is no more adequate than bilateral agreements to prevent buildup of military stockpiles. In spite of the controls on reactors supplied by foreigners, the amount of plutonium under safeguard is only a fraction of total world production. Outside of any international controls are the amounts produced for military purposes and the enormous quantities that are a byproduct of the civil nuclear installations. Control of the latter on a limited scale is now being developed and will be discussed later.

While the possibilities for control by international authority through bilateral agreements appear to be limited, there may be better prospects from an accord between countries with the necessary levels of technology to design and construct reactors. At present only nine countries have the abilities to develop and manufacture large nuclear reactors—the Soviet Union, the United States, Great Britain, France, China, Japan, West Germany, Canada, and Sweden—and five other countries may be in a position to do so quite soon—Italy, India, Czechoslovakia, the Netherlands, and Belgium. This means that most countries would have to have reactors built by foreigners and would have to import most of the important components. These would include assembled fuel elements, even if the operator could obtain the uranium ore from local suppliers. Suppliers of reactors are in a position to specify conditions for inspection and fuel handling, either through a bilateral agreement between the two parties or in conjunction with an international authority such as the IAEA. Operators, on the other hand, may accept only the most beneficial tender and other factors than cost may be taken into account: a preference for bilateral agreements with smaller suppliers has already been noted.

During discussion of the Non-Proliferation Treaty objections were raised to inspection of facilities on the grounds that this would amount to commercial espionage. Sir John Cockcroft believed that these objections were misplaced for several reasons.* It is customary for detailed designs of nuclear power stations to be published during the late stage of commissioning, in order to encourage further sales, so that by the time production starts, and long before the first fuel is withdrawn for chemical reprocessing for plutonium recovery, there is little if any need for commercial secrecy. Since it is necessary to freeze designs so that components can be manufactured, it

---

*John Cockcroft, "Control of Nuclear Energy," Survival (November 1967).

has been said that any reactor that is built is already obsolescent. The essential requirements for commercial success in the civil nuclear field are not secrecy but an experienced design team capable of further advances, the necessary scientific and engineering research and development staff and their laboratory and test facilities, and good sales and credit facilities.

The second form of control that may be introduced with the contract is on the arrangements permitted for recovering plutonium from the irradiated fuel. Many agreements stipulate that the irradiated fuel shall be returned to the original supplier for extraction of the plutonium and that this should be purchased at some agreed-upon figure.

In developing countries the fact that they would not have the resources to process spent fuel for recovery of plutonium would itself be a safeguard. This would not apply, however, to the same extent to those countries able to supply reactors; in many cases they already have chemical separation plants for the recovery of plutonium. Control of plutonium manufactured by the nuclear powers is quite another problem and will be discussed later. A serious political problem that affects the type of controls that may be instituted lies in attempting to impose stricter conditions on developing countries than those imposed on the nuclear powers, which already have large stockpiles of fissile materials.

FUTURE SAFEGUARDS

Requirement for Reactors

At present nuclear power is competitive with more conventional fuels in only a few areas and, even then, only when installed in very large operating units; nevertheless, nuclear power still offers the prospect of very cheap power, which could transform the economies of many countries. A few countries, notably Great Britain, have already initiated important nuclear power programs for the production of electricity, many other countries are about to do so, and even more countries operate research reactors. One of the reasons for operating research reactors is to provide a cadre of trained personnel, who would be essential for a future power program. Apart from this requirement it would otherwise be difficult to justify this employment of rare skills and expensive equipment in some of the less developed countries.

While nuclear power now represents only a fraction of total power installations, it is expected to play a much more important part in the future. By the year 2000 nuclear power could represent about half of the installed electrical generating capacity in the United States, and investments on a similar scale are likely in the technologically advanced countries of Europe, Japan, and Canada; in addition nuclear power will provide unique opportunities for economic development, when combined with desalinization plants, in such arid areas as the interior of Australia and large tracts of North Africa, Siberia, Mongolia, and Antarctica. Although deposits of low-cost uranium may be barely adequate for such an ambitious program, there are possibilities for the discovery of new ore deposits. There are also available considerable quantities at higher cost to extract; and thorium, which is about as plentiful as uranium, may also be converted to nuclear fuel. The most important possibility, however, is the development of fast breeder reactors, which would reduce requirements for imported uranium to initial fuel charges only.

Glen Seaborg estimated cumulative production of plutonium to be as follows:*

Year	Kg Plutonium
1970	10,000
1980	180,000
2000	4,000,000

These amounts should be compared with the estimated requirement for a weapon of 5-7 kg.

Possible Forms of Control

In view of the potential threat of worldwide dissemination of plutonium-producing facilities, some writers believe that it is necessary to examine with a greater sense of realism and urgency the present position and the possibility of installing control before the problem becomes insoluble.

---

*Glen Seaborg, "Nuclear Power: Two Years After Geneva," fifth annual lecture to the British Nuclear Energy Society (October 24, 1966).

Doubts as to the efficiency of present safeguards have caused Leonard Beaton* and others to propose more stringent procedures for the physical control of plutonium.

Possible solutions are the following:

Physical possession of plutonium by the IAEA, as is permitted by the charter, or by nominated countries, such as the nuclear powers or other agencies

An international agreement to sell back all spent fuel containing plutonium to the IAEA or some specified country

An agreement to sell back all plutonium to the country that supplied the reactor.

Physical control of plutonium by the IAEA would restrict reprocessing for the recovery from spent fuel elements to a few plants which could be readily inspected. On the other hand, it might hinder economic exploitation of a valuable resource; and precautions would have to be taken to protect the plutonium stocks that might be stored in several, or even many, countries from capture by agents of the host or other country, dissident groups, or even criminals. It might even be necessary to provide an international force of armed guards. If the object was only to stockpile plutonium, it might be possible to evolve suitable protective barriers and automatic warnings, but it is much more likely that there would be a fair amount of movement in and out of store; and whilst it might be possible to telemeter these movements, it is unlikely that everyone would be satisfied without some form of human safeguards. Aspects of control of stocks of plutonium in process will be examined later. Some of the difficulties mentioned here will also arise.

On the other hand, an advantage gained by forced purchase of plutonium by the original supplier or even by the IAEA or a consortium of suppliers would be to make available the large stocks of plutonium that are necessary for fueling of fast reactors. There will probably be a shortage of plutonium for initial fuel charges for fast reactors over the next few decades. Employed in this way, much of the plutonium

---

*Leonard Beaton, "Safeguards on Plutonium," Nature (December 31, 1966).

would be safely hidden inside reactors or in process; during most of this time it would be associated with highly dangerous radioactive fission products and, in addition, subject to national accounting, which would have to be severely applied for economic reasons and to guard against nuclear criticality accidents. Thus it might be possible to control plutonium more easily when in use than when stored.

A monopoly on plutonium by the IAEA or by the United Nations would, as the requirements for fuel for fast reactors increase, place the possessor in a powerful position; and while this could be seen as possibly leading to a powerful, wealthy world government (and thus would be welcomed by many individuals), it is likely to be resisted by governments whose primary concern is the well-being of their people and by more cautious individuals who suspect concentrations of power. Apart from such hesitancies, the handing over of plutonium could deprive a nation of the income from its sale, its use as a fuel in the future, and, of course, the option to convert it to nuclear weapons. Any forced sale agreement would suffer from the same problems, but the economic difficulties could be overcome by including a right to repurchase from the IAEA an equivalent amount of safeguarded plutonium. From the point of arms control, the most important advantage arising from the physical possession of plutonium by the IAEA and its delivery to a specified country for processing would be that only a few chemical separation plants need be constructed, and these could be more easily inspected or supervised by IAEA.

Inspection of Plutonium-Producing Facilities

Following from the remarks above, the increasing use of nuclear power in provision of electricity might be seen as an opening for the clandestine diversion of nuclear fuels. While it is certainly true that without a nuclear industry a nation would not have nuclear fuel to divert to military purposes, there are little-appreciated safeguards that can apply in countries with a civil nuclear industry. Nuclear power stations tend to be of distinctive and well-understood designs; and the output in electricity is specified, and even widely publicized, for the purpose of national prestige and to encourage further orders. The yield of by-product plutonium can be fairly easily assessed, within limits, from the published details and from information from the contractors, if they are from another country. As plutonium begins to have a domestic and world market value as an alternative fuel, there will be pressures to declare stocks as indicators of economic stability; indeed, it has been suggested—and not without justification—that at some time in the future world currencies might be related to a plutonium rather than a gold standard.

Examination of the flow sheet of the nuclear industry shows that there are key processes that must be controlled to a high degree, whereas other processes do not require such elaborate precautions. Plutonium facilities that would require a high degree of control would be reactors, chemical separation plants, plants for the manufacture of fuel elements, and stores.

Inspection of Reactors

The principle of inspecting reactors to prevent diversion of plutonium to military purposes is to form an estimate of the amount of plutonium manufactured in the reactor, and thus the amount removed with spent fuel. The average amount of plutonium in spent fuel elements can be calculated from the neutron flux and the time of irradiation; and the former can be derived from the electrical power output in the case of power reactors and the position of the fuel in the reactor.

Inspection of reactors is facilitated by the fact that for military purposes the Pu-239 should be as pure as possible. To avoid too high a content of nonfissile Pu-240, a rapid turnaround of fuel and a lower operating temperature are necessary. Much more handling is required when a reactor is operated in this way than when it is operated solely for the production of electricity; in the case of a large power reactor this factor may seriously affect the design and, with the lower operating temperature, mitigate against the optimum production of electricity. An inspector would pay particular attention to these operating parameters.

Access for inspection would be continuous for large installations, which might have several operating reactors, and only occasional for small reactors. The main purpose of such visits would be to monitor the amount of new fuel received, the amount of spent fuel dispatched, and the irradiation history (and hence the amount of plutonium produced). The average amount by which the fuel was irradiated can be cross-checked from the integrated electrical power output of the station. Falsification of records would thus be made more difficult because it would involve two different sets of documents, one of which would be closely related to domestic and industrial power usage.

Inspection of Chemical Separation Plant

Plutonium, when it is produced in a nuclear reactor by the transmutation processes described earlier, is intimately mixed with the remaining uranium and with highly radioactive fission products. The spent fuel, as it is withdrawn from the reactor, is too radioactive to be handled directly and the fuel elements are stored underwater, to shield the operators from harmful effects and also to remove the heat released by continued radioactive decay. While in the cooling ponds the fuel elements can be visually identified and counted but can be moved or stacked only by use of remote-control handling equipment. After some weeks of storage the radioactivity has decayed to a level when the fuel elements can be transferred to the next page.

For transporting fuel to the next stage special "flasks" are required. These are large containers, often of cast iron or steel and weighing several tons. They are designed to hold a relatively small number of fuel elements under water, which is still required to remove the heat from continuing decay. The flasks are designed to contain a buildup of pressure, and to avoid injury of workers or the public by radiation penetrating the walls of the flasks or by spillage of the contents. Heavy cranes and special road or rail cars are needed for transporting the flasks. Precautions have to be taken against accidents during the journey, with a communications system set up; and accident control and decontamination teams at the consigning and receiving ends have to be on alert. In addition it is necessary to warn rail and other public transport officials, and police and fire brigades along the route whenever a movement is to take place. These aspects of movement planning and control are stressed to indicate the number of individuals who have to cooperate, and to indicate the nature of the equipment and precautions. Diversion during this stage could be made even more difficult if all flasks were numbered or identified in some way by the inspectorate and the location of each flask could be monitored.

When spent fuel arrives at the chemical separation plant, it is still too radioactive for direct handling. Briefly, the processes to be carried out are removing the metallic cans that provided protection against corrosion while in the reactor; dissolution of the fuel in acid; a number of stages in a complex chemical process that separates the plutonium, uranium, and fission products into separate streams; and the production, in the case of plutonium and uranium, of solid products, generally high-purity salts such as oxides or fluorides. All of these processes, except the last, have to be carried out behind six-foot-thick concrete shielding, with apparatus that can be remotely controlled and monitored and with special precautions for removing samples.

The chemical separation plants are as small as possible for two reasons: to limit the amount of plutonium that can accumulate in any part of the plant to less than the minimum critical mass, in order to avoid the risks of a nuclear explosion, and to economize on shielding and remote-control handling equipment. In order to achieve a satisfactory throughput plants are of the continuous-flow type. Chemical separation plants are in operation in the United States, the Soviet Union, Great Britain, France, and India; there is also the Eurochemic plant in Belgium.

The next stage of the process is to convert plutonium into a form suitable for nuclear weapons or for nuclear reactor fuel. This stage is more likely to involve batch processes for the production of metallic plutonium for nuclear weapons and oxides, carbides, or other compounds of plutonium for fuel. Because of the very high toxicity of plutonium and the ease with which it is oxidized in air, the batch processes are carried out in glove boxes, that is, in enclosures made of Perspex sheets, with any direct manipulation through arm-length gloves sealed at the shoulders to the panels of the boxes. The boxes in many cases are filled with argon. When removed for transfer to the weapons production plant or the fuel element plant, the plutonium has to be wrapped or encapsulated to prevent oxidation by air and to protect workers and the public from the alpha rays that are emitted. However, while great care is essential to see that these precautions are properly carried out, the actual form of the transport containers is in no way distinctive unless made so by warning labels. Additional difficulties, from the arms control point of view, are that for avoidance of criticality accidents, only relatively small amounts of plutonium would be in each container; and since alpha particles have little penetrating power, the containers have only to be thick enough to provide protection against mechanical accidents. Containers for plutonium need not, therefore, be particularly large or distinctive.

From the foregoing it seems obvious that diversion of plutonium for nuclear weapons would be difficult at any stage; but the most vulnerable stage is when the plutonium has been reduced to metal, that is, in the condition necessary to be fabricated into weapon components. The most intensive inspection therefore would be required at the output stage of the chemical plant. In fact it is only at this stage that physical custody by the inspectorate would be possible, since at earlier stages the plutonium is either mixed with radioactive fission products or is in a continuous flow process.

There is, however, a technical means of control which could be used to reduce the possibilities of diversion of metallic plutonium. Because of its rather peculiar physical properties, plutonium, unlike natural uranium, cannot normally be employed as a metallic fuel but in some cases is used in a ceramic such as the oxide or carbide or, less frequently, in an alloy with another metal. It might be possible to have an international agreement to prevent the holding of stocks of metallic plutonium except in very small quantities for research purposes, with a ban on production-scale equipment for reducing plutonium salts to metal or for separating it from its compounds and alloys.

As far as existing agreements are concerned, the verification arrangements between Great Britain and the IAEA do not include inspection of the chemical plant; but methods for the control of chemical reprocessing plants are being investigated in the United States.

Since the plutonium, U-235, and enriched uranium that are produced by separation plant can all be used in nuclear weapons, inspection of the plant would involve continuous monitoring, at least of the final stages, where the likelihood of diversion is highest. Other checks might be necessary at the input and intermediate stages. Any stores of fissile material associated with the chemical separation plant would also be subject to inspection and occasional stocktaking. It might be possible to introduce physical controls of stores with locks, the keys to which were held, and could only be used, by the inspectors. (Other problems of inspection of stocks are considered below.) Inspection of material in process and of stocks would be greatly assisted by the system of records and procedures to avoid criticality accidents.

To ensure that there are no clandestine facilities engaged in separation or fabrication of fissile material, the inspectorate might require access to any suspected plants, or at least permission to inspect inputs and outputs.

Monitoring of activities at suspected plants, as at known plants, would be much facilitated by many technical requirements of the processes. The size and shape of buildings would give some indication of their suitability, as would the presence of the thick concrete shielding that is necessary to protect the workers and the public from radioactivity in both reactors and chemical separation plants; electrical power in large amounts is required for uranium isotope separation by the diffusion process; plants for the gas centrifuge processes are not so well understood, but it is likely that the equipment will be very unusual and easily recognized; in any plant in which radioactive materials are handled, special precautions have to be taken to protect the health of the workers, such as medical examinations, monitoring for radioactivity, and special clothing, and in the design of containers for equipment, such as glove boxes and hot cells. Other precautions have to be taken to protect the public by treatment of effluents from the plants and by sampling and monitoring for radioactivity deposited by gaseous effluents in the neighboring countryside.

Identification of nuclear facilities is also considered in Chapter 7.

INSPECTION OF STOCKS OF PLUTONIUM IN PROCESS

Problems of safeguarding the large stores of plutonium that could be held by the IAEA or other authority have been discussed. We now examine a problem that already exists in the present nuclear powers.

Buffer stocks of plutonium and other fissile material that have been built up after the chemical reprocessing stage, prior to being processed to fuel elements, would have to be inspected in the same way as stocks at the earlier stages. But because the plutonium is now highly purified, it is particularly suitable for nuclear weapon components; and since it is not associated with radioactive fission products, it could be fairly easily diverted without detection. At this stage the manufacturing process is particularly vulnerable to diversion. Fortunately there is a technical feature that would facilitate control: plutonium for weapons has to be in the metallic state; but as such it is generally unsuitable as a fuel for nuclear reactors, for which compounds such as oxides or carbides, or alloys with other metals, are more suitable. Prohibition of the reduction of plutonium compounds to metal (unless immediately embodied in an alloy under international observation) could materially assist control. To avoid clandestine processing, equipment for reduction of plutonium salts to metal would have to be prescribed. To prevent diversion of plutonium salts to clandestine reduction plants, permanent inspection would be required for stocks of a certain size, while for smaller stocks there would be long range telemetry, depending on measurement of the radioactivity of plutonium. The aim would be to ensure that stocks could not be seized and converted to weapons before countermeasures could be taken.

CHAPTER

6

ENRICHMENT OF URANIUM

GASEOUS DIFFUSION PROCESS

The first nuclear weapon to be used in an attack on a city was based on uranium-235, and the second was based on plutonium. The manufacture of plutonium in reactors and its extraction from spent fuel in chemical separation plant were described in Chapter 5. This chapter is concerned with the processes for separation of uranium-235, which constitutes 0.7 percent of naturally occurring uranium, the remainder being mostly U-238.

Small differences between the atomic weights of U-235 and U-238 affect the rate of diffusion and electrical, magnetic, interatomic, and intermolecular forces. Of these differences in properties, four were considered to have some possibilities as the basis for a large-scale separation process and were further investigated. This investigation showed that processes could be developed that depended on the small difference in the rate of diffusion between gaseous molecules containing U-235 and U-238 isotopes. The requirements for a suitable compound were severe: not only did it have to be in the form of a gas at temperatures and pressures that could be achieved in chemical engineering plant, but it also had to be possible for it to be manufactured on the process scale, as a relatively simple compound, so as not to reduce the already small difference between uranium isotopes. Furthermore, the other element or elements in the compound should not be present in several isotopic forms; otherwise the process would sort for these differences just as much as for the different isotopes of uranium.

Fortunately a suitable chemical compound, uranium hexafluoride (UF_6), was discovered. This compound can be manufactured, albeit with great difficulty, and is gaseous at slightly elevated temperatures, so that the whole of the processing plant would have to be heated. There were other difficulties: uranium hexafluoride was chemically very unstable and was readily decomposed by moisture in the air, leaving a solid residue, so that air intake for the plant was liable to be blocked, while leaks to the atmosphere were hazardous to operating personnel through ingestion of radioactive uranium and poisonous hydrofluoric acid. In addition to these problems "Hex" is very corrosive, and special materials and surface treatments for the equipment had to be developed.

The atomic weight of fluorine is 32, so that the weights of the two molecules to be separated are 235 + 6 x 32 = 427 and 238 + 6 x 32 = 430, that is, a difference of only 3 parts in 430, roughly 0.75 percent—about half the difference between atoms of U-235 and U-238. With this small difference many stages of diffusion would be required to obtain almost pure U-235. It was realized that the number of stages could be reduced if forces acting on the molecules could be increased differentially, as would be possible in a centrifuge—in which the heavier atoms would tend to be thrown to the outside. However, at the time of the first development of nuclear weapons and for some time afterward, it was not possible to solve the engineering problems of high-speed centrifuges. Recourse was made to a relatively simpler process, although one not without its own serious problems, in which the uranium hexafluoride gas was brought into contact with a membrane: the lighter molecules tended to diffuse through each membrane at a slightly higher rate than the heavier molecules, so that a mixture somewhat richer in U-235 could be fed to the next stage up the cascade of cells, while the residue was fed to a cell further down the line. The process therefore required an immense quantity of gas to be circulated and recirculated, for a relatively small output of U-235. To provide this circulation large numbers of high-grade pumps are required and the plant has to be raised to a suitable operating temperature. A gaseous diffusion plant, then, has to be on a very large scale and requires the input of electricity equal to that for a city. These distinguishing features and the precautions that have to be taken with plants handling radioactive materials, such as those relating to the health of workers and public and the control and monitoring of effluents, would make a gaseous diffusion plant difficult to conceal.

Few details of the gaseous diffusion process have been revealed, but it has been independently developed in the United States, Soviet Union, Great Britain, France, and probably China. The delays and high cost of bringing the French plant into operation have probably been due to the technical difficulties referred to above.

Weapons-grade U-235 has to be highly enriched, that is, almost pure. Fuel for reactors does not always have to be so pure, although there are some reactors fueled with highly enriched U-235. Many reactors require uranium fuel that contains 2-5 percent U-235, and the demand for this low-enriched grade of uranium is likely to increase as more recently developed types of reactors are built and as smaller units are installed in more isolated urban communities.

INSPECTION OF THE GASEOUS DIFFUSION PROCESS

The formidable technical difficulties of the gaseous diffusion process, the size of plant compared with its output, and the enormous electrical power consumption together act to hinder dissemination of the process to many countries because of economic constraints and would also make the plant difficult to conceal, thus facilitating verification by an opponent or an international inspectorate.

Production of U-235 so far has been a government monopoly in each of the countries where the gaseous diffusion plant has been developed. While it is likely that most countries will continue with the present arrangements, in the case of the United States these are contrary to the traditional limitations on government enterprise; and as emphasis has shifted from military to civil requirements, there has been increasing pressure for the diffusion plants to be operated by commercial companies. Such a change could complicate verification, in that there could well be a reluctance to expose commercial secrets and, with the increasing international market for U-235, commercial operation may increase the possibilities of dissemination of knowledge of the process and proliferation of plants through commercial licensing, subsidiaries, and cartels. Already arrangements have been made for uranium of Belgian origin to be converted to tetrafluoride (UF_4) and to hexafluoride (UF_6) in France prior to enrichment in the United States.

Some of the technical features of the gaseous diffusion process can be used to facilitate control. It has already been pointed out that the sheer size of the plant, its requirement for electricity and the precautions necessary in its operation would make it difficult to conceal. Other features can be used to reduce the possibility of diversion.

In the plant the quantity of gas being handled at each stage becomes less as the degree of enrichment increases, so that at the high enrichment end the pumps and other components are much smaller.

Inspection of a plant would reveal any capability to produce highly enriched material: if the plant did not have small pumps and other equipment it would not be able to separate highly enriched uranium, so a ban on equipment under a certain size (except for laboratory-scale equipment for research purposes) might be an effective means for prohibiting the capability.

If production of uranium hexafluoride containing more than, say, five or 10 percent U-235 were prohibited, then even if some diversion did take place, a very large plant would be required to enrich this material to weapons grade, with consequently increased chance of detection.

When uranium hexafluoride is transported, it is carried in special vessels. To avoid criticality accidents the minimum size of the container must be related to the degree of enrichment. Highly enriched uranium hexafluoride can be carried only in small amounts, and a prohibition on small containers would hinder the safe transport of enriched uranium.* (See Chapter 7.) Of course, such a prohibition on mobile equipment would be much more difficult to enforce than one on fixed equipment such as pumps.

An indirect means for checking the output from the highly enriched end of the plant would be to check the output from the depleted end of the plant. This would bear an exact relationship to the highly enriched output and added together, they would, over time, be equal to the input.

THE GAS CENTRIFUGE PROCESS

At the time when the different processes for enrichment of uranium were being considered, the advantages of the gas centrifuge were recognized.* Subjecting the gaseous mixture of isotopes to high centrifugal forces would accentuate the differences between the molecules of different masses so that each stage of enrichment could be more efficient. The theoretical ratio of enrichment at each stage for the gas centrifuge process is 1.05, as compared with 1.005 for each stage of the gaseous diffusion process. While these differences may appear to be small, the gaseous diffusion process requires ten

---

*"U-235 by Centrifuge," Scientific American (May 1969).

stages to effect the same degree of enrichment as one stage by gas centrifuge.*

The problems with a gas centrifuge plant include those which relate to the high chemical activity of "Hex" (uranium hexafluoride) and to the requirement to maintain the whole of the apparatus at a temperature and pressure at which Hex is in the gaseous form. In addition, severe operating conditions were imposed by the very high speeds of rotation of the centrifuges—that is, the materials had to be strong enough to avoid disintegration and resistant to corrosion by Hex, bearings had to be developed that would permit long runs without wear and seizing; and leakproof connections were required.

These problems could not be solved in time for the process to be a rival to gas diffusion. However, experimental work continued, and there have been continuous advances in engineering technology that have gone a long way toward solving the problems. The repercussions of development of a successful process were only too obvious to governments; and at the beginning of the 1960's actions were taken to reduce the possibility of dissemination of the techniques. In the United States work being conducted by private industry was taken over by government agencies in order to preserve secrecy similar to that applied to the gaseous diffusion process. In Europe a gentleman's agreement was reached between Great Britain, West Germany, and the Netherlands not to divulge details of their research to others.**

The possibilities of the gas centrifuge's becoming a serious rival to the gaseous diffusion process became more widely known when the three European countries—Great Britain, West Germany, and the Netherlands—announced their intention to explore the possibilities of setting up two manufacturing plants in Europe. While the stage in technical developments that had been reached gave the capability to build plants, the incentive to do so was the long-delayed but coming economic advantage of nuclear power over fossil fuels.

---

*C. F. Barnaby, "The Gas Centrifuge Project," Science Journal (August 1969).

**For details, see "Centrifuges Promise Cheaper U-235: Holland; Germany and the UK Move to Corner Market," Science Journal (February 1969).

The United States has an advantage in the production of enriched uranium by the gaseous diffusion process because of the low cost of hydroelectricity, so that without the gas centrifuge process the greatly expanded nuclear power industry of Western Europe could be dependent upon supplies of enriched uranium from America. The gas centrifuge process only requires 10-15 percent of the electrical power input of gaseous diffusion and thus is more suitable for the European market. Another advantage from the European point of view is that a gas centrifuge plant could be brought into service unit by unit, rather than the whole plant having to operate together.

A great number of centrifuge and other units, the number running into the millions, would be required; and these would be of new materials and produced to very high standards of engineering quality. Given the high level of engineering skill in Europe, there does not appear to be any reason why there should be any major problem in manufacturing the equipment to the necessary standards. At the same time, new industries would have to be created for high-precision machining—industries, moreover, that would have an assured and expanding market, at least in the beginning; it is such industries that are leading the technological revolution in the United States. A spillover of advanced technology into other fields could occur, as has already happened in the construction of nuclear reactors.

Britain and France already have gas diffusion plants that were built to supply U-235 for thermonuclear weapons. The British plant at Capenhurst was put on a care-and-maintenance basis following an agreement with the United States for an exchange of uranium U-235 for British plutonium, and it ceased production of U-235 for military purposes in 1963.

As the emphasis changed in the British civil nuclear power program from the Stage I "Magnox" gas-cooled reactors to later types of reactor that were fueled with low-enriched uranium, the early stages of the Capenhurst plant were brought back into service again.

THE GAS CENTRIFUGE AND PROLIFERATION

Installation of nuclear reactors on a worldwide scale for the production of power will confer on many countries an option to manufacture nuclear weapons, and this has given serious concern to a number of writers on strategy: the Non-Proliferation Treaty is seen as an inadequate instrument to guard against this possibility. However, so far plutonium can be used only to make atomic—that is, fission—

weapons, the maximum yield from which is on the order of .50 megaton (this is discussed later). It would, therefore, be necessary also to have available delivery systems of fair accuracy.

Proliferation of facilities for separating U-235 are regarded as even more alarming, since the way would then be open to production of nuclear—that is, fusion—weapons, for which U-235 is thought to be required for the fission trigger.* Fusion weapons could be of such high yield and could devastate such large areas as to make the accuracy of delivery less significant; relatively crude means, such as civil aircraft, could be employed. Other countries could more easily acquire nuclear weapons, and this could be done without the indicators from the development and testing of sophisticated nuclear delivery systems. Doubt of intentions and suspicion of perhaps quite innocent activities could increase, perhaps causing international incidents from interference with civil airlines and shipping. Now that international collaboration has been established in the development of the gas centrifuge process, and however well justified it is on economic grounds—or even from the practical point of view as regards control—it might be more difficult to deny know-how to other countries with nuclear power programs.

THORIUM AND URANIUM-233

Thorium is more abundant than uranium and can also be used as a fuel in some nuclear reactors. Thorium is a fertile material, that is, although itself unable to sustain a nuclear chain reaction, when it is irradiated with neutrons in a reactor it is transmuted to uranium-233, which is fissile in the same way as U-235 and Pu-239.

Research and development have demonstrated that thorium can be employed in this way, but at present there does not appear to be an economic justification for using it on a large scale. The fuel elements that contained thorium can be left in the reactor so that some of the U-233 is "burned" in situ, or the fuel elements can be removed and the U-233 extracted in a chemical separation plant. An experimental reactor fueled with U-233 has been operated at the Oak Ridge National Laboratory of the U.S. Atomic Energy Commission.

From the arms controller's point of view, U-233 is another fissile material like U-235 and Pu-239 that can be used as a fuel in civil

---

*The technical reasons why this is so have not been published.

nuclear reactors, or as an explosive in nuclear weapons. Controls that apply to the other fissile material must also apply to thorium. Because U-233 is chemically different from the unconverted thorium in spent fuel, separation can be done in a chemical plant—which, despite the precautions necessary to protect the workers and the public, would be easier to develop, build, and operate than either of the plants depending upon diffusion. Use of thorium as a fuel for nuclear reactors would therefore provide a simpler and cheaper route for separation of a pure fissile material (U-233) than the processes for production of U-235, and probably would also be cheaper than the processes for manufacture and separation of pure plutonium.

It has not been revealed in the open literature whether U-233 is suitable, like U-235, as a trigger for a fusion (hydrogen) weapon.

CHAPTER

7

CONTROL OF NUCLEAR MATERIAL

NATIONAL PRECAUTIONS FOR NUCLEAR FACILITIES

In earlier chapters the production of plutonium and of uranium-235 was discussed and some attention was given to special features of the process and materials themselves that could be used to enhance control. In this chapter more general problems of the control of nuclear materials will be examined, commencing with the controls that have to be imposed for the safety of operatives and the public. In general there are three kinds of precautions: those required to prevent inadvertent uncontrolled nuclear chain reactions; those to prevent exposure to or ingestion of radioactive materials by operatives or local public during normal operation of the plant; and emergency procedures to protect the citizenry at large and even those in neighboring countries from the effects of a serious accident.

The first kind of accident is generally referred to as a criticality incident and may be accompanied by an explosion—not in itself likely to be of great magnitude, although some radioactive material might be scattered about. The precautions taken to prevent criticality incidents are discussed below.

The second kind of accident would most likely arise from what can be regarded as poor housekeeping in a plant and could involve some of the operatives. The public locally could become involved through inadvertent discharges of liquid or gaseous effluents. As will be shown later, the necessity for taking precautions to safeguard the operatives and public can be used to help identify nuclear facilities, and this applies also to the emergency procedures for large-scale accidents. The latter include explosions, inadvertent criticality, damage to the structure of nuclear reactors, and serious fires in nuclear materials processing plants. Furthermore, monitoring of some of the safeguard systems may also be a form of control.

Because of the danger of criticality accidents and the dangers from handling radioactive materials, countries with nuclear power programs have legislation and regulations to protect the operators and public against exposure to radiation. Precautions that are taken against external irradiation and ingestion of nuclear materials include assessments of the risks by independent experts and routine monitoring of manufacturing plants, their environments and effluents, the wearing of film badges by operators, and regular medical checks.

CONTROL OF CRITICALITY

Bringing together more than a critical mass of fissile material will cause a self-sustaining nuclear chain reaction, with the release of fission energy and a flux of radioactivity that can damage human tissue and, if the exposure is enough, cause death. A few nuclear accidents have resulted from the inadvertent bringing together of super-critical masses, and in these accidents most of the injuries have been from neutrons. The release of energy has seldom been enough to cause an explosion; and the heat generated has generally blown the assembly apart, so that the mass is no longer critical and the chain reaction has been self-limiting.

To generate the enormous explosion of a nuclear weapon, the fissile material has to be held together long enough for enough of it to be consumed to produce the explosive yield required. In a nuclear reactor during normal operations the neutrons in excess of those for a just-critical chain reaction are absorbed in control rods that automatically adjust to maintain the power release at the level set by the control instruments.

The designs of nuclear reactors are intended to prevent serious accidents. Since nuclear reactors contain many minimum critical masses of fissile material, they are built, as far as possible, with natural and built-in safety features, such as an increase in the loss of neutrons at high temperatures and automatic shutdown mechanisms that react to excessive neutron flux.

In handling fissile materials there are a number of ways in which the risks of criticality accidents may be controlled.[1] Generally precautions can be divided into administrative and physical controls. It is not necessary to describe in detail the various methods, but two examples will be given. A typical administrative control is to prohibit more than a stipulated batch size that is less than half the critical mass, so that even if by mistake two batches are together in an area and an emergency occurs, there will still be no possibility of accident. The worst emergency is generally flooding with water, which is both a moderator and a reflector for neutrons—most accidents have been with fissile material in solution. An example of a physical control would be the use of "safe-by-shape" vessels in a chemical plant. Vessels of this type are so narrow that most of the neutrons that are released can escape from the surfaces, and a chain reaction is impossible however much fissile material the vessel contains.

The minimum critical mass depends upon the purity of the fissile material, and generally much larger batches can be handled if nonfissile material is also present to separate the fissile atoms and to capture the neutrons. Exceptions to this generalization are moderators and absorbers, such as graphite and water, which, as described above, can make a noncritical mass into a critical mass. In the case of natural and enriched uranium the U-235 is diluted with U-238. Some idea of the effect of dilution is shown in Table 5 for nuclear safe masses—that is, amounts that are less than half of the minimum critical mass when fully reflected by water, to allow for both accidental double batching and flooding at the same time. From considerations such as these it can be suggested that a possible precaution the inspecting authority could impose would be that only movement containers above a certain size were available. This would ensure that the would-be violator had the choice of making his movement in rather large, obvious, and probably identified containers which, if filled completely, would contain more than a critical mass and be dangerous, or attempting to smuggle small quantities of material in prohibited containers.

Small amounts of fissile material required in metallurgical, chemical, and physical laboratories for research purposes would at first sight appear to be difficult to control. However, it is necessary to have elaborate accounting systems to prevent more than a critical mass of fissile material in the laboratories, working areas, or glove boxes in order to avoid an accident. Because of the high costs of these materials and their toxicity, particularly that of plutonium, avoidance of loss is an important part of the management of the facilities. Many of the operations with plutonium and uranium-238 are carried out in glove boxes, that is, totally enclosed containment, to prevent spread of toxicity and to retain an inert gas atmosphere that prevents unwanted oxidation. Transfer in and out of the boxes requires special

TABLE 5

Nuclear Safe Masses for Uranium

Composition		Mass
Nearly pure	U-235	0.35kg
Enriched to 10%	U-235	0.60kg
Enriched to 2%	U-235	2.00kg
Enriched to 1%	U-235	20.00kg

Source: A. J. Mallett, "Mass (Batch) Control and Its Application," in Criticality Control in Chemical and Metallurgical Plant, Karlsrune symposium (Brussels: European Nuclear Energy Agency, 1961).

precautions. Because of the high cost of fissile materials, special experimental techniques were developed that used only small quantities. Taking into account these restrictions, if the inspectorate had access to movement records it would be difficult to divert fissile material on a significant scale without falsifying numerous book entries and involving a number of individuals.

INTELLIGENCE AND INSPECTION FOR CONTROL OF FISSILE MATERIALS

Intelligence is an effective and continuously operating control, and it is often possible to know in advance at least the main direction in which progress is being made in other countries. Atomic weapon development is thought to require, at a minimum, several hundred scientists and a great deal of equipment, and to take several years: it is difficult to hide such activities completely. It is not even necessary to depend upon espionage for much of the information: directories of scientific manpower, attendance at national and international scientific conferences, research publications, personal contacts, and special training being given at universities, will provide indications that can be supplemented by direct visits, consular activities, etc. In addition to the fissile materials, nuclear reactors require other special materials. While it is not likely that these could be controlled, since they are also used in other industries, monitoring of their usage could help in identifying some nuclear activities. Typical of these special materials are graphite, heavy water, and some hydrocarbons and sodium used as moderators and coolants, canning materials such as zirconium and beryllium; materials for construction, such as large steel and concrete vessels; and components such as pumps, valves, nuclear instrumentation, and control devices. Most nonnuclear countries permit fairly unrestricted travel; of the Communist countries where there are restrictions on travel, most visitors are under close surveillance. However, there are limitations on the confidence which can be given to an intelligence system alone, and an official inspection system has particular advantages:

It would lend extra stigma to violations

It would increase the confidence in the assessment that states are not engaged in weapons manufacture: even a slight gain in confidence might be sufficient to prevent a local arms race

Without overt inspection it would be difficult to reassure a government that its neighbors were not engaged in nuclear activity, if the only evidence was that provided by the intelligence organization of another country.

IDENTIFYING NUCLEAR FACILITIES

For the purposes of "national verification" systems—in other words, intelligence—and for international or adversary inspection, it would be necessary to be able to identify plants that might be concerned with the processing of nuclear materials.

A nuclear plant does not have one unique distinguishing feature; but it does have many features that, taken together, would tend to indicate its presence and purpose. Elaborate precautions have to be taken to safeguard the workers in the plant and the general public against radioactivity. The workers may be required to wear overalls and shoes or boots that must be left in the plant and not taken home. Laundries for the clothing would be more elaborate than usual and would contain monitors for radioactivity.

Special protective clothing or gas masks would be required for some operations, along with washing and shower facilities and equipment for monitoring personnel for radioactivity. The workers would be given periodic medical checks that would be somewhat more extensive than those normal in industry, and the medical services and arrangements would be on a sufficient scale and coordinated for dealing with large accidents. The plant would be required to have health physics personnel who would be responsible for monitoring the plant for radioactivity, for ensuring that certain workers carry film badges or dosimeters, that the level of radioactivity in effluents is within the permitted level, and that there is no buildup of pollution in the environment. For this purpose samples would be taken of air, water, soil, and herbiage outside the perimeter of the plant. From time to time exercises would be carried out to test the emergency procedures, and some of the larger-scale exercises would involve the police and local authorities.

We have already seen that one of the objects of an inspection system for known plants would be to attempt as far as possible to ensure that if diversions did occur, they would be at stages where only a large clandestine plant could complete the processing—and such a plant would be more easily discovered.

In addition to control arrangements made locally, some kinds of central organizations would also be required to supervise these precautions and to ensure that national standards were being applied consistently, to keep overall records and files, and to issue film badges, to process them after use, to record the exposures of personnel, and to conduct inquiries when statutory doses are exceeded. In addition other officials would be responsible for permits to discharge solid, liquid, and gaseous effluents and for ensuring that the quantities released were not excessive and that undue contamination of the environment was not resulting from these discharges. In a modern industrial state that could support a nuclear power program, the activities described above would be the responsibilities of a number of different government departments; and while it might be difficult for a foreign inspectorate to get an overall view of the different activities, access to many different kinds of records at the detailed level would provide many opportunities for cross-checking.

FORMS OF INTERNATIONAL CONTROL

The Baruch Plan

Immediately after World War II had been concluded by a demonstration of the power of nuclear weapons, the U.S. government put forward the Baruch Plan, designed largely by scientists, for internationalizing civilian nuclear power. In retrospect the Baruch Plan can be seen as impossibly idealistic, since it would have put immense power in the hands of an international atomic development agency. Apart from what would now be regarded as the naïveté of the ideas, international authority of this scope is quite contrary to the Soviet principles of national sovereignty and the great power veto. The Baruch Plan has been represented by its critics as an attempt to retain U.S. monopoly, since the United States said it would surrender its nuclear weapons only when an effective organization was in existence. Raymond Aron has stressed in this connection, "An agreement on partial disarmament has no serious chance of being approved unless it gives neither side an advantage, in appearance or reality."[2]

At the time the Baruch Plan was put forward, it was thought that there would be a rapidly increasing demand for civil nuclear power. However, partly because of improvements in management, the conventional fuel industries became much more economic and the demand for nuclear power has been delayed. In the opinion of some writers, if the United States had been concerned with maintaining its lead in nuclear engineering, particularly because of the advantages of a military monopoly, a better policy would have been to encourage the reduction in costs of conventional fuels so that these remained more economically attractive for other countries. Instead, the United States made large investments in research and development in civil nuclear engineering, both for reactors and for civil engineering projects, and in addition provided power and research reactors at advantageous terms to a number of countries, thus providing not only possible access to plutonium but also a cadre of trained personnel in countries that would have had great difficulty in mounting operations of the same magnitude with indigenous resources. On the other hand, if nuclear reactors had not been supplied by the United States and other countries, it is possible that some of the recipient countries would themselves have made greater investments in research and development and would have built reactors that would not have been subject to bilateral or international control.

Cutoff in Production of Fissile Material

The world stockpile of nuclear armaments has been estimated to have a total yield equivalent to about 320,000 million tons of TNT, that is, about 100 tons of TNT equivalent for every living person.

The quantities of fissile material already produced are vastly in excess of what could be rationally required in any circumstances, and several proposals have been made for a cutoff in production. The U.S. delegate to ENDC suggested that the elements of a cutoff agreement would be the following:[3]

At an agreed date nuclear-weapon states would halt all production of fissionable material for use in nuclear weapons

Production of fissionable material for peaceful purposes would continue

The IAEA would be asked to safeguard the nuclear material in each state's peaceful nuclear activities and to verify the shutdown of facilities for production of fissionable material that are closed.

This latter point represents a change in policy by the United States, which had previously believed that adversary inspection was more appropriate for this type of agreement.

The purpose of inspection for a cutoff agreement is to provide a high degree of assurance that there would be no significant increase in existing stockpiles of materials for weapons use after the coming into force of the agreement. The proposed system would subject three types of facility to inspection: U-235 separation plants, which produce enriched uranium; nuclear reactors, which also produce fissionable material; and chemical separation plants, which isolate the products of reactor operations. There would be no need to inspect mines, nor would there be any requirement to inspect nuclear stockpiles.

The first stage would be a declaration of the numbers, sites, and outputs of U-235 separation, reactor, and chemical separation plants, both those to remain in operation and any to be shut down, together with schedules of production for different purposes—for example, research, power and propulsion reactors, and explosives for civil purposes, together with transfers to other states and international organizations.

With these declarations the objectives of inspection would be the following:

To check that closed plants did not resume operation

To guard against overproduction or diversion from operating plant

To ensure that no undeclared plants were engaged in clandestine production of fissionable material for use contrary to the agreement.

For a closed plant an initial inspection would be followed by infrequent and irregular visits, since restarting a plant is difficult and time-consuming. Monitoring of allowed production of U-235 is much simpler than might be thought. In the first place, perimeter inspection systems would be required round the processing block to check input, output, and tails (i.e., wastes containing some uranium) for U-235 content. A similar arrangement would be required at any U-235 storage areas. Occasionally special arrangements might be required when discrepancies occurred through inconsistencies in analysis and weighings and when unaccounted-for process losses reached some maximum figure. Exactly the same checks would in any case be necessary to avoid criticality accidents, and it might be possible for inspection to serve both purposes: control of throughput to avoid diversion to nuclear weapons and prevention of large accumulations that could be dangerous, with the international inspectorate supervising and checking a national system.

Cutback in Production of Fissile Material

While it has not been possible to obtain an agreement to cut off production of fissile material, parallel declarations of the shutdown of some military production facilities have been made by the United States, the Soviet Union, and Great Britain. No arrangements were made for inspections to be carried out and the cutback was essentially unilateral, unverified, and difficult to challenge.

A more recent development in cutback has been in connection with the Non-Proliferation Treaty. Many of the nonnuclear powers have seen the treaty as very one-sided, requiring them to give up their nuclear options with little reciprocal sacrifice by the nuclear powers. It may have been partly to disarm these criticisms that in 1966 the United States and Great Britain made agreements with the IAEA to place some of their nuclear facilities under safeguard. The British contribution was the twin-reactor station at Bradwell, with an output of 1,100 milliwatts (thermal), which was, at the time, the largest single installation in the world. The first inspection was carried out in the November following signing of the agreement, the purpose of this and subsequent visits being to ensure that plutonium yielded as a by-product in the manufacture of electricity was not used for weapons. Since the British chemical reprocessing plant is not inspected, the plutonium entering the plant loses its identity and an equivalent amount of plutonium leaving the plant is earmarked. The problems of inspection and control of a chemical reprocessing plant are being investigated in the United States. While those reactors which are safeguarded in the United States and Great Britain represent only a fraction of the civil capacity to manufacture plutonium, the experience gained should enable suitable techniques to be developed for both gas and water-cooled reactors.

As a means of control of cutback and cutoff, there would be fewer technical problems if particular plants were completely shut down than if output were reduced or part allocated to civil purposes.

Reduction of Stocks of Fissile Material

The stage after cutoff in the production of fissile material would be a reduction in stocks of nuclear material held by the nuclear powers. An organization to control stocks would, of course, operate most successfully when there was no preexisting fissile material economy. Where such an economy had existed, the task would be much more difficult. The main tasks of the organization would be to ensure the accuracy of records and stocks in existence, to ensure that no fissile material was being diverted to weapons, to ensure the control of continuing operations, and to guard against the possibility of there being clandestine plants for the manufacture or separation of fissile material.

In order to divert material from current production it would be necessary to reroute part of the flow of material at some stage or stages of manufacture. The problems would be essentially similar to those discussed earlier in relation to the nonnuclear powers but, because of the number of existing facilities and the possibilities of hidden stockpiles, the problems of control would be much greater. A control scheme that embraced all stages from mining on would be unduly costly in men and funds, and some stages would be difficult to justify. A more viable scheme would be to concentrate attention on those specific stages to which attention was drawn above.

The basic methods of control of fissile materials are physical security and technical surveillance. Most practical schemes would rely on one or other at particular stages, with the other means of control as a secondary check. During its history, from the time it is mined or created in a reactor, fissile material undergoes various chemical and physical processes that change its chemical composition and form. At some stages it can be counted, weighed, or measured; at other times it is combined with other materials and processed, often in continuous-flow plants, through a series of stages: here input and output would have to be measured over a period of time. Material in transit and store could be controlled by a system of invoices and receipts, which could be supervised or operated by the inspectorate.

During the time material was in the plant, technical surveillance would be necessary to ensure that all fissile material entering the plant could be accounted for as output, in wastes, or in accumulations within the plant. The inspectorate would have to ensure the accuracy of the records system and of procedures for weighing, measuring, sampling, and analyzing, by spot checks on instruments and methods. The accuracy with which the inspectorate could verify the amounts of fissile material would depend to some extent on the plant itself, its history, its performance, and the degree of managerial control.

The accuracy of declarations of past production would lead to some uncertainties. Material accounting processes used in the past might not have been accurate and reliable; and in addition to systematic errors, from time to time there would be other discrepancies due to adventitious mistakes and losses which could not be accounted for and would have to be written off. It would not be obvious to the international inspectorate whether all or some of these discrepancies had been used to cover diversions in anticipation of an agreement, or if the records had been consistently faked over a long time to disguise diversions. Another source of doubt would be that original records might not be preserved for more than a few years, even if summaries were available. Measurements of the quantities of by-products—that is, fission products and depleted uranium—could be used to check on the total amounts of fissile material produced.

A determined violator would have no technical difficulties in falsifying the totals shown in the records in the ways indicated above; but this would be at some cost, and a great number of people would be involved, so that there would be a probability that the activities would be revealed to the international inspectorate. In addition, there would be some likelihood that the clandestine plants to process the diverted material would themselves be discovered.

The international inspectorate would have to prepare a balance sheet of all the fissile material entering the system, that leaving the plants in various forms, and losses in the plant and in weapons trials. The latter would pose particular difficulties; and an accurate accounting might involve a knowledge of the designs of weapons exploded, because otherwise it might be claimed that more fissile material had been destroyed than actually had been the case because weapons involved were inefficient (i.e., used more fissile material).

The initial work of installing the system and verifying past production could be carried out only by very high grade personnel, probably available only from the nuclear powers; and it might be necessary to secure such staff for a year or two, while the personnel for more routine long-term operations were being recruited and trained. A source for the latter personnel could be retired military officers from technical branches.

Existing International Control Agencies

Present international systems for the control of atomic energy are the following:

Bilateral systems of Canada, the United States, and Great Britain

Western European Union (WEU)

European Nuclear Energy Agency (ENEA)

Euratom

International Atomic Energy Agency (IAEA).

Bilateral systems were designed to prevent diversion of fissile materials to weapons. Generally this was achieved by incorporation of a prohibition in the agreement. The physical means adopted was to require that the spent fuel elements be returned to the supplier for extraction of plutonium and of U-235. A weakness of such a system that has already been mentioned is that there would be a suspicion, if no more, that in order to secure a commercial agreement against competitors, the terms themselves or their enforcement was not sufficiently rigorous.

Because of these doubts and in order to strengthen the IAEA, many bilateral agreements, as they have come up for renegotiation, have been converted to agreements with the IAEA.

The WEU Arms Control Agency has little power and no nuclear experts: its inspections are by agreement with the inspected party and thus appear weaker than those of other agencies. On the other hand, it has built up valuable and unique experience and techniques in identifying key items in weapons systems, including nuclear delivery systems and dual purpose systems—fields in which other agencies have no responsibilities, and possibly no expertise. It has built up library and reference resources relating to weapons manufacture of a kind not normally available in international agencies.

The ENEA is distinguished by having a sanctions system and a court of judges, but it controls few plants. In the past it has played only a minor role in the control of nuclear power in Europe; but in the late 1960's it became responsible for the safeguards for the Eurochemic international reprocessing plant in Belgium, that is, a key stage at which plutonium could be diverted most readily.

Euratom has more extensive responsibilities than inspection and is involved in many facets of the commercial exploitation of nuclear power in Europe. It has a strong team of inspectors who have powers of access to data, places, persons, and facilities under their control; and it monitors the flow of material between plants. Once they have been accredited, inspectors can exercise their functions throughout the EEC. Hence a tight system of control exists.

Thus Euratom is concerned with the kind of nuclear materials management that exists in the nuclear powers and is concerned not only with inspection but also with the most economic procurement of supplies and raw materials, the most profitable allocation of resources within the system, guarding against process loss and pilfering, and ensuring that unpremeditated and other releases of radioactivity that might endanger members of the public or workers are avoided.

In a fully integrated national or regional system it would be possible to reduce international inspection to a few key processes. Euratom, for example, requires submission of plans for chemical reprocessing facilities but not of individual reactors. It also has the right to scrutinize the design of experiments that might complicate the safeguarding of fissile material. In addition Euratom has other responsibilities that include consultation on significant investments by member countries, development and implementation of technical and managerial standards, and responsibilities relating to the safe design and operation of plants. It follows that inspection to prevent diversions of material for military purposes can rely on extensive cross-checks. In a fully international organization there would exist a potential for the leakage of important commercial and military information: Euratom would tend to limit dissemination of much of the information to members of the control system.

Inspection Under the Non-Proliferation Treaty

During negotiations for the Non-Proliferation Treaty (NPT) two pressures developed: many states pressed for the IAEA to become the inspecting authority, while Western European states demanded that the IAEA delegate its authority for inspections to Euratom, claiming that inspection would be more effective and at the same time preserve commercial security. Since designs and specifications for nuclear plants, such as reactors, are generally published about the time they are first brought into operation, this concern about commercial security may have been somewhat exaggerated; and the claims for secrecy have aroused probably quite unjustified suspicions as to the motives for favoring Euratom.

A particularly important case is that of France, which as a nuclear power would be exempt from inspection by the IAEA under the terms of the NPT, but under the Euratom agreement is the most closely inspected nuclear power. The possibilities of dissemination of French military information to other members of Euratom are obvious; on the other hand, if France were not inspected, there would be an incentive for other European powers to attempt to have their sensitive nuclear developments carried out in France.

Under the NPT prime responsibility for inspection would go to the IAEA. The IAEA has 102 member states and has limited authority over power-producing reactors. On the other hand, in 1967 the IAEA had only 13 inspectors; and it has been estimated that 200 would be required in the future for operating on a world-wide scale. The IAEA appoints its own inspectors, that is, they are not loaned or seconded from national authorities; but countries whose facilities are to be inspected have rights of objection to individual inspectors. For political reasons the inspectors will have to be recruited from many countries, and possibly some will be without great experience in nuclear power processes, so that a very considerable training program would have to be mounted. Results of inspections are assessed centrally in Vienna and the data is open to international surveillance, which can be compared with the type of EEC inspection in Euratom. The arrangements for inspection depend on the size of the facility and vary from periodic inspections to appointment of resident inspectors. The IAEA specifies one inspection per year for every five kg of fissionable material installed in the facility or in the annual throughput. When more than 60 kg of fissionable material is involved, continuous residual inspection may be imposed.

As has been said, the IAEA is taking over bilateral arrangements with 13 countries, but these are mostly for research reactors that require only occasional visits. The IAEA has not yet had the opportunity to demonstrate its competence in dealing with large-scale inspections: earlier we saw that the United States and Great Britain have both made arrangements with the IAEA for inspections of large civil nuclear reactors producing plutonium, and this will no doubt provide experience and aid in developing techniques. Apart from these arrangements, which seem to be intended mainly for the investigation of techniques, another important development has occurred.

In order to reduce the possibilities of transfer of information on nuclear weapons, the United States for many years preferred to advocate a system of adversary inspection between the nuclear superpowers; but in the late 1960's this policy changed and, as we saw earlier, the United States has announced that under an agreement to open up its major facilities, it would do so to the IAEA.

Barnaby suggests that the IAEA should be strengthened by the provision of more funds and support to make it the ". . . body recognised as having the major responsibility for international co-operation in the development of nuclear energy."[4] Not only could provision of nuclear power reactors to developing countries be more effectively organised, but the operation of the nuclear power industry itself, and the spread of nuclear weapons, could be more strictly controlled. Besides carrying out assessment studies, the IAEA could act as a consultant on the choice of reactor systems and hire out fuel, so that spent fuel would have to be returned for processing to the IAEA and the plutonium recovered would be in custody until hired out as fuel for fast reactors. Countries able to build reactors and those able to supply fuel and uranium could cooperate with agreed export policies aimed at avoiding proliferation. The nuclear powers could provide the IAEA with information on national safeguards systems and participate in further studies.

While many who are concerned about the spread of uncontrolled nuclear facilities would echo these sentiments, much depends on the degree to which the nuclear powers would cooperate and support the IAEA.

TECHNICAL FEATURES OF NUCLEAR FACILITIES

Little attention appears to have been paid to technical requirements that will make the tasks of inspection easier.[5] Some of these have been described earlier. The separation of fissile materials from reactor fuel requires a complex and expensive plant. U-235 could be separated from natural uranium feed, but the feed would first have to be converted to uranium hexafluoride, a difficult procedure, and then processed in a gaseous diffusion plant. The technical details of the gaseous diffusion plant have not been published, but it is obvious from the French experience that bringing a plant into production is a difficult and costly process. Movement of irradiated fuel elements requires very heavy transport flasks because of the high level of radiation; and the chemical separation plant has to be designed for remote handling, the operators controlling the procedures from behind a thick concrete wall.

The only way in which these processes can be avoided is by the purchase of pure U-235 or plutonium, so that a ban on the sale of more than experimental quantities of these materials would seal this source of supply. Fortunately, pure fissile materials are unsuitable as such for power and research reactor fuels; they are used in alloys (natural uranium can be so regarded) or in compounds—carbides, oxides, and nitrides. Recovery of pure fissile materials from these alloys or compounds would involve difficult chemical processes; hence an additional difficulty could be placed in the path of possible makers of clandestine weapons if there was an agreement to supply fissile material only as compounds or alloys and not to supply pure fissile materials in more than small quantities.

ENFORCEMENT OF INTERNATIONAL CONTROLS

Several treaties and proposed treaties would permit withdrawal in the case of overwhelming national interest. This is in some senses a weakness, but it is doubted whether governments would be prepared to sign agreements without such a clause. In addition, the ability to withdraw can be used by a nation as a counter to political and diplomatic pressures.[6]

It may be for this reason that comparatively little attention has been paid to considering actions that could be taken to prevent violation of agreements, such as the application of sanctions by cutting off supplies of uranium; this might not be immediately successful, since at this time it is likely that a stockpile of fissile material will have been accumulated and the country could be exploiting its indigenous sources of uranium. There are economic reasons for stockpiling plutonium and U-235 at particular times to provide the hundreds of kilograms of fuel for fast reactors, or for use in thermal reactors to replace part of the natural or low-enriched uranium fuel, either by direct addition or as separate fuel elements, a procedure known as "spiking." Legitimate stockpiling could act as a cover for accumulation for weapons production.

BENEFITS TO A WEAPONS PROGRAM FROM CIVIL NUCLEAR POWER

Many nontechnical writers have expressed deep concern with the possible advantages that a civil nuclear power industry could have for a weapons program. To anyone familiar with both industries it is often quite surprising how little contact there can be at the working level, and how different are the particular areas of research and technology. Essentially, the nuclear weapons industry is concerned with prompt and fast neutrons and physics research is oriented to determining facts about their release, lifetime, capture, etc., while the civil nuclear power industry has until recently been concerned mainly with the control and fate of delayed and slow neutrons. Metallurgists in the weapons industry are involved with the fabrication of batches of a few kilograms of pure fissile material; in the civil power industry they are concerned with the processing to fuel elements of ton quantities of natural or low-enriched uranium or with alloys or compounds. Engineers in the nuclear weapons industry are engaged in planning and conducting trials in remote areas, while their colleagues in the civil nuclear power industry build complex industrial plants. No less an authority than Sir John Cockcroft subscribed to the view that there is very little carry-over from one industry to the other.[7] However, on reflection it appears to this writer that a civil nuclear power industry would be able to assist a weapons program in many more ways than merely by providing raw materials.

In the first place, workers who transferred would already have a basic knowledge of the theory of nuclear fission, which is required in all the various disciplines; in addition other skills are quite directly transferable, such as health physics and the provision of such safety precautions as the control of effluents, the issuing of safety clothing, design of special laboratories and of "hot cells," chemical analysis, specialized engineering skills, and many other supporting activities. On balance it seems that a civil nuclear industry provides a strong potential for a weapons industry. This potential consists in a large part of human resources in the form of a reservoir of skilled managerial, scientific, and technically trained personnel available for either or both military and commercial industries. It also includes processes that are identical for both requirements, as shown in Figure 1. This potential may on the one hand be a threat, and on the other a deterrent, to other states considering the manufacture of weapons. As a threat it could induce other powers to acquire a counterthreat; as a deterrent it could make other powers cautious of actions that would make the threat into a reality.

NOTES

1. For example, see J. T. Daniels, "Criticality Inspection by the Authority Health and Safety Branch," U.K. Atomic Energy Authority paper AHSB (S). R-150 (1968).

2. Raymond Aron, On War: Atomic Weapons and Global Diplomacy (London. Secker and Warburg, 1958), p. 17.

3. A. S. Fisher, in Conference of Eighteen Nations Disarmament Committee Verbatim Record PV 401 (April 8, 1969).

4. C. F. Barnaby, Alan Lee Williams, and Geoffrey Lee Williams, The Nuclear Future, Fabian Tract 394 (London: The Fabian Society, June 1969) p. 38.

5. But see U.K. Delegation to the Eighteen Nations Conference on Disarmament, "The Technical Possibility of International Control of Fissile Material Production," ENDC/60 (August 31, 1962).

6. See D. Carlton, "Verification and Security Guarantees: Lessons from the past," in C. F. Barnaby, ed., Preventing the Spread of Nuclear Weapons (London: Souvenir Press, 1969).

7. John Cockcroft, "Perils of Nuclear Proliferation" in Nigel Calder, ed., Unless Peace Comes (New York: Viking Press, 1968).

CHAPTER

8

NUCLEAR WEAPONS

NUCLEAR FISSION

When a neutron is absorbed into the nucleus of a uranium-235 or a plutonium-239 atom, the nucleus is made highly unstable and almost instantaneously splits, generally into two fission fragments and two or three neutrons. The fission fragments are the nuclei of newly formed atoms and carry high electrical charges; thus they repel each other violently, losing kinetic energy as heat by colliding with other atoms. At the same time there is an instantaneous release of binding energy.

Some of the neutrons released are absorbed in nuclei of other fissile material to continue the chain reaction, while others may be absorbed by impurities or lost from the surface. Criticality occurs when, for each neutron absorbed, there is one fresh neutron to continue the chain reaction. In a supercritical mass the chain reaction spreads almost instantaneously.

To prevent premature criticality, the fissile material in a weapon must be separated until the explosion is required.

FISSION WEAPONS

To produce an explosion with fissile materials, several conditions are necessary:

The fissile mass must exceed that for the minimum critical mass when in its final configuration

The mass must be brought together rapidly

The fissile material must be held together until enough fissile material has fissioned.

If the fissile material is less than the critical mass, too many neutrons escape from the surface for a chain reaction. If the mass is not assembled rapidly and held together, fission heating will distort, melt, or evaporate the material, leading at the worst to a minor explosion. This will also happen if the mass is not prompt-critical, that is, critical with the neutrons released at the moment of fission. In a nuclear reactor the assembly of fissile material, moderator, and reflector is slightly subcritical for prompt neutrons and is made just critical by the release of delayed neutrons; control rods that absorb neutrons may be inserted or withdrawn so that the assembly is exactly critical.

The fission of one pound of U-235 or Pu-239 will release energy equivalent to that from 8,000 tons of TNT. Hence the fissile material actually fissioned in a 20 kiloton weapon would be almost 2.5 pounds.

The critical mass of U-235 or Pu-239 depends on a number of factors; loss of neutrons from the surface is at a minimum from a sphere and is reduced still further by surrounding the mass with a neutron reflector and by increasing the density. In the form of a sphere of metal the critical mass of U-235 is about 22 kilograms (48 pounds); the critical mass is about 0.8 kilograms when dispersed in water (which both reflects and moderates, that is, slows down, neutrons and increases the probability of capture). The critical mass for a weapon is between these limits; the exact mass required depends upon the skill and ingenuity of the designer in face of the constraints imposed in achieving a fully reliable assembly that can be readily stored, transported, maintained, armed, and detonated.

An essential requirement for a nuclear weapon is the very rapid bringing together of a supercritical mass of fissile material and holding it together for a fraction of a second for the chain reaction to spread throughout the mass. To achieve these requirements two types of nuclear weapons have been developed and described: the implosion and gun-barrel types. The implosion weapon consists essentially of a hollow sphere of fissile material surrounded by a heavy metal tamper (outer casing) and, outside this, high-explosive shaped charges. When these charges are simultaneously detonated, the sphere is collapsed inward so that the fissile material is brought together as a compressed, compact, solid supercritical mass, held together momentarily by the tamper. In a gun-barrel weapon two hemispheres of fissile material occupy either end of a heavy metal tube. A high-explosive charge is used to drive one hemisphere into the other.

A requirement for a weapon is that it explode at the designated time, and a desirable feature is that the weapon be as small as possible, to ease the problems of delivery.

By convention all fissile weapons are known as atom bombs, or atom weapons, while the terms "nuclear bombs" or and "nuclear weapons" are used generally for all weapons depending on a nuclear process.

FUSION WEAPONS

The energy released by an atomic bomb is from fission (splitting) of heavy atoms. Some of the energy from a thermonuclear weapon comes from the release of binding energy from fusion (joining together) of the nuclei of light atoms and the remaining energy comes from the explosion of a fissile device, which is essential to raise the temperature for the initial fusion to take place. So far the only fissile material that will provide the high temperature required is uranium-235; plutonium, as far as is known, cannot be used. The reasons have not been published why U-235 and not plutonium can be employed in the trigger of a fusion weapon. Other means are being investigated for obtaining the high temperature essential to initiate the fusion process. There are a number of nuclear fusion processes that can release energy, but only a few of them can be utilized in a weapon because of the very high initiating temperatures and the time required for the reaction to take place. It is easier to obtain fusion in a mixture of deuterium and tritium, heavy isotopes of hydrogen, than in any other reactions. Both of these isotopes are gases at ordinary temperatures, and for the first thermonuclear devices a refrigeration plant was incorporated to liquefy the isotopes. Other disadvantages of this design are that tritium has to be manufactured by irradiation in a nuclear reactor and decomposes when stored. This so-called "wet bomb" was superseded by the "dry bomb," which is packed with lithium hydride; when irradiated by neutrons from the explosion of the fission core, lithium is converted to tritium. Lithium hydride is a solid, so that refrigeration is not necessary.

FISSION-FUSION-FISSION WEAPONS

A third nuclear process adds to the vast energy release in the fission-fusion-fission weapon.

Initiation of the explosion is by the fission process; the second stage is the fusion process, from which vast quantities of neutrons are released that can be utilized to cause fission in uranium-238. As much as 80 percent of the total yield can be supplied from fission of the outer casing, or tamper, of natural or depleted uranium. There is no real limit for the yield from such an explosion; and the Soviet Union has tested a device of this type that, with relatively minor modifications, could have exceeded 100-megaton yield.

The evolution of nuclear weapons by the different nuclear powers is shown in Table 6.

EFFECTS OF NUCLEAR WEAPONS

Phenomena associated with explosion of nuclear weapons are the following:

Air blast

Ground and water shock

Thermal radiation

Nuclear radiations.

The particular effects, and their ratios, from an explosion will depend upon the design of the weapon and the environment in which it is detonated.

An explosion is the result of a rapid release of large amounts of energy within a limited space, with all the materials present at the point of explosion converted into hot, compressed gases. These gases at high pressure expand rapidly and initiate a shock wave in the surrounding medium. As the shock front passes, there is a sudden increase in pressure that gradually decreases to normal. In air the shock wave is referred to as a blast wave because it is accompanied by a strong wind.

Although the destructive effects of nuclear weapons on most targets are mainly from blast and shock, and in this way are similar to those from high-explosive weapons, there are differences:

The scale of nuclear weapons effects is vastly greater, on the order of thousands or millions of times

TABLE 6

Evolution of National Nuclear Weapons Programs

	Fission Weapons			Thermonuclear Weapons			Delivery Systems			
Nation	First Explosion	Fissile Material	Production	First Explosion	Fissile Material	Production	Subsonic Bombers	Supersonic Bombers	Long-Range Missiles	Missile Sub-marines
United States	1945	U-235	Gas Diff.	1952	U-235	Gas Diff.	1945	1961	1959	1960
Soviet Union	1949	Pu-239	Reactors	1952	U-235	?	1949	1961	1956-57	1961-62
Great Britain	1952	Pu-239	Reactors	1957	U-235	Gas Diff.	1957	None	Abandoned	1968
France	1960	Pu-239	Reactors	Not Yet	—	—	—	1964	1968	1969
China	1964	U-235	?	1967	U-235	?	1967	?	1968	?

Source: Derived from Leonard Beaton, "Nuclear Proliferation," Science Journal (December, 1967).

A fairly large proportion of the energy is emitted as electromagnetic energy, manifested as thermal radiation—that is, light and heat

The explosion is accompanied by an instantaneous burst of nuclear radiation

Debris remaining and distributed by the explosion contains residual nuclear radioactivity—that is, fallout.

Predicting the effects of nuclear weapons is complicated by difficulties in obtaining accurate measurements and in relating these to the environment in which the explosion takes place, and by differences between the effects of different designs of weapons of the same yield.

Estimating the range of effects from the yield is made uncertain because of the limited amount of data available: it was particularly difficult to derive survival data in Japan because of the wide range of conditions—from "free-field" victims (those caught in the open) to those who were sheltered in some way. The extent of injury from secondary effects such as flying glass depended on proximity and placement of windows. Apart from such variations, the number of casualties would also depend on whether mobile survivors could escape from the area.

The principal weapons effects in different environments are shown in Table 7.

ADVANCES IN WARHEAD DESIGN

The first atomic devices used for test purposes were large and unwieldy and were emplaced on towers. The first weapons exploded over the cities in Japan were still large and were transported by large bombers; the weapons were dropped by parachute. With further development atomic weapons became smaller and could be carried in large conventional bomb casings. The first thermonuclear devices were also large, and some had to have associated refrigeration equipment. With further developments thermonuclear weapons were also reduced, first to a size that could be carried by heavy bombers. The great area of destruction from a thermonuclear weapon compensated for the lower accuracy of missiles, as compared with bombers, so that long-range missiles, which at first were too inaccurate to be used with atomic warheads, were sufficiently accurate for thermonuclear warheads. The first long-range missiles had to be large enough to carry the then large warheads. With further developments the size of warheads was further reduced and missile accuracy increased, so that much smaller, solid-fueled missiles, which are very much cheaper to manufacture and require much less maintenance, were possible and are the main type deployed in the United States.

The very high accuracy of modern long-range missiles is such that they are suitable for attacking soft targets and even some hardened targets with warheads of about .25 megaton yield. Yields of this magnitude could be obtained with fission weapons based on plutonium. In other words, U-235 would not be so necessary for very accurate strategic long-range weapons, so that there would be less dependence on the gaseous diffusion or gas centrifuge processes and reliance could be placed on nuclear reactors that might be ostensibly for a civil power program.

Refinements of weapons components have continued, and advantage has been taken of important advances in solid-state physics for microminiaturization of avionics (the electronic components in the command, control, and guidance equipment) and airborne computers.

As the stocks of fissile material held by the superpowers have increased, it has become possible to mount several smaller warheads on one missile. This has been done with the Poseidon missile, which is scheduled to replace Polaris missiles in many U.S. nuclear-powered submarines, and also with the Minuteman-3 land-based missiles. Both of these missiles, and the proposed advanced ICBM, are all larger than those they are intended to replace. (See Chapter 13 for more details on advanced weapons.)

Basically, the problem of attainment of thermonuclear conditions in a suitable mixture of deuterium and tritium is of cramming enough energy into a small volume of dense material to raise the temperature to that at which nuclear fission will begin. In a fusion weapon, where the process, once initiated, is uncontrolled, the initial heat is produced by the explosion of a fission device (bomb) of plutonium. Recent advances in initiating thermonuclear reactions offer the possibility of developing weapons that do not depend on a uranium trigger. In experiments exploring the release of controlled fission energy, dense gas plasmas have been contained in magnetic bottles; but so far this has not proved suitable for a trigger.

There are other possible approaches to the development of the high temperatures needed. Essentially, the method is to "ignite" a small quantity of deuterium and tritium with an intense field emission

TABLE 7

Effects of Nuclear Weapons

Type	Altitude	Blast	Shock	Crater
High-Altitude	Above 100,000 ft.	Small	None	None
Air Burst	Below 100,000 ft. fireball above surface	Most when reinforced by reflection from ground	Some	None
Surface	On or just above surface	Proportions depend on height of burst		
Subsurface	Underground/ underwater	Some, depending on depth	Most	Depends on depth; size increases to maximum, then decreases.

Thermal (Heat and Light)	Electro-Magnetic	Prompt Neutrons	Fission Products	Irradiated Material
X rays and very large, low-energy fireball: long-range effects, radio blackout and interference	Very long-range		Distributed in stratosphere: no local fallout	Virtually none
Intense fireball, effects to long ranges, screened and reflected by clouds	Long-range effects	Long-range	Widespread, little local fallout	Not important
Small fireball, mostly screened by ground	Short-range	Mostly absorbed locally	Mostly deposited locally as intense fallout	
Mostly screened, with local heating	Short-range	Absorbed locally	Very high locally if shallow, little if deep	

Source: Samuel Glasstone, The Effects of Nuclear Weapons (Washington, D.C.: U.S. Atomic Energy Commission, 1964). For a review of the full range of effects see Tom Stonier, Nuclear Disaster (Harmondsworth: Penguin, 1964).

discharge—a great spark. High-intensity electron beams of a million megawatts lasting up to 10 nanoseconds have been produced in the laboratory. In the projected fission initiator a large bank of capacitors would be discharged through a concave electrode, which would force the burst of energy onto a small target. So far the energy levels attained in this way are too low to act as a trigger. As an alternative to bulky capacitors, there have been proposals for storing the energy in a superconducting ring, from which escape is prevented by its own constraining magnetic field.

STRATEGIC TARGETING

Military targets are of two kinds, "point" targets and "area" targets. Strategic point targets are, for example, missile silos and command posts, while area targets could be cities and bomber bases. However, in terms of an attack with nuclear weapons, the essential difference between point and area targets is not their size but their hardness.

The hardness of a target is its resistance to damage and is measured in terms of the minimum weapons effect required to ensure a given level of damage to the target. The level of damage does not have to be complete destruction; for example, an attack would be successful if it damaged all of the aircraft on a base so that the least damaged might require several days for repair; if only a few aircraft survived and could be used within a few hours to deliver a counterblow with nuclear weapons, then the attack would have failed. The concept of minimum level of damage varies with the type of target, as a few illustrations will make clear. Typical successful attacks would be to crush or displace a concrete silo so that the missile inside could not be launched; to inflict severe damage on one-third of the houses in a town, that is, with roofs stripped, windows smashed, doors torn off their hinges; or so to contaminate an area with fallout that troops would not be able to pass through it. These are examples of minimum damage; nearer the point of detonation the damage would be more severe.

The damage radius or lethal radius is the distance from ground zero to which the required minimum level of damage from prompt effects of the weapons explosion extends. The effects of fallout cannot be calculated in this way, and it is usual to consider the collateral damage from fallout as a "bonus" that may not be included in calculations of damage. The lethal radius depends on the weapons effect specified to give the minimum level of damage and on the yield of the weapon. The harder the target, the greater the effect to cause damage must be and, consequently, the smaller the damage radius and the area damaged to the required extent. The higher the yield, the further the lethal radius extends and the greater the area damaged. Another way is to look at this from the point of view of accuracy of delivery; to damage hard targets, the weapon must be exploded near the target (i.e., of high accuracy) or be of high yield.

Military targets on the ground could be attacked by ground bursts or air bursts. Compared with a ground burst, blast from an air burst will extend further, ground shock will be much less, and radioactive fallout will be less and more widely dispersed—but fusing of the weapon might be more difficult. Warheads that penetrate the ground produce more ground shock and excavate a larger crater—unless they go in very deeply and create an underground cavity rather than a crater.

Calculation of the effect of an attack with nuclear weapons involves knowledge of the probabilities of the system's behavior at all stages. The main parameters in the calculation are availability for launch, that is, the missile is not under maintenance; that it is launched on its correct trajectory; that it is not destroyed in flight by an ABM; the accuracy; the yield; the hardness of the target; and the number of warheads allocated to the target. Values for parameters are obtained from test firings but, of course, full system tests with live warheads are not often carried out. Other factors that cannot easily be included in the calculations are the effects of a nuclear attack on the objectives and capabilities of the opponent and the circumstances of the attack. For the purpose of calculation it is usual to assume that the enemy will make his attack when everything is in his favor; if this maximum possible attack cannot achieve its objectives, a lesser attack certainly will not.

The statistics of impacts around a target, which depend on the above factors, can be described in a mathematical expression; and from this it is possible to calculate the number of targets that would be destroyed for different values of the parameters. (This topic is returned to in greater detail in Chapter 12.)

Another aspect of targeting is to see it as the allocation of a limited number of warheads against a list of targets arranged in order of priority.

FALLOUT

From the early days of discovery of artificial nuclear energy, scientists have been concerned about the effects on human beings of fallout from nuclear weapons tests. Fallout is the debris from the explosive device. The debris contains fission products—atomic nuclei of many isotopes: many fission products are radioactive, emitting particles and energy as they decay to more stable forms. The rate of decay depends on the species and can vary from fractions of seconds to many years. The emissions can be harmful to body tissue. Fission products tend to become attached to other matter, such as the ejected and pulverized soil and rock, some of which may also be transmuted to radioactive species by irradiation, so that from a ground burst fallout is local and intense. From an air burst, however, the fission products tend to be carried up by the hot rising gases into the upper atmosphere: the particles, being minute, drift down to earth over several months or years. During this time most of the shorter-lived radioactivity has decayed, and the long-lived isotopes are distributed widely throughout the northern hemisphere.

Protection against radioactivity from some of the short-lived isotopes that emit beta and gamma rays can be obtained in shelters shielded with concrete, steel, and earth—which, if sufficiently thick, will reduce the dose received to below an immediately harmful level (the somatic dose). Alpha rays (or particles) penetrate only a few inches of air: however, some alpha-emitting isotopes (the most important of which is strontium-90) are particularly dangerous if ingested: because of their chemical resemblance to calcium such isotopes are deposited in the skeleton and the short range of the alpha particles means that the energy is absorbed and creates damage locally in the bone marrow, where blood constituents are formed. Strontium-90 decays relatively slowly, so that any returning from the upper atmosphere is still harmful; and any inhaled or ingested with food continues to irradiate the body over a lifetime.

The deleterious effects of large doses of radiation have been well known for many years through study of diseases contracted when radioactive material, such as radium, is handled. What has been more controversial, however, is whether these effects persist at very low doses, affecting only a few of the population. Two views have been advanced: that there is no limit below which some damage occurs, but that it would be impossible to predict which individuals would be affected; and that there is a threshold below which self-repair of cells will obviate any effects. What this threshold level is cannot be stated with any certainty and, as a practical matter, the doses permitted in industry and medical uses have generally been limited to a fraction above the natural background radiation.

The controversy over the effects of small doses has been sharpened by an analysis of infant deaths in the United States by E. J. Sternglass.[1] According to this evidence the smoothly falling curve of fetal morbidity has been disturbed by fallout from atmospheric testing of nuclear weapons; following cessation of testing by the United States, the Soviet Union, and Great Britain, a similar rate of decline was resumed. There is supporting evidence that higher fetal death rates were associated with measured deposition of fallout. Sternglass predicted that whereas many adults would survive a nuclear war, there might be no children to succeed them.

This work has been criticized on a number of grounds. The assumption that the rate of infant deaths would continue to decline at a constant rate can be challenged: there will at some stage be deaths that are unavoidable with the existing state of knowledge. Another ground for criticism is that many factors known to affect fetal deaths were not taken into account. Furthermore, follow-up studies in Japan and studies in areas with high natural background radioactivity do not show similar trends.[2]

SOCIAL EFFECTS OF NUCLEAR WAR

R. A. Dentler and P. Cutwright (and others) have studies what the effects of various levels and kinds of nuclear war would be on the population, economy, political organizations, and physical environment of the United States.[3] An attack of between 1,000 and 2,000 megatons (i.e., 50 to 100 20-megaton warheads, only a small fraction of the stocks of the nuclear superpowers) would have a catastrophic impact on the major components of the American social system. Taking into account the experience of the recovery of Germany after World War II, it was concluded that no reasonable parallel existed with the economic disorganization that would follow a nuclear war. In addition to immense physical damage there would be devastation of vital sectors of the labor force and ecological effects of unpredictable magnitude; it is doubtful that political organization and public order adequate to the challenge could remain. Survival of anything resembling present society would be unlikely. A subsequent but more limited study came to very different conclusions, but the level of the attack was comparatively low.[4]

Recovery of a city after a devastating attack depends critically upon the amount of aid given by the surrounding populations. After the attacks on German and Japanese cities, aid was available from neighboring cities and from military forces. There is little reason to believe that this help would be available after a nuclear attack.

The effects of a nuclear attack, even at a lower level, on the densely urbanized countries of Western Europe could be even more devastating: while fairly simple precautions, if carried out in time, would suffice to protect many of the public against prompt effects of the attack—collapse of buildings, broken glass and other missiles, heat flash—without immediate, massive, and organized help from outside, which would not be available, the survivors could not be dug out of the ruined buildings or evacuated before fire swept the area or the arrival of fallout from radioactive material that returned to the surface and would jeopardize the victims and any rescuers.

NOTES

1. Ernest J. Sternglass, "Infant Mortality and Nuclear Tests," Bulletin of the Atomic Scientists (April 1969); "Can the Infants Survive?," ibid. (June 1969); "Has Nuclear Testing Caused Infant Deaths?," New Scientist (July 24, 1969).

2. L. A. Sagan, E. S. Weiss, and D. J. Worth, "Infant Mortality Controversy," Bulletin of the Atomic Scientists (October 1969).

3. R. A. Dentler and P. Cutwright, "Social Effects of Nuclear War," Nuclear Science Abstracts, XVII, 20 (July 1963).

4. U.S. Office of Civil Defense, Post-Attack Recovery from Nuclear War, proceedings of a symposium, National Research Council, National Academy of Sciences, November 6-9, 1967.

CHAPTER

9

ARMS CONTROL AND NUCLEAR WARHEADS

NATIONAL SAFEGUARDS SYSTEMS

As far as civil nuclear installations are concerned, national and international legislation has been introduced to regulate industrial operations and thus, as far as possible, to prevent accidents involving nuclear materials: inspectorates have been set up to ensure that the legal requirements are met and to provide an organization for study and advice on these problems. In Great Britain there is the Inspectorate of Nuclear Installations, and other responsibilities in this field are carried by the Factory Inspectorate. Since many of the problems encountered in the industrial and military fields are similar—for example, the transport of nuclear materials—there would seem to be many advantages to be gained from close collaboration between the responsible military and civil agencies.

INTERNATIONAL EXCHANGES ON CIVIL SAFEGUARDS

There is considerable international exchange of information on safeguards in connection with civil nuclear installations: international standards and regulations have been adopted with regard to the maximum permitted doses to workers in the nuclear industry and to members of the general public and also with regard to precautions in the transport of radioactive material. Within nations that have well-developed nuclear industries the regulating organizations have been responsible for interpreting and enforcing the international regulations. Even countries without civil nuclear programs can be deeply involved if they provide harbor facilities for nuclear-powered vessels.

NATURE OF NUCLEAR ACCIDENTS

Nuclear weapons, even when elaborate precautions are taken, are potentially very dangerous because, even with a low probability of accident, the results could be so catastrophic. Accidents with nuclear weapons can be placed in four categories:

In the lowest there is no release of radioactivity, that is, even if the weapon is dropped, the casing remains intact

The next category is that in which there is a release of radioactivity from the exposure of fissile material, perhaps made worse by a fire

The third type of accident would involve both a nuclear explosion and the scattering of radioactivity

The most feared is an accident that could trigger a nuclear exchange—but it is not essential in this kind of accident that there be an explosion or release of radioactivity: the launching of a missile or even the malfunctioning or misinterpretation of a radar system might be sufficient.

The possibility of triggering a nuclear war by accident has been much reduced by the philosophy of the second strike, that is, the ability and intention to absorb the opponent's first strike and to have enough well-protected weapons survive to deliver a devastating retaliatory blow. Also contributing to an increase in security are the better appreciation of the effects of a nuclear war and the lowering of international tension, which make the possibility of an attack without warning less to be feared.

Other factors that would contribute in some way to the results of a nuclear accident within the categories listed above would be the yield, time, place, weather conditions, and other fortuitous circumstances. Even a minor nuclear accident can involve and endanger people outside the territory of the owner of the weapon, either through drift of radioactive debris with the wind or through the worldwide deployment of aircraft and submarines.

ACCIDENTS WITH NUCLEAR WARHEADS

In discussing accidents with nuclear weapons, a clear distinction should be made between those involving assembled nuclear weapons in service, storage, or transport and a more general class of accident involving fissile materials. It is only the first kind of accident, that involving assembled nuclear weapons, that could lead to a nuclear explosion of great magnitude and thus to loss of life and destruction of property.

The service safety record for nuclear weapons is extraordinarily good, considering the numbers available and the lack of experience in their deployment and use. No accident with a weapon has so far led to a nuclear chain reaction. Some accidents have led to the release of the radioactivity from the fissile components of weapons. Chain reactions have occurred in research laboratories, in reactors, and in processing plants; but the effects have been localized, although some operating personnel have died from the effects of radiation.

Such accidents are unlikely to be of great magnitude because nuclear explosions require the fissile material to be in the configuration of a warhead. In accidents involving nuclear weapons but in which critical conditions are not achieved, the scale of the effects is much less than from a nuclear explosion; casualties are likely to be confined to those quite close, unless there is an accompanying release of radioactive material that could contaminate an area downwind of the event. The "no yield" record for accidents with nuclear weapons is possible because the superpowers have had enough time to develop and install safety devices and administrative procedures, have had the skilled manpower to undertake the work, and have been able to allocate funds for development and testing of safety devices and accident procedures. In the future these advantageous conditions may not exist in all countries that acquire nuclear weapons; and from what is known about the causes of accidents, there appears to be a greater possibility of accidents that might result in a nuclear yield or scatter fissile material.

UNILATERAL PRECAUTIONS WITH WARHEADS

The principles of several control systems that have been applied to U.S. nuclear weapons are the two-key arrangement, the electronic lock, and the two-man arrangement.

The original two-key arrangement for control of nuclear weapons was to have two ordinary keys held by two officers, one American and the other from the host country, who wore their keys round their necks. A check on this system found it to be very inadequate: the American officer could be overcome and his key taken.

To provide a more secure control of nuclear weapons deployed abroad, a remote-control lock that gave a compromise between security and ease of opening was required. The device chosen was a combination lock, the code of which could be sent in the same message that gave the order to fire. Hearing of these precautions, the Russian ambassador in Washington made enquiries in 1966, and the principles of the device were revealed to him on presidential instructions. Although installation of locks was opposed by some military officers, particularly when the system was applied to weapons in the United States as well as those deployed abroad, it was welcomed by some strategists as conferring greater flexibility in forward deployment. For example, a single-seat aircraft could now take off carrying a nuclear weapon, while arming could be controlled from elsewhere and without the risk of the pilot, on his own initiative, making an attack.

The two-man arrangement requires that nuclear weapons be designed so that important operations in the preparation of a weapon can be carried out only by two persons working at some distance from each other. Accidents with nuclear warheads and unilateral precautions are further considered in Chapter 14.

EFFECTS OF PROLIFERATION ON WEAPONS SAFETY

It has long been one of the dogmas of those who oppose proliferation and dissemination of nuclear weapons that either will increase the possibility of accidents involving nuclear weapons. There are good reasons for believing this to be true. In the first place, the mere increase in numbers of weapons, other things being equal, will increase the statistical chance of an accident occurring. Thus, if at a particular time it is computed that with the existing stocks of weapons there is a chance of one accident in ten years, then if the number of weapons is doubled, there will be a calculated probability of an accident every five years. But things do not remain the same. As the number of weapons increases within a state, there will no doubt be some improvement in safety procedures and systems. But, at the same time, there will be an increase in the number of personnel involved in handling nuclear weapons, with perhaps a more or less inevitable reduction in the skills of the individuals and also in their specific feelings of responsibility.

On the international level the situation could be even worse. Countries intent on becoming nuclear powers will in many cases not have such an abundance of highly skilled manpower that enough can be spared from urgent tasks of weapons design, manufacture, and testing to work on safeguards design and enforcement. Furthermore, it is likely that secret crash programs will be initiated to prevent possible rivals from taking the lead or even mounting a preventative attack, and there will be insufficient time and money for deep consideration of safeguards philosophy and problems. Indeed, there will be pressures and incentives to push the program forward at high speed, with less regard for safety than is justified, considering the nature of the risks.

INTERNATIONAL EXCHANGES ON SAFETY OF WARHEADS

In 1961 Senator Hubert Humphrey introduced a resolution in the Senate asking the president to instruct the U.S. representative in the U.N. Security Council to ask that the nuclear powers, to an extent consistent with their security, report the measures taken to prevent mishaps with nuclear weapons.

Although no international action was taken, some information on the precautions taken in the United States to safeguard nuclear weapons has been published. On the other hand practically nothing has appeared in unclassified literature on the precautions taken by the Soviet Union, Great Britain, and China. The French minister of the armed forces, Pierre Messener, said that parallel chains of command existed in France, one for missiles and the other for warheads, and that nuclear delivery vehicles had a black box installed that was remotely controlled by political authority.[1]

Joel Larus has advocated international exchanges of information on safeguards applied to nuclear weapons.[2] Anticipating the main objection to such exchanges as being loss of national security and the possibility of disseminating information on weapons technology, Larus has gone into considerable detail about procedures that could at least reduce these problems. The exchanges would be generally designed to be conducted with the participation of nuclear powers at different levels, according to their capabilities and weapons systems, starting with problems that are less sensitive to the superpowers but of importance to nuclear powers with less highly developed systems. In the first phase of discussions there would be exchanges on the common functions of storage and transportation: individual topics could be principles of stores and dumps, materials of construction, layout, security and guarding procedures, securing of weapons during transport, methods and equipment for lifting, emergency and accident procedures, mechanical and electronic locks and warning, and means of transportation.

Phase Two would concentrate on weapons systems that are obsolete or obsolescent for the superpowers but of current importance to later nuclear powers. The manned bomber is in this category, since the United States and the Soviet Union are allowing their bomber fleets to decrease and there is a possibility that no more will be built. It would be expected that methods of control for manned bombers would be well established, that national security of the superpowers would not be jeopardized by revealing the principles, and that this information could be applied to improve the safety controls of those nuclear powers relying on manned bombers. After the first stage of Phase Two, discussion could be extended to describe precautions relating to fighter-bombers and ground attack aircraft that might carry tactical nuclear weapons.

Phase Three of the discussions would start with precautions for strategic missiles vulnerable to a first strike, that is, missiles that are both liquid-fueled (and require some time for bringing to a state of alert) and not stored in hardened silos or carried in submarines. This type of weapons system is of decreasing importance in the armories of the superpowers but could conceivably be a stage of evolution for other nuclear powers. When this part of Phase Three was concluded, the next stage would be concerned with weapons systems designed to survive a first strike and to respond before a second wave of attack: in other words, missiles with storable liquid or solid fuel, held in hardened silos or submarines. While this stage of discussion would be the most sensitive to inadvertent disclosures of information and to the attitudes of the participants, the fact that the earlier stages had been successfully concluded, and that the forum was by now reduced to the superpowers, would produce an atmosphere for discussions that would be more likely to lead to valuable results than had the problem been tackled without the other stages.

THE LIMITED NUCLEAR TEST BAN TREATY

In 1958 a conference of experts from the nuclear powers met in Geneva to discuss means for reducing the risks of war. While nothing was achieved immediately, it was the increase of understanding then reached that led to negotiations in 1962-63 with the aim of producing an agreement on a comprehensive nuclear test ban to prevent all testing of nuclear weapons. Some experts involved in these negotiations considered that agreement was nearly achieved. J. B. Wiesner has examined the reasons why this conference failed.[3]

Although the conference did not reach a formal agreement, there was an unofficial moratorium on weapons testing that was observed by both the United States and the Soviet Union, until broken when the latter resumed testing (September 1, 1961), followed soon afterward by the United States. After both superpowers had completed a series of planned tests, agreement was quickly reached to limit nuclear tests to those which could be conducted underground without release of significant quantities of radioactivity to the atmosphere.

The Limited (or Partial) Test Ban Treaty (August 1963) was the first significant arms control treaty to come out of 17 years of negotiation between the Western allies and the Soviet Union. The treaty prohibited testing by the signatories of nuclear weapons in the atmosphere, outer space, or underwater, under their jurisdiction, and, in the words of the treaty:

> . . . in any other environment if such explosion causes radioactive debris to be present outside the territorial limits of the State under whose jurisdiction or control such explosion is conducted. It is understood in this connection that the provisions of this subparagraph are without prejudice to the conclusions of a treaty resulting in the permanent banning of all nuclear test explosions, including all such explosions underground, the conclusions of which, as the Parties have stated in the preamble to this Treaty, they seek to achieve.[4]

METHODS FOR DETECTING NUCLEAR WEAPONS TESTS

At the time the Limited Test Ban Treaty was signed, effective methods existed for detecting nuclear explosions in the atmosphere, in space, and underwater. The main methods for detecting nuclear explosions in the atmosphere available in 1958 were detection of acoustic waves and radioactive debris: explosions in space could be detected by light and heat flash and also by a flux of neutrons and from secondary effects on natural phenomena.[5]

Acoustic waves in the atmosphere have an amplitude that is proportional to the cube root of the explosive yield and to the distance from the point of explosion; they are also dependent, to some extent, on atmospheric conditions. The distance for detection depends upon the upper wind direction: a one-kiloton explosion could be detected at 500 kilometers upwind and 2,000-3,000 kilometers downwind. With these figures the site of the explosion could be located within 100 kilometers for explosions up to an altitude of 30 kilometers. Deep underground and underwater explosions do not produce strong air waves and cannot be detected to long range by acoustic sensors. However, underwater explosions produce strong hydroacoustic waves that can be detected to great distances. Acoustic waves are subject to misinterpretation by interference from waves from natural sources such as meteors, volcanoes and undersea earthquakes, so that acoustic records alone would not be sufficient for identification.

A nuclear explosion releases radioactivity equal to 300 million curies per kiloton of fission yield one hour after the explosion. (A curie is the rate with which radioactivity is emitted from 1 gram of radium.) Thermonuclear explosions will yield carbon-14, tritium, and other radioactive species that can be detected and used to identify the explosion and even the materials used. Depending upon the power released, the altitude of the explosion, and weather conditions, the debris will be scattered and will spread in the atmosphere. The maximum opportunity for detection and identification is at 5-20 days after the explosion, when debris has drifted with wind but has not decayed or scattered too much to affect the instruments.

Sensitive radiochemical techniques could (in 1958) detect a sample that had 10^8 fissions and could identify the time of an explosion from a sample containing 10^{10} fissions by comparing the relative ratios of short-lived and long-lived isotopes: fallout could be detected in rain and a one-kiloton explosion could be detected with control posts at ground level on a 2,000-3,000-kilometer grid. Underground and underwater tests could also be detected and identified from radioactive samples, but not so reliably and not to the same range as for tests in atmosphere. The method would have to be supported by other techniques. With other evidence of an explosion, the cloud of debris from an atmospheric burst might be located and sampled by aircraft. It was appreciated in 1958 that the method of sampling for radioactivity would improve in sensitivity as the atmosphere became freer from old debris and with improvements in radioactivity counting techniques.

In 1958 the possibilities of seismic methods for detection of underground and underwater explosions were appreciated: underground explosions of one-five kilotons could be detected at quiet sites at 1,000-3,000 kilometers, depending on the noise level at the time: undersea explosions could be detected to even greater range. Explosions could be discriminated from natural events if records were available from five stations, but the range of detection was not sufficient for explosions at sites in the middle of a continental power to be unambiguously identified beyond the national frontiers.

Atmospheric explosions generate radio signals through the release of radiation; but the signals from underground, underwater, and specially shielded explosions could not be detected at great range. Those from atmospheric tests could be detected worldwide, and the location and time of the test could be determined with very great accuracy in favorable circumstances. Lightning flashes emit signals that appear similar at the greatest ranges, and there are up to several hundred flashes per second: techniques for discrimination existed but were not always satisfactory.

It was anticipated that high-altitude tests could be detected from satellites by the intense burst of gamma rays and neutrons, and satellites are now orbited with suitable detectors. In clear weather it would be possible to observe the light emission from a nuclear explosion. It was also suggested that a high-altitude burst would produce intense ionization of the upper atmosphere, which would interfere with cosmic noise, but that some natural events could also have the same effect.

The experts in their report on the 1958 conference proposed standard equipment for a control net of nuclear explosion detection posts, which would be located inland, on islands, by the shore, and in ships.[6] With such a control net it was estimated that it would be possible to detect and identify nuclear explosions down to the low-yield range of one-five kilotons. The experts also considered that the system should be under the direction of an international control organization to ensure the following:

Further development, testing, and installation of suitable equipment

Observations at the control posts for detection of explosions

Communication of data, reports, supplies, and personnel between the control posts and the control organization

Analysis of results and further inspection of unidentified events.

The characteristics of the control posts would be determined by the minimum size of events to be detected, the number of control posts it was decided to install, and the probabilities of correct identification of events. The experts recommended 160-170 land-based posts and about 10 in ships. The net would not be uniform; stations would be closer together on land and in seismic areas. About 30 workers of varying qualifications and disciplines would be required at each post. In addition, air sampling would be carried out by regular aircraft flights, supplemented when necessary by special flights. Unidentified events would be investigated on the supposed site of the event by mobile teams.

In Table 8 methods for detecting nuclear tests listed by Samuel Glasstone, which include those described above, are tabulated.

The above discussion shows that long-range detection and verification of explosions in space, the atmosphere, and water have been possible for some time by several methods, but that a large number of stations would have been required for detection and identification of underground tests. The long-range systems could be operated by many powers from within their own territories and with their own resources, such as airlines, ships, and overseas bases.

LONG-RANGE SEISMOGRAPHY AND ON-SITE INSPECTION

Underground explosions were omitted from the prohibition on testing ostensibly because at that time it was not possible accurately to identify tests of nuclear weapons, particularly those of smaller yield, from other events such as earthquakes. By 1962-63 improvements in seismic detection methods had been developed and new information showed that there were fewer earthquakes in Russia than had been thought, with many of them at sea or in other areas otherwise not suitable for testing. Furthermore, the need was not to detect a single violation but to be able to detect one of a small series of tests: a single test would not be militarily significant. In this new situation it appeared that effective monitoring could be conducted by long range seismography, without the need for a close net of stations, provided that suspicious events could be examined more closely by on-site inspection. Controversy centered around the precise number of on-site inspections that the superpowers would permit on their territory. The United States was prepared to agree to a minimum of six or seven on-site inspections per year, while the Soviets were prepared to accept up to three or four on-site inspections per year. Although the gap was so narrow, it was not possible to achieve an agreement.

TABLE 8

Methods for the Detection of Nuclear Explosions in the Atmosphere, Water, and Space

---

Ground-Based Techniques

Airborne radioactive debris
Light scattering of debris trapped in upper atmosphere
Acoustic waves in air with microbarometers
Seismic waves from underground and undersea explosions
Electromagnetic (radio) signals, which may be difficult to distinguish from lightning at long range
Visible light, for very high-altitude tests
Fluorescence; X rays absorbed by air reemitted with characteristic wavelengths
Back-scatter radar; changes in electron density in atmosphere that may persist for some time
Cosmic noise absorption of radio waves from space
Very low-frequency anomaly; change in transmission time between transmitter and receiver, giving a rapid phase shift
Ionosonde measurements; height of ionized layers in atmosphere may be disturbed
Disturbance of magnetic and electrical fields

Satellite-Based Techniques

Thermal X rays
Gamma rays
Neutrons
Beta particles

Source: Samuel Glasstone, The Effects of Nuclear Weapons (Washington, D.C.: U.S. Atomic Energy Commission, 1964).

It is obvious that, with the technical requirements of the two sides so close, a compromise was possible without much loss of detection ability or of security. It is possible that it had not been anticipated that so close an agreement could be reached; and the hurried withdrawal by both sides reflects the cautious attitudes of defense-minded groups, who traditionally distrust the motives of the other side. Even given a great deal of caution, and the requirement for substantiation and proof, scientists and technologists from both sides were able to come close to agreement. From the American point of view the central block to progress in disarmament is the fear of secret military activities, which is aggravated by Soviet unwillingness to accept inspection. On the Soviet side there appears to be a fear that espionage might reveal military weaknesses that could be exploited. However, there have been much improved technical methods for intelligence gathering and parallel improvements in inspection methods—and, perhaps as important, a much better understanding of the purpose of inspection. Continuation of these trends could improve the chances of agreement on technical matters; however, we should never forget that technical problems are often advanced as barriers to agreement when in fact it is other factors that cause the problem.

CONTINUATION OF UNDERGROUND TESTS

Important gains that were expected from the Limited Test Ban Treaty were restrictions on further developments in nuclear weapons because it would be difficult to conduct the necessary trials, and the prevention of further releases of dangerous radioactivity into the atmosphere.

The effects of an increase in radioactivity above that naturally occurring were not known, nor are they still known with certainty. What was appreciated was that continuation of atmospheric testing might be harmful to living systems, including man. The treaty was successful in permitting a steady reduction in the excess background radiation until Chinese and French tests in the atmosphere commenced (in 1964 and 1960, respectively). (Effects of fallout were considered in Chapter 8.)

The expected limitation on weapons tests was not achieved. The Partial Test Ban Treaty was signed in the United States against strenuous opposition that believed the treaty would reduce the security of the United States. Consent of the Joint Chiefs of Staff depended on assurances of the following safeguards:

A vigorous underground testing program

Maintaining an ability to resume atmospheric testing at short notice

Strengthening of capabilities to detect weapons tests

Maintenance of modern laboratories and production facilities.

The last point received considerable attention: it was thought that without objectives, including carrying out at least occasional nuclear tests, it would be difficult to retain interest and morale in the scientific and engineering teams; particularly in those countries that could not direct individuals into occupations, the most able would probably depart for more interesting and rewarding work.

The United States, the Soviet Union, and, to a limited extent, Great Britain continued to carry out tests of nuclear weapons, although these were underground and so did not produce high levels of fallout. Occasional relatively small releases of radioactivity that have occurred, even when detected outside the national boundaries, have been ignored rather than jeopardize the agreement. Neither France nor China signed the treaty and, as nuclear weapons were developed in these countries, they carried out tests in the atmosphere. However, both France and China have also carried out some of their most recent tests underground, and it may be that eventually they too will only test underground.

REQUIREMENTS FOR DETECTION SYSTEMS

Early proposals for the detection of underground nuclear explosions depended on the instruments then available, which were those of a rather recondite science relating to earthquakes and similar natural events. These instruments were by no means ideally suited to the new requirements, which involved not only detection of events but also identification, to a high degree of assurance, of both explosions and earthquakes. Since the early days of application of seismology to detection of underground tests, considerable advances have been made; and seismology still remains the best method for detecting events at long range.

The early proposals for a grid of about 180 stations were based on the idea that a more or less uniform coverage was required of the land masses, that is, the system should have a capability for detecting tests carried out anywhere. There is in fact a more limited immediate requirement, the ability to detect tests carried out in the land areas of the nuclear powers. While the earlier proposal would have required stations manned by nonnationals within the boundaries of the superpowers, the new requirement appeared to be attainable by teleseismic means. However, it would still be necessary to confirm suspicious events by on-site inspection, and a number of proposals have been made in this connection. Another easing, concerning the efficiency of both seismic analysis and on-site inspection, is that it is now not considered, at least as far as the present nuclear powers are concerned, that every test should be identified as such but that a series of tests should be discovered.

In an attempt to overcome the lack of agreement about the annual number of on-site inspections that would be permitted, scientists in the Pugwash movement have suggested that the efficiency of the long-range detection system could be enhanced by a network of local unmanned sealed detection units—black boxes. The black boxes would be placed in position and retrieved by a team from the adversary country. Lack of political agreement and improvements in long-range seismology have prevented this plan from being put into operation.

THE NEW SEISMOLOGY

A seismometer or seismograph is essentially a very simple instrument. It consists of a case that is attached to, and moves with, the earth; inside, carried by a spring or pivot system, is a weight. During an earth tremor the weight tends to remain stationary from inertia, and relative movements between the weight and the case can be measured and recorded. Early seismometers depended upon a thin wire tracing movements on a sheet of smoked glass. From this primitive beginning considerable developments have taken place: first by recording on sensitive paper, then on film; now movement can be sensitively detected by electrical capacitance and recorded on magnetic tape for analysis by computer. In these more advanced systems movement can be magnified thousands of times.

The frequency of the waves to which a seismometer is most responsive depends on the details of the construction of the instrument. Sensitivity at a station will be increased by having several instruments of the same or different characteristics.

The Problems to Be Solved

There are three problems with which a seismologist is confronted in relation to nuclear explosions—detection, discrimination, and location.

Detection is concerned generally with the sensitivity of the instruments and the local noise level at the station, that is, the probability of recording distant events. Discrimination is the possibility for distinguishing the signals from an explosion from those of more numerous natural events. Location is of importance not only in determining as precisely as possible the area in which the event occurred, for the purpose of carrying out inspection or other confirmatory examination, but also because location of the event may be an additional guide to its nature—thus a signal originating underwater is not so likely to be from an explosion; an event away from a known earthquake area is more likely to be an explosion than if it occurred in a natural seismic area. For events that have been located in a possible test area, the principal factors that can be used to distinguish an explosion from an earthquake are the following:

The depth, since it would be difficult to explode a device at great depth, both because of the engineering difficulties of emplacement and because of instrumenting such a trial: explosions are not likely to be more than five kilometers below the surface

The first motion from an explosion is compression in all directions, while that from an earthquake varies according to the direction of the station from the fault line

An explosion is essentially rather a simple event, is less rich in shear waves, is less likely to be followed by secondary events, and is thus less likely to result in complex signals.

Detection, discrimination, and location may be improved by installation of an array of seismometers, to be discussed later.

The questions that faced the experts meeting at Geneva in 1958 were related to detection and identification capability. The problem with detection capability was the minimum yield that could give an observable record at a number of stations (in order to provide confirmation) and how this yield is related to the smallest yield of a nuclear explosion that would be of value in the development of a weapon. On identification, the questions were whether explosions of this minimum yield can be identified as weapons tests and differentiated from natural events, how many earthquakes would produce signals of comparable magnitude, and what fraction of these could be identified as earthquakes. A number of factors can contribute to answering these questions. The first is the size of the record from the event as compared with the natural background of "noise" and isolated natural events. Any recognizable features that are specific either to explosions or to earthquakes will aid differentiation. It would be valuable to know how the size of the signal at different distances from an event is related to the yield. Arising from these considerations, it is important to be able to estimate reliably how many signals from explosions or from natural events will be interpreted incorrectly, and whether the signals from an explosion can be reduced or disguised in some way.

An underground explosion or an earthquake will generate a series of shock waves that spread through the earth. These waves are of two different kinds: compressions and decompressions spreading out from the event more or less in a radial direction, and shear waves, a vibrating motion at right angles to the direction of propagation. Another feature of the waves is that some tend to travel through the body of the earth, while others tend to follow the surface. The strength of a signal will obviously depend to some extent on the distance from the event, but this relationship is by no means simple. Waves that follow the surface decrease in amplitude as the distance increases from the event, while waves that penetrate the earth (body waves) are refracted if the density of the medium varies and are reflected at interfaces in the medium. Hence, at the seismic detection station the record tends to be confused by a mixture of different kinds of waves, with different arrival times and different and often complex propagation routes.

Thus the waves from an event have either a compression-dilation or a shear motion, and either of these wave forms propagates through the body of the earth or along the surface.

For the purpose of interpretation, the waves are classified in the order in which they usually arrive at the detection station:

P (primary) waves, which travel through the body of the earth as a series of compressions

S (secondary or shear) waves, which also travel through the earth and have a vibrating motion

L (Love) waves, named after their discoverer, are S waves trapped into following the surface of the earth and appear as sideways motion

Rayleigh waves, which also follow the surface of the earth, move with a circular motion that resembles that of waves in the sea.

The ability to be able to analyze incoming signals into these components helps in identification of the type of event and in tracing its path through the earth. Analysis is facilitated by recording on magnetic tapes, which can be presented to a computer, so that the records from different recorders can be easily compared and outputs superimposed with time delays. Arranging a number of seismometers in an array can be used to amplify the response and also, by taking into account differences in arrival times, to establish the direction of arrival of the signal.

Differentiation between earthquakes and nuclear explosions is made possible by, among other things, the differing relative magnitudes of surface and body waves. Nuclear explosions produce smaller surface waves than earthquakes of comparable magnitude. Analysis shows that the two types of event can be separated graphically and nuclear explosions distinguished, in 98 percent of cases, by observations made on the same continent.

The waves travel at different relative speeds: P waves travel half as fast again as S waves, and at different speeds in different rocks; thus P waves have different speeds at different depths. This is the reason for the diffraction of the P-wave front already mentioned; in addition, P waves reflect at discontinuities and also generate other wave forms. Waves that penetrate deeply to strike the Mohorovicic discontinuity between the earth's mantle and crust, at which there is a sharp change in density, are transmitted along the boundary at higher speed than waves that propagate by reflections within the crust. Because of different arrival times of waves at the seismic detection stations, only the beginning of the record, that is, the first arrival of the P wave, gives a fairly clear record; afterward the record becomes increasingly complex.

When observations are made on different continents, the reliability is less because of aberrations at the continental margins. Also, the level of detection depends on the local seismic noise level, but the effects can be reduced by technical improvements that will be discussed below.

Source Phenomena

At the source earthquakes and explosions are very different. Earthquakes can be seen as being caused by a stress in the earth's crust that builds up until it exceeds the strength of the rock, which suddenly fails in shear, that is, a fracture develops that enables a block of rocks to slide sideways relative to the mass to which it was attached. An explosion, on the other hand, is an almost instantaneous buildup of enormous pressure acting in all directions. Thus, from an earthquake the first P wave is compression in some directions, and extension (dilation) in other directions, while the first P wave from an explosion is a compression in all directions.

Analysis of Signals

The important data to be recorded are the time of arrival of the first signal, the amplitude (strength), and the period (the time between peaks of the major waves). Arrival times of P and S waves at a number of stations and a knowledge of the (variable) speed of waves through the earth can be used to predict the location of the event. The time interval between the first pulse and a second pulse that is reflected from the surface of the earth above the event serves to indicate the depth of the event. Basic data used for these calculations, e.g., the velocities of waves in rocks, are continually updated. The actual determinations are now made by computer. Since it is only the first part of the P wave that is not contaminated by other and less direct waves, criteria that will identify the nature of the event are sought in the first motion. Application of sophisticated mathematical techniques of analysis may increase the length of record from which useful results may be extracted.

Instruments are designed to respond to waves of different amplitude: short-period signals are used to detect body waves: long-period instruments, surface waves. In the design of a station, a choice has to be made between the extremes of a broad-band instrument, which records most movement whatever the amplitude, and a narrow-band instrument, which records (more or less) only one wavelength, but this with high sensitivity. There are, however, overall limitations on the sensitivity because of earth movements from a variety of sources, such as the motion from sea waves, minor earth tremors, traffic, industrial activity, and so on.

Interference with Signals

Besides the signals from important distant events, a seismometer may also record other signals from local and distant events, from local scattering of the wanted signal, and from the man-made and other sources mentioned above.

Some of the interference can be eliminated or reduced in the design of the instruments and observatory. Ocean waves, for example, have a period of between four and eight seconds, which falls between the peak responses for short-period (.01 to 1 second) and long-period (10 to 100 seconds) seismometers. A depth of a few meters below the surface is enough to reduce the effects of wind, but a greater depth may be indicated by the nature of the terrain; and the bore holes for the seismometers may be sunk to the depth of the bedrock. Experience has shown the advantage of siting observatories away from the coast, main roads, railways, industrial installations, and, of course, in an area of low seismic activity. Unfortunately some areas already selected for seismic observatories have levels of random noise that are not much below the signals from an event of seismic magnitude 4.0 in a zone from which body waves can be most clearly received.

Seismic stations that are on the continent where underground testing is taking place have a high detection capability. At the longer-range teleseismic distances, seismic detection stations have a lower capability. The Canadian seismic observatory network, for example, can identify explosions of 4.5 seismic magnitude in Nevada but can only detect events of 5.9 magnitude in Central Asia—an identification capability for energy release of 10 or 20 kilotons in the North American continent but of 200 kilotons in Asia. Observatories have very low capability for detection of events on the other side of the earth, which is in the shadow, as it were, of the core on the earth, from which waves tend to be deflected by the Mohorovicic discontinuity. Stations for the detection of teleseismic events therefore have to be sited in relation to the areas that are to be kept under observation.

PROBLEMS OF A BAN ON UNDERGROUND TESTING

The more elaborate requirements to monitor a ban on underground testing made it impossible to reach a comprehensive agreement. A possible solution—a close network of posts, frequent movement of personnel and communications, and perhaps with mobile teams to visit suspected events—appeared to be open to infiltration by espionage. Unattended stations—not available at the time, but which could be developed—were open to interference or deception. Underground tests themselves could be disguised, or at least there were some possibilities for making tests resemble earthquakes. These factors were advanced as reasons for not being able to reach agreement on underground tests. It is difficult to know the importance of the political pressure for an escape clause that would permit continued testing by the superpowers but would make it hard for others without elaborate resources and experience to carry out tests without the odium from release of radioactivity into the atmosphere.

SEISMIC ARRAYS

Modern teleseismic observatories tend to be elaborate installations and involve arrays of seismometers, since the difficulties attendant upon attempts to monitor underground testing at long range have led to special requirements not encountered when local observatories only were considered.

The signal-to-noise ratio at a recording station can be improved by superimposing signals from a number of separate instruments: pulses from the main event are additive, while the pulses from local events do not affect all instruments to the same extent and at the same time—that is, the local noise will tend to be out of phase at the different instruments, so that by adding together several recordings a more or less uniform level of background results. The maximum theoretical gain in the signal strength relative to the background noise is proportional not to the number of instruments, as might at first be thought, but to the square root of that number. In practice this theoretical improvement is not attained; but some improvement may be achieved by more widely separating the instruments, so that the background noise is even more incoherent, and by replaying the magnetic tape records from the different instruments with time delays to combine the major pulses. Measuring relative time delays between arrival of the first pulse at the different instruments permits the array to be "steered" to "point" in the direction of the incoming signal. In other words, the first seismometer to encounter the signal is on the side of the array from which the signal is approaching. If the first pulse is recorded almost simultaneously on all instruments, then the wave front must have traveled deep through the earth's crust. This technique can also be used to discriminate between two events that arrive at about the same time but from different directions.

The system of stations coordinated by the British Atomic Energy Authority consists of four arrays operated by different national organizations at Eskadalemuir in Scotland, Yellowknife in Canada, Gavribidunar in India, and Warrawonga in Australia, which supply information to the Atomic Energy Authority Data Center at Blacknest. The UKAEA concentrated on L-shaped arrays with straight arms; the advantages of this type of array are that with suitable time delays the records of first motions can be added, while noise, which travels at different relative speeds, tends to be smoothed; that with different time delays the records from other waves can be added to make a clearer picture; and that by using time delays in the two arms the array can be apparently "steered" and "pointed" in the direction of the signal. These arrays are equipped with short-period seismometers, with the outputs stored on magnetic tapes. At the same time a reference frequency is also recorded on the tape so that any variation of speed of the tape can be compensated for. Other means of recording are also used, including a visual record for identifying events that require analysis.

The Large Aperture Seismic Array in Montana (United States) is arranged in concentric circles, each with four subarrays having 25 instruments. Including the subarray at the center, there are 625 seismometers in LASA spread over an area 20 kilometers in diameter. Each subarray can have its signals added, and the whole array may be steered. For the most accurate analysis all the seismometers in the array can be steered. LASA is used for research studies. (A similar system has been installed in Norway.)

French seismologists have developed methods that may prove to be cheaper to install than the methods so far discussed and that operate with a few spaced-out seismometers that are designed to filter out all signals except those within a narrow band of frequencies where the signal-to-noise ratio is particularly favorable. It is claimed that these relatively small but sophisticated installations give detection levels that are as good as those from large arrays.

In order to provide worldwide coverage many stations are necessary: the United States, the Soviet Union, and Great Britain each have a number of stations connected to data analysis facilities. The Russian system has 44 stations; the U.S. World Wide Standard Seismological Network (WWSSN) has over 100 stations with standardized instruments, and there are also about 100 stations at universities and other institutions with their own choice of instruments. The United States and Great Britain have arrangements for collecting and collating results on a worldwide basis.

In order to increase world coverage, both the United States and the Soviet Union have used underwater stations that record over a period and then return to the surface or report by telemetry on demand. As would be imagined, the noise level is rather worse than that in bore holes on land, but a seabed station may be nearer to the event or have other advantages.

EARTHQUAKES AND WEAPONS TESTS

The energy release from natural events extends over a wide range from continuous minor earth movements through major and infrequent earthquakes. It is impossible to estimate the energy release from a single event very accurately. Thus a logarithmic scale is used in which, for each increase of one unit on the magnitude scale, the energy released in the event increases by a factor of 250. Large earthquakes have magnitudes of about six or seven. The magnitude recorded from a nuclear explosion depends not only on the energy release (the yield) but also on the medium in which the explosion takes place. Unlike earthquakes, which result from the fracturing of rocks, nuclear explosions may take place in rock or in softer material. From an explosion in granite the seismic magnitude is similar to that from an earthquake of similar energy release, but in tuff (a material of volcanic origin in which much underground testing has been carried out) the shock wave, and hence the apparent magnitude, is less; and from an explosion in alluvium (low-density material deposited in ancient river-beds) the explosion is even more muffled. A one-kiloton explosion in hard rock would be recorded as of seismic magnitude four, but in alluvium it would require a 10-kiloton explosion to give about the same signal.

THE SEISMIC THRESHOLD

The number of earthquakes recorded increases rapidly at lower seismic magnitudes and, with the decrease in signal strength, there must be a magnitude at which it becomes difficult to be certain of detecting or discriminating an explosion from an earthquake and, of course, vice versa.

Between seismic magnitudes five and four a very high probability of detection and identification changes to a very low probability. Unfortunately this range represents that for small but militarily useful nuclear tests, particularly if they are carried out in soft material. Other factors that have to be taken into account are the distance between the event and the detection station, the nature of rock formation at the event and observation station and the intervening strata, and variations in the level of noise from local and distant events. Lowering the level of detection to 10-kilotons in hard rock (even if higher in a softer medium) would constrain a potential violator to work at only half this magnitude, that is, at a level that would be of much less value for the development of powerful weapons.

RESEARCH IN SEISMOLOGY

The effects that it has been necessary to identify in monitoring for nuclear weapons tests are usually much smaller than those with which geophysicists had been previously concerned, so that more sensitive instruments had to be developed capable of discriminating the required signal in the background noise from natural events. Fortunately, during the past few years scientific expertise in general problems of communications has rapidly increased, particularly in reading a signal against a high background of noise. In Great Britain, for example, seismic research has been backed by the large-scale instrumental and computing facilities of the Atomic Energy Authority, so that any advances can be rapidly applied in the seismic area. In the period 1963-70 some $200 million was spent on basic seismic research in the United States alone. During this time important advances have been made in seismology and a better understanding has been gained of the way shock waves are generated from natural and artificial events, as well as how they are transmitted and reflected through the body of the earth and across its surface. In addition a great deal of new statistical information has been gained on the occurrence of natural events of various magnitudes, their frequency, their localities, and their depths, and earthquake areas have been located and studied in detail.

Seismic research is carried out in a number of countries and exchanges of information are made on a voluntary basis; a number of more formal meetings of experts from different countries have also taken place. In addition Canada has been pressing at ENDC for a survey of information that governments are prepared to make available; and the Swedish government has financed the International Peace Research Institute, which has an international staff. SIPRI arranged an important conference of experts that produced a report on the problems of detecting underground tests.[7]

In order to provide basic data against which instruments in all parts of the world can be calibrated and effectiveness of detection, discrimination, and identification checked, and to provide material for further research, the United States and Great Britain have carried out a number of explosions with conventional high explosives for various purposes connected with the detection of underground nuclear explosions, and the United States has carried out underground nuclear explosions for the same purpose: Projects Sterling and Rulison.

PROJECTS STERLING AND RULISON

Project Sterling was the explosion (in 1966) of a nuclear device of about 0.35 kiloton, which was detonated in an underground cavity made by an earlier nuclear explosion. The purpose of the test was to examine the degree of decoupling that could be achieved. Decoupling is the muffling effect that was described in connection with explosions in soft material—that is, a reduction in signal strength because the full force of the explosion is not transmitted to the surrounding media. Its connection with the disguising of nuclear tests will be discussed later.

A later series of tests was announced by the United States. These underground explosions were to be part of the Plowshare Project to develop natural resources, but were also to be used as a contribution to a worldwide investigation of the detection of underground testing. The first explosion of this series, Project Rulison, was detonated in 1969. Before the event details of the preparations were supplied to the participating countries; immediately before the explosion seismic observatories were alerted, and after the event other parameters—such as the exact time, depth, and yield—were disseminated. The yield for Rulison was 40 kilotons, which was released in a gas-bearing stratum, similar to that for an earlier explosion, Gas Buggy, part of the Plowshare Program on the peaceful uses of nuclear explosives.

SEISMIC MAGNITUDES AND IDENTIFICATION

It will be recalled that experts meeting at Geneva suggested a triangular grid of 180 seismic detection stations; as a result of subsequent work Great Britain was able to suggest that 20-25 control stations only were necessary. These stations would be at specially selected sites, as far as possible from local noise. An advantage of long range (teleseismic) signals of 3,000-10,000 kilometers is that they are much less distorted by irregularities of the earth than are shorter-range signals. Great Britain suggested that explosive signals down to seismic magnitude four could be identified; but a later test showed that anomalous signals were produced in the vicinity of the test area when distorted by the terrain, and so the magnitude for identification was revised upward.

Theoretical work has suggested that the ratios between different types of waves is different for earthquakes and explosions. Using this and other evidence, the SIPRI group convened to discuss the detection of underground tests came to the conclusion that yields down to 10 kilotons in hard rock could be identified with suitable systems, but that explosions in alluvium could be as much as a factor of 10 higher for the same signal strength. For identification of tests of lower magnitudes, new equipment might have to be developed. Great Britain concurs with this view and believes that present systems are "unlikely to provide an identification threshold at teleseismic distances, much, if at all, lower than the 20-60-kt agreed by the SIPRI group."[8]

Seismographers have designated different means for identifying nuclear explosions as positive identifiers or as diagnostic aids. A positive identifier is unambiguous in pointing to a nuclear explosion, while a diagnostic aid points to a degree of probability. Some means of identifying earthquakes that are only diagnostic aids for events of lower seismic magnitude become positive identifiers at high seismic magnitude.

ON-SITE INSPECTION

Following the failure to obtain agreement on a small number of on-site inspections, there has appeared to be little incentive to pursue the matter. However, in some circumstances this might be the only satisfactory way of quelling doubts one way or another, particularly for the majority of states that do not command the technical resources necessary for other means of verification.

Seismic events cannot be located precisely by seismometers alone, but only within an elliptical area on the surface of the earth. It is usual to specify the ellipse as one in which there is a 95 percent probability that it will contain the event. The larger the release of energy, the more easily the location is specified, that is, the smaller the ellipse. At the lower levels of discrimination the ellipse might be about 2,000 kilometers in area, although better knowledge of travel times will improve the location of events. The personnel making an on-site inspection would thus need considerable liberty to explore the area in which the test was thought to have taken place, and freedom to conduct tests. Apart from such obvious steps as checking mining and other industrial facilities within the area, the inspectors could be equipped with apparatus to take samples of gases from below the surface; detection of particular radioactive species would show that a test had been conducted, and ratios between the species would indicate when the test had been conducted.

SERIES OF TESTS

A single underground test of a magnitude even as high as on the verge of detection would not be of much value in the development of nuclear weapons, so a number of such tests would have to be carried out; and this would increase the chances of detection. If tests were being conducted at the threshold for identification and at a rate of one-third of natural events in the area under surveillance, the probability of detecting a single test would be one in three; but the probability of discovering at least one test out of two is better than even. The calculated successes of a number of inspections are tabulated in Table 9, from which it can be seen that, with four inspections during the period of the trials, there would be 80 percent chance of discovering at least one clandestine test and of demonstrating that the treaty was being broken.

With the introduction of surveillance satellites, the preparation of sites for underground testing would become more difficult to conceal from the superpowers; but interpretation of photographs and other sensor records might be difficult to produce as evidence, both because of the difficulties of interpretation by nonexperts and because it might not be thought wise to reveal the capabilities of the surveillance systems.

A possible alternative or supplement to on-site inspections could be further development of sealed and tamper-proof black boxes. The problem of collection of records might be overcome by periodic

TABLE 9

Detection of Clandestine Weapons Tests

Number of Inspections	Probability of Detecting One or More Tests
1	0.33
2	$1-(1-0.33)^2 = 0.56$
3	$1-(1-0.33)^3 = 0.70$
4	$1-(1-0.33)^4 = 0.80$

interrogations from satellites, with rapid transmission of data followed by scrubbing and reuse of the magnetic tape, so that the black box could continue to supply information until the batteries or other components failed. As an example of such a capability, it will be recalled that a seismometer was placed on the moon during the first manned landing, and the instrument telemetered observations some 250,000 miles to earth. Small seismic detectors are already in use by the military to monitor the passage of men and vehicles in tactical situations.

A number of suggestions have been put forward for making on-site inspections more acceptable. For example, Great Britain suggested that they should be carried out only after agreement by a majority of an international committee; Sweden has suggested inspection only on invitation; and various annual quotas of inspection visits have been proposed.

DISGUISING UNDERGROUND NUCLEAR EXPLOSIONS

Agreement on banning of underground nuclear test explosions is unlikely to be reached if there is a high probability that an opponent could be carrying out undetected clandestine explosions. Since this is the crux of the problem, a great deal of attention has been paid to methods that might be used by a determined violator. Generally, three possible methods could be tried. The first is to explode the device at the same time as a local earthquake of higher seismic magnitude, so that the signals from the explosion are swamped. The difficulties are obvious: testing would have to be carried out in an earthquake region, and the test detonation would have to await a natural event. The second method is to make a test explosion resemble an earthquake. This might be done by exploding two devices, so that a first and a second wave are produced, the timing of arrival at the station appearing to indicate a deep earthquake with a primary pulse and a following pulse reflected from the earth's surface. The third method is to reduce the coupling between the explosion and the surrounding medium. Partial decoupling by exploding in alluvium was discussed above, but it is possible that the device could be not emplaced at sufficient depth in the relatively shallow beds of alluvium to prevent cratering or ground subsidence that could be detected from a satellite. A fully decoupled explosion could be carried out at great depth in a spherical hole. The problem is in making the hole. A hole to achieve decoupling of a reasonable-size explosion would be a difficult engineering feat, since a vast quantity of rock would have to be mined and the cavity prevented from collapsing. When spherical holes for demonstration and test purposes have been used, they have been made by the previous explosion of a nuclear device. Apart from the fact that this explosion itself could be detected, access to the hole for the emplacing of the second device is delayed for many months or even years because of residual heat and radioactivity.

Experimental work of this nature has been conducted, and the purpose of Project Sterling was to examine the degree of decoupling that could be achieved. Some details were given of the range at which this comparatively small explosion could be detected. The yield was probably too low for really useful information in the design of weapons, for which the minimum yield might have to be about 10 kilotons. It has been mentioned that creating cavities by underground nuclear explosions has special problems, whatever purpose the cavity is to serve. The high temperatures of the walls of the cavity subside only slowly because of the low thermal conductivity of rock strata. The cavity for Sterling was created by Project Salmon (in 1964); two years afterward the walls were still at 200°C, and a refrigerator unit had to be incorporated with the nuclear device for Sterling. When the refrigerator failed, the test had to be advanced by three days to avoid an unplanned explosion of the conventional explosive component in the device. (This kind of failure could be serious in a highly instrumented test that depended upon closely coordinated experiments by a number of scientific and technical groups.)

On the other hand, it has been calculated that with a sufficiently large cavity almost complete decoupling would be possible and a 20 kiloton explosive would then give a seismic magnitude of three—that is, well below the limit of certain detection.

Clandestine nuclear tests are most likely to be carried out in areas of natural seismic activity. These are well-known, as they lie in lines of weakness in the earth's crust. Underground explosions in these areas have led to considerable concern that they might trigger earthquakes. Some of the underground explosions in the United States have been followed by earth tremors, but it has been argued that an underground weapons test is likely to release only those earthquakes that are imminent. A great deal of concern was expressed about very large-scale tests on Amchitka in the Aleutians, at Millrow in October 1969, and Cannikin in November 1971; but firing of the shot was not followed by serious earth movements in either case.

USE OF NUCLEAR EXPLOSIVES FOR CIVIL ENGINEERING

The possibility of using nuclear explosives for civil engineering has been considered for some years,[9] with the greatest effort being by the U.S. AEC in their Plowshare Program. The types of operation that have been considered include digging of canals and harbors, underground mining, creation of storage cavities, and the release of natural gas and oil. Since nuclear explosives have not yet been used widely for civilian purposes, the design of the first devices was not optimized for civil uses—that is, mainly low cost and low fallout of radioactivity—as against military requirements, which emphasize compactness and low weight.

The cost of using nuclear explosives for civilian purposes depends on a number of factors. Assessing the hazards and the precautions to be taken is a much more serious problem than in conventional civil engineering; the cost of emplacement and fusing will no doubt be considerably less than for quantities of high explosive; unlike conventional high explosive, the cost of an explosion is not proportional to yield, and it is more economic to use a few high-yield devices rather than many low-yield shots; there are the costs of obtaining control of land for some time, evacuating the population, and carrying out post-explosion surveys; finally, there are problems of venting radioactive gases and the fallout of radioactive debris. Nuclear explosions will release radioactivity from the fission reaction; and if the fusion reaction is employed, there will be a release of radioactive tritium. In addition, irradiation by neutrons will induce radioactivity in surrounding materials. Design of devices to reduce the amount of radioactivity produced has recently been optimized so that they release only 1 percent of the amount of the radioactivity that would have been released by the same yield a few years ago.

When the intention is to shatter rocks or produce a cavity underground, much of the radioactivity will be trapped; escape to the atmosphere will be limited to radioactive gases and volatile vapors, and some of the latter will be absorbed in the soil. However, thermonuclear devices that generate radioactive tritium may contaminate water and oil so that, if these are to be recovered, "all-fission" devices may be preferred. On the other hand, when constructing canals and harbors, the crater would be dug in the surface of the earth and fission products could not be trapped; hence the fission content of the device must be at a minimum, and irradiation of surrounding soil may be reduced by surrounding the device with neutron-absorbing materials.

Apart from the hazards to man from the release of radioactivity, there is the problem of detection of radioactivity beyond the national frontiers, prohibited by the Non-Proliferation Treaty. So far there has been no detailed discussion of how civil nuclear explosions can be reconciled with the extremely sensitive methods available for detecting traces of radioactivity at long range.

Another problem that arises from the possibility of using nuclear explosives for civil engineering is whether the development of such devices by a nonnuclear weapons country would be tantamount to development of a technology for nuclear weapons. In the opinion of the nuclear experts advising the secretary-general of the United Nations,[10] and other experts who have spoken on this matter, there is little difference in the design of civil and military nuclear devices. (But see below.)

Countries with undeveloped natural resources and without adequate transport and low density of population could use civil nuclear explosions for gaining access to these resources and for exploiting them—for example, the digging of harbors and canals, opening up road and rail routes through mountain ranges, loosening and removing overburdens from ore deposits, creating underground water storage, or releasing oil and natural gas. There is thus considerable reluctance by these countries to be constrained in development of nuclear civil engineering by international treaties such as the NPT. However, apart from the complications of the NPT, the costs of developing nuclear explosives devices are very high and must be compared with the prices that could be offered by the nuclear weapons powers that already have these devices and have offset the development costs against their weapons programs.

Nuclear explosive devices must be at least as sophisticated as nuclear weapons in order to fulfill some of the requirements, such as minimal fallout, predictable yield, small diameter to facilitate installation, and neutron shielding to reduce induced radioactivity. It therefore appears unlikely that a country developing nuclear explosives for the first time could compete with the present nuclear powers, or even with countries where considerable development has taken place.

The status of development in the Soviet Union is not known, although a number of underground explosions have been carried out; and while these may all have been for the development of nuclear weapons, there will undoubtedly have been some experience generated of value to civil explosions. It is also known that the Soviet Union has highly developed techniques for very large explosions with conventional high explosives that are suitable for civil engineering tasks. It is, therefore, possible to marry these different techniques. Soviet spokesmen at ENDC have said that there is little basic difference between civil nuclear explosions and nuclear warheads, but that they can foresee no difficulty in providing a service to countries without nuclear programs after the NPT is signed.

Nuclear explosive devices have advantages over conventional explosives in civil engineering in situations where a very large concentrated yield is an advantage; in such circumstances a nuclear device is smaller and more easily handled, and much more easily emplaced. However, nuclear explosives always involve such a concentrated release of energy that some is wasted in producing unwanted effects, such as vaporization of rocks. Many civil engineering tasks, such as bringing down the face of a cliff, can be better performed by a large number of small, discrete charges. As part of their program the Russians have carried out a number of tasks using large quantities of conventional high explosives; these tasks included the loosening or removal of overburden to give access to bodies of ore near the surface and the damming and diversion of rivers. They appear to have built up a body of unique experience in these techniques; and it may be that their lack of enthusiasm, as compared with the United States, for nuclear explosives in engineering is related to their apparent success with other means.

Practically all that is known publicly about the history and practice of nuclear explosives for civil purposes comes from the United States, including the engineering textbook by Teller and his associates.[11]

The United States has carried out studies and some trial explosions in the Plowshare programme. (Some of these have been already mentioned.) Much nuclear work is carried out by private companies, and it may be thought that here there is more possibility of dissemination of information than would be the case with direct government agencies, particularly when the private companies wish to become members of international consortia in order to compete to better advantage. Problems of the release of radioactivity from cratering explosions would occur when digging canals or creating harbors. In the case of a second canal to run parallel with the Panama Canal, which has been studied in considerable detail, several of the possible routes could be dug with a series of nuclear explosions; the health hazard from fallout could be reduced by carrying out the explosions over a few years, the intervening time being used for civil engineering tasks, and also by selecting times of settled weather, when the radioactive debris would be blown out to sea. However, the sensitivity of methods of detecting radionuclei is such that it is highly likely that debris would be detected beyond the national frontier, thus breaking the Limited Test Ban Treaty. Some kind of relaxation or dispensation would be necessary, and it is possible that this could be linked in some way with international inspections.

Costs, too, have to be taken into account; these include not only special precautions that must be taken with a nuclear device and temporary evacuation of areas liable to fallout but also, in the case of high explosives, the much more extensive work of emplacing the charges, the large quantities of explosives, and transport to the site. Here the costs might be much more favorable for a nuclear device.

From the arms control point of view, the main problem is whether development work on a civil explosive device is closely related to that for developing a weapon. At the suggestion of General Burns the international experts who had advised the secretary-general of the United Nations were asked for their opinion; their answer was that there was no essential difference between the requirements for civil and military explosives.[12] The nuclear superpowers indicated that they would be willing to negotiate separately to provide a nuclear explosives service, which Burns characterized as "a good bargain," since much of the development costs had already been charged against weapons development. Agreement on conditions may be achieved in the private discussions between the United States and the Soviet Union on the problems of use of peaceful nuclear explosives, which were held first at Vienna in April 1969, and subsequently at Moscow in February 1970.

COMPREHENSIVE TEST BAN TREATY

The Swedish delegate to the ENDC tables a draft treaty on 1 April 1969.[13] Provisions in the draft that have technical importance are the following:

Article II

> 2. Each state party to this treaty undertakes to cooperate in good faith in an effective international exchange

of seismological data in order to facilitate the detection, identification, and location of underground events.

3. Each state party to this treaty undertakes to co-operate in good faith for the clarification of all events pertaining to the subject matter of this treaty. In accordance with this provision, each state party to the treaty is entitled:

a. to make enquiries and to receive information as a result of such enquiries.
b. to invite inspection on its territory or territory under its jurisdiction, such inspection to be carried out in the manner prescribed by the inviting party.
c. to make proposals, if it deems the information available or made available to it under all or any of the preceding provisions is inadequate, as to suitable methods of clarification.

4. Each state party to this treaty may bring to the attention of the Security Council of the United Nations and of the other parties to the treaty that it deems another party to have failed to co-operate to the fullest extent for the clarification of a particular event.

The purpose of the treaty, as explained by the Swedish delegate, was not to provide complete intelligence or judicially conclusive evidence but to act as a deterrent. The decision as to what was an "adequately verifiable treaty" was a political decision. As far as the nonnuclear countries were concerned, this treaty would be a second lock on further development and dissemination of nuclear weapons in addition to the Non-Proliferation Treaty.

In the view of this writer, the question to be answered is not entirely political; it is whether, with existing techniques and with advances that could be made, it would be possible to verify clandestine nuclear testing to a high level of probability before the results of such tests could be applied to upset the strategic balance.

This is largely a technical question; the political element is the choice of the criterion for the level of probability of detection—is this to be 80 percent (one chance in five of escaping detection), 90 percent, 95 percent, or 99 percent (one chance in a hundred)?

Put in this way, not only does the violator have to carry out his tests in such a way as to escape detection but he also has to be able to use the results to gain a substantial military advantage. What this would involve would be very different for the superpowers than for the nonnuclear powers; in the former case the new weapons would have to confer a first-strike option, that is, some hundreds of new weapons would have to be deployed. In the case of the nonnuclear powers, the local strategic situation could be entirely upset by only a few weapons, or even the proven ability to make them. It is likely that an important barrier to agreement to a Comprehensive Test Ban Treaty is the fear on both sides that the other would maintain a present advantage. As at least a partial answer to this problem, Great Britain has suggested a quota of annual tests, decreasing over a number of years until complete prohibition is achieved.

PREVENTION OF PROLIFERATION AND DISSEMINATION OF NUCLEAR WEAPONS

The terms "proliferation" and "dissemination" often tend to be used rather carelessly, and even interchangeably. Succinct and useful differentiations have been given by Sir Solly Zuckerman that are sufficiently operational for this text: proliferation is "make it yourself" and dissemination is "get it from someone else."[14] To add further confusion, the term "vertical proliferation" is sometimes used for an increase in the stock of nuclear weapons in one of the nuclear powers. The Non-Proliferation Treaty relates to both "proliferation" and "dissemination" as defined above but not to "vertical proliferation."

Views on proliferation vary from country to country. It is to the advantage of the present nuclear powers that no other countries acquire nuclear weapons because this would reduce the advantages that the nuclear powers believe they now have in comparison with the nonnuclear powers. The United States, the Soviet Union, and Great Britain have played leading parts in the negotiations for the Non-Proliferation Treaty. France has announced that she will not sign the treaty but will observe its general requirements. French official policy is not to sign treaties that are not genuine disarmament treaties. A view strongly advocated in France is that as each country reaches the stage of industrial development at which it can produce nuclear weapons, it should do so, to be in a position to threaten to retaliate against an attack on its vital interests. However, this attitude is not shared by a number of the "civil nuclear powers," that is, those with resources to become nuclear military powers: several have been in a position to develop nuclear weapons for some years and have made a conscious choice not to "go nuclear." In other cases the choice is more delicately balanced because of different apparent threats. A lesser fear by some countries is that the treaty would prevent the development and use of nuclear explosives for civil engineering.

Proliferation of nuclear weapons has been less than many would have anticipated. There are several reasons for this.

The present nuclear powers wish to retain their advantage in military power and to exert pressure on other nations to persuade them not to proliferate; they consider that they are the best to be trusted with this great power and thus take steps to avoid passing on information and materials. There is a general desire to limit the number of fingers on the nuclear trigger; and governments realize that further dissemination, once begun, would be difficult to limit, whereas the present balance is fairly stable. The scale of damage would be so great that even the greatest countries would suffer terrible losses from even a limited attack, while small countries could be destroyed; and in present circumstances many nonnuclear countries are able to pursue sufficiently independent national policies to satisfy their aspirations.

THE NON-PROLIFERATION TREATY

Prevention of dissemination and proliferation is now almost universally accepted as being in the interests of individual countries and of the international community. This has not always been so: following wartime collaboration the United States materially assisted the British nuclear weapons program, first by sharing information on the design of nuclear warheads and second by provision of Polaris missiles. The Soviet Union is believed to have provided some help to the Chinese. France has had an indigenous weapons program, but the cost appears to have been enhanced by lack of know-how from external sources. The French attitude is against the dissemination from one country to another but, as we have seen, not against proliferation within individual countries.

The principal reason advanced for opposing both proliferation and dissemination is that the possession of nuclear weapons by more countries would increase the possibilities of nuclear war. These arguments are generally well known and will not be repeated. However, one point that might be stressed is that the chance of nuclear war is increased not only in proportion to the number of countries possessing nuclear weapons but also (probably more nearly) in proportion to the number of pairs of such countries. Thus, with five nuclear powers there are 10 such pairs, while with seven nuclear powers there would be 21 pairs—more than doubling the chances of a nuclear war.

The attitudes of countries toward the NPT depend on their present situation and future prospects. The present nuclear powers see one of its advantages as preserving their military status and, even if not prepared to sign, are in practice willing to adhere to the provisions that prohibit transfer of know-how. Countries that have developed civil nuclear industries are divided into those which have decided that possession of nuclear weapons will not improve their security and those which have doubts. Countries without any highly developed nuclear resources generally approve entirely, since they see further proliferation as a possible direct and indirect threat.

The main technical problems that have given concern are the adequacy of controls over fissile materials and of means for verification, the fear that the treaty might inhibit the transfer of information on civil nuclear reactors and cause restriction on the use of nuclear explosives, and how much "spin-off" there can be between civil and military technology (and thus any consequential restrictions on civil developments). Political objections to the Non-Proliferation Treaty relate to its apparent one-sidedness, in that it imposes limitations on the nonnuclear powers without any reciprocal concessions by the nuclear power signatories. A particular cause of concern to some countries is the use of nuclear explosives, which appears to hold great potential for the kind of civil engineering required to exploit their natural resources.

The early drafts of the Non-Proliferation Treaty appeared to place the nuclear weapons powers in a privileged position, which was resented by those countries whose plants would be open to inspection. Offers by the United States and Great Britain to open some commercial plants for inspection helped to mitigate the problem but, of course, other countries realized that this would still leave military plants uninspected and, in any case, this arrangement would not involve the other nuclear powers. To satisfy the nonnuclear powers a promise was required of further steps to follow the NPT, with opportunities for the nonnuclear powers to monitor and approve progress. Article III of the treaty, relating to inspection, was omitted from the first openly published draft (August 1967); and negotiations of the wording were prolonged and subject to frequent amendment. The Non-Proliferation Treaty finally came into operation on 5 March 1970 with signing by the United States, the Soviet Union, and Great Britain.

ORGANIZATIONS FOR INSPECTION UNDER THE NON-PROLIFERATION TREATY

Problems of agreeing on safeguards for the Non-Proliferation Treaty—and, for that matter, for other treaties involving inspection—are complicated by the number of international agencies with inspection responsibilities. The International Atomic Energy Agency appears in many respects to be the natural body for such responsibilities: it is an agency of the United Nations and has an international staff and a fairly limited range of objectives, among which inspection is prominent. However, for a worldwide inspection organization it is understaffed.

Euratom is a constituent of the Organization for Economic Cooperation and Development; and while it has wide responsibilities, the inspection arm is particularly well developed. Furthermore, inspection is already mandatory and not by invitation of the two parties concerned, as it is at present with IAEA; and about one-third of the installations inspected by Euratom are in France—indeed, France is probably the most inspected country. However, Euratom inspection is regional rather than international, and it has been objected to on the grounds that it is a kind of self-inspection in Western Europe. On the other hand, the countries concerned in Western Europe prefer inspection by Euratom on grounds of commercial secrecy. In practice, collaboration between IAEA and Euratom should not be difficult to achieve and would appear to ensure that the region where there is the greatest technical potential for proliferation and dissemination would be most closely inspected. Even apart from the question of inspection, it was inevitable that closer collaboration between the two bodies would in any case have developed with the expansion of the nuclear power industry.

(A more extended discussion on IAEA and Euratom appeared in Chapter 7.)

INSPECTION REQUIREMENTS

An important criterion for the success of the Non-Proliferation Treaty is the number of signatory countries that have developed nuclear and other relevant industries. Many countries have nuclear reactors that could be used to produce plutonium for military purposes, but only a limited number—Germany, Japan, and Canada, followed by Sweden, Italy, and India—have more or less immediately available materials and skills for the manufacture of warheads and nuclear delivery vehicles, such as missiles and aircraft.

The countries named, and others, have nuclear reactors for research or production of electrical power. In many cases these reactors and fuel were supplied to them by other countries under some form of bilateral agreement, usually with conditions to control the plutonium produced. These agreements are either bilateral between the supplier and the operator or under an international agreement. It is conceivable that there could be diversions from current production for clandestine military purposes; and there might be an even greater danger in the accumulation of stocks of plutonium over years of operation, perhaps to fuel a fast reactor, with the seizure of these stocks by the government—which might be of a totally different political complexion from the one that signed the treaty. One solution might be a complete ban on the building of reactors and other facilities in other countries; but this would not be acceptable to countries hoping to sell reactors, nor to those countries hoping to install them for the generation of electricity. And, politically, it would appear to discriminate against those countries whose need is greatest. Without going to the length of a complete ban on the building of reactors for others, there are several other ways in which pressure may be exerted to injure commercial activities, such as restrictions applied to supplies of materials such as uranium ores and, in the future, thorium and plutonium, and restrictions on the export of essential plant, technical assistance, and know-how. Particular activities that are considered to be closely related to weapons development could be prohibited, and an external inspection system could itself hinder the processes in many ways and give rise to fears of commercial espionage.

There is, in addition to these problems that face the nonnuclear weapons powers, the loss that the nonnuclear powers believe they may suffer in terms of a substantial spin-off of commercial value from a nuclear weapons program: this is not the same thing as the transfer of techniques and skills from the military to civil nuclear industries and vice versa. It is argued elsewhere that, while there may not be very direct similarities in the core science of nuclear physics, there are in fact large areas of supporting technologies that are required by both and a generalized knowledge and experience common to both industries. However, there is little evidence that there are transfers of great importance to other industries from the nuclear weapons industry; there is, on the other hand, from civilian nuclear power, the widespread impact of the availability of radioactive isotopes, which are used in medicine and many industries in a number of different ways. The actual construction of nuclear power stations actively engages large segments of the civil engineering and construction industries, and the special requirements have undoubtedly introduced new techniques and standards into these industries. It must not be too readily assumed that the resources allocated to a nuclear weapons program have an immediate spin-off to the civil sector.

The purpose of inspection is to verify to the satisfaction of the nuclear powers and the other nonnuclear powers that the nonnuclear countries are not producing nuclear weapons. Inspection will bear most heavily on the nonnuclear powers and can be seen as an infringement of national sovereignty. There are also objections on the grounds of industrial espionage and restrictions on peaceful nuclear activities.

The United States favors vigorous safeguards of all civil nuclear facilities of the nonnuclear countries, eventually extending controls to the nuclear powers, even though this would not be related to the concept of proliferation within the context of the treaty. The Soviet Union has not imposed particularly severe legal safeguards on those states to which it has supplied aid. On the other hand, it has maintained practical controls: for example, all fuel has to be returned to the Soviet Union for reprocessing, and there have been restrictions on the type of fuel—that supplied to Yugoslavia and China was limited to 2 percent enrichment, while to other Communist countries it was limited to 10 percent. Non-Communist countries have been given help only with small research facilities, and often Soviet technicians are employed.

Each country has its own problems, whether they arise from the present stage of its nuclear industry, its foreign policy and alliances, or its appreciation of threats. The position of the nuclear powers can be summarized as follows:

Soviet Union—sponsored treaty but will not permit inspections

United States—sponsored treaty and will permit inspection of civil industry

Great Britain—supports treaty, will permit inspection of civil industry, but could be embarrassed by transfer regulations

France—will not sign treaty but will adhere to principles; civil industry already inspected

China—denounces treaty but shows no sign of disseminating information.

NONNUCLEAR ZONES

Another way in which nuclear weapons may be controlled, besides a complete restriction on nuclear tests and general nonproliferation, is a prohibition of all nuclear weapons in a particular geographical area. The only areas for which such an agreement has been reached are Latin America and Antarctica, under the Treaty of Tlatelolco and the Antarctica Treaty. This kind of agreement is essentially political and has little technological content that has not been dealt with elsewhere.

Other areas for which treaties have been suggested are the Balkans and Africa, and a degree of denuclearization has been proposed for Europe under various proposals made by Polish government sources. (Limitation of nuclear weapons on the seabed is considered at the end of Chapter 13.)

NOTES

1. Pierre Messener, Our Military Policy (Washington, D.C.: Press and Information Service, Embassy of France, May 1963). Quoted in Joel Larus, Nuclear Weapons Safety and the Common Defense (Columbus: Ohio State University Press, 1967).

2. Larus, op. cit.

3. J. B. Wiesner, Where Science and Politics Meet (New York: McGraw-Hill, 1965).

4. Article I. 1(b), "Treaty Banning Nuclear Weapons Tests in the Atmosphere, in Outer Space, and under Water" (Moscow Partial Test-Ban Treaty, August 5, 1963). See also ENDC/100/Rev 1 (July 30, 1963).

5. United Nations, "Report of the Conference of Experts to Study the Possibility of Detecting Violations of a Possible Agreement on the Suspension of Nuclear Tests," Document A/3897 (1958).

6. Ibid.

7. D. Davies, rapporteur, Progress Report of the Seismic Study Group (Stockholm: International Peace Research Institute, February 1970).

8. Conference of the Eighteen Nations Disarmament Disarmament Committee, Vertabim Record PV 428 (August 14, 1969).

9. For details, see Edward Teller, Wilson K. Talley, Gary H. Higgins, and Gerald W. Johnson, The Constructive Uses of Nuclear Explosives (New York: McGraw-Hill, 1968). Also see Kenneth Parker, "Engineering with Nuclear Explosives," New Scientist (April 2, 1970).

10. United Nations, "Report to the Secretary-General on the Effects of the Possible Use of Nuclear Weapons and on the Security and Economic Implications for States of the Acquisition and Further Development of These Weapons," A/6858 (October 10, 1967).

11. Teller et al., op. cit.

12. United Nations, "Report to the Secretary-General . . . ."

13. Sweden, "Working Paper with Suggestions as to Possible Provisions of a Treaty Banning Underground Nuclear Weapons Tests," ENDC/242 (April 1969).

14. Sir Solly Zuckermann, The Control of Proliferation: Three Views, Adelphi paper no. 29 (London: Institute of Strategic Studies, 1966).

CHAPTER

10

STRATEGIC NUCLEAR DELIVERY VEHICLES

TYPES OF NUCLEAR DELIVERY VEHICLES

There are problems in defining weapons delivery systems because many can deliver both conventional and nuclear weapons. However, the more costly long-range weapons systems would not be cost-effective, and probably ineffective militarily, if armed only with conventional warheads. At the lower end of the range of strategic nuclear weapons systems there is no clearly marked transition to tactical nuclear weapons systems. Shipborne systems could be used, for example, armed with tactical nuclear or conventional high-explosive warheads to deter nonnuclear weapons states or to attack coastal targets. Field-force dual-purpose tactical nuclear weapons could be used with kiloton-yield nuclear warheads or conventional high explosives to attack a range of targets such as troop concentrations, bridges, railheads, airfields, etc. An agreement on strategic nuclear weapons would have to specify which weapon systems were to be included. The main characteristics of various nuclear weapons systems are described in Table 10.

One of the most important factors in deciding which nuclear delivery vehicle is to be selected as a deterrent system is the vulnerability to a disarming first strike by the enemy. The importance of retaining invulnerable second-strike forces is that the promise of devastating retaliation will inhibit a first strike. Indeed, the second strike may well cause more casualties than a first strike aimed at military targets, since the surviving second strike could be retargeted, if necessary, against cities. It should be noted, on the other hand, that a counter-force strike against hardened military targets might cause more casualties than the same number of weapons bursting over cities,

TABLE 10

Characteristics of Nuclear Delivery Systems

Aircraft
Vulnerable on ground, particularly to surprise attack; small number only on immediate (airborne) alert; high cost of alert; the obvious threat during practice alerts and simulated attacks may be useful as a deterrent or dangerous; not vulnerable when airborne until they reach enemy territory; high attrition rate crossing enemy territory; extreme accuracy; can select new targets or targets of opportunity; possibility of successive missions; available for nonnuclear missions; less liable to discharge of weapon; may avoid strongest defenses, or attack them, by launching short-range attack missiles.

Light Bombers
deployed near enemy territory; constant threat, but very vulnerable to counterforce strike; arming of weapons may be only on command; political problems.

Heavy Bombers
deployed in home territory; less obvious, at least not so vulnerable to first strike; possibility of recall; very heavy loads.

Strike Fleet
aircraft carrier is not fixed in position and can be moved to evade detection and to areas of different targets; flexible targeting; some vulnerability to aircraft, submarines, and surface-to-air missiles; encourages a maritime defense; few aircraft on immediate alert; because of short range, may not be possible to recall; political problems; no collateral (i.e., fallout) damage if attacked.

M/IRBM
Medium and Intermediate Range Ballistic Missiles
May be sited near opponent's territory and are then an obvious threat; if on field sites, vulnerable to first strike; cheaper than ICBM's; not highly accurate and require larger warhead; much collateral damage; if liquid-cooled, problem with fueling, and not all immediately available except for short stand-by periods; if mobile, some safety against first-strike, but logistic problems and reduced accuracy.

ICBM
Intercontinental Ballistic Missiles
Vulnerability reduced by hardening (i.e., containment in underground concrete silos), so that to ensure their destruction a number of attacks may be required; constant alert, with automated checking of systems and countdown; command and control can be hardened and duplicated in airborne control posts; large amount of collateral damage (from fallout) if attacked; cannot be recalled, but have possibilities of autodestruction or delayed arming of weapon; in flight fairly invulnerable to countermeasures; accuracy inferior to bomber, and for same targets must carry large (megaton) warhead; solid fuel does not require refrigerated storage and pumping facilities.

SLBM
Submarine-Launched Ballistic Missiles
Submarines are difficult to detect and locate, move at high speed, and can remain submerged for long patrols; with alternate crews, can remain on station for long periods; refueling is very infrequent; invulnerable to a high degree; range of SLBM's may restrict patrol stations; overseas bases may be required to exchange crews and provide facilities for shore leave; problems of command and control; problems in selecting, training, and retaining personnel; very complex and costly system; reduced accuracy of missiles, best suited for second-strike role; position at sea may be used to signal increased or decreased threat (this may be used as arms control measure).

Space Vehicles
Cost-ineffective; vulnerable to counterattack; numbers required would be obvious threat; banned by treaty.

Note: Tactical nuclear delivery vehicle systems such as field artillery, SAM's and short-range missiles, are not considered here, nor are such possible future strategic systems as seabed missile platforms and highspeed surface ships or the advanced manned strategic aircraft.

because ground bursts to damage silos may create much more and more highly concentrated radioactive fallout.

In general terms the relative advantages and disadvantages of different strategic systems depend on the following criteria:

Cost-effectiveness of alternative systems

Effect on deterrence and in war

Amount of collateral damage if attacked

Effectiveness and reliability of command and control

Vulnerability to preemptive attack

Rate of obsolescence (military and technical)

Political effects on allies, neutrals, and opponents

Status in international law

Susceptability to arms control and inspection agreements.

Subcriteria are accuracy, nature of threat, ability to penetrate defenses, flexibility, usefulness in escalation or deescalation, target discrimination, acceptability in the neighborhood, modifiability, and dispersion of launch sites.

FIRST AND SECOND STRIKES

A power with long-range nuclear delivery systems confronting a nonnuclear weapons state has a first strike option in that it can attack without the risk of nuclear retaliation; relatively few nuclear weapons would be required for this purpose. For a first-strike option against another power armed with nuclear weapons, a capacity would also be required for destroying in a single onslaught most of the opponent's strategic nuclear weapons, with any surviving weapons capable of inflicting only a limited amount of damage, insufficient to deter the first strike. A first-strike capability would deter almost any action of an opponent by threat of "massive retaliation."

A second-strike capability exists when enough nuclear weapons could survive a first strike to pose a threat of retaliation of such magnitude that a would-be attacker would be deterred from launching his first strike.

The modern form of mutual deterrence exists when both sides have second-strike capabilities. With sufficient numbers, sophistication, and variety, mutual deterrence is not likely to be upset either by rapid production of more weapons by one side or by a rapidly exploited technical advance.

Strategic nuclear delivery systems can be preserved for retaliation in various ways. The first method was to provide very early warning of an attack and an ability for almost instantaneous response, so that weapons could be launched before the attack arrived. This was obviously so dangerous—in that it depended on interpretation of radar signals and hair-trigger command and control, and increased the chance of war—that strategic systems were designed, at least in part, for a second-strike role. This could be achieved in several ways. A large initial deployment ensures a greater chance that enough will survive. A variety of systems complicates the first strike in a number of ways, for not only may a different attacking system be required for a highly effective attack on each target but, in an all-out attack, each of these attacking systems would have to act simultaneously to prevent the launching of retaliation. Mobility of systems makes them difficult to locate; and, even when they are located, information on the new positions must be fed back into retargeting of the attacking systems. Systems may be hardened to survive the effects of weapons up to a high level, weapons systems may be defended by other systems that can attack the incoming warheads or nuclear delivery vehicles.

NATIONAL CAPABILITIES AND DEPLOYMENTS

U.S. Capabilities

Immediately after World War II the United States deactivated the very large military forces it had mustered; but it has since rebuilt modernized forces, some of which are deployed outside the country, principally in Southeast Asia and in Europe as part of NATO.

The main elements of the U.S. military forces are a large, almost completely deployed force of ICBM's in underground silos in the United States, mostly solid-fueled and with secure command and control; a force of intercontinental bombers, reequipped for extended service, mostly stationed in the United States; a fleet of nuclear-powered submarines armed with nuclear weapons; strike fleets built around aircraft carriers, with aircraft capable of carrying nuclear weapons; balanced military field forces with all arms, including tactical nuclear warheads for delivery by artillery, missiles, and aircraft; long-range aircraft and some shipping for rapid intervention, together with marines and other specially trained troops; and fleets of warships of various categories, some armed with tactical nuclear weapons.

Russian Capabilities

Russian capabilities stemming from the forces in World War II, and, as later developed, consist of a large and growing force of ICBM's, some solid-fueled and in underground silos, including a high proportion of large liquid-fueled missiles with multi-megaton yield warheads; a small force of intercontinental bombers; a deployment of liquid-fueled medium- and intermediate-range ballistic missiles, mainly threatening Western Europe; heavily armored land forces, integrated with armies of other members of Warsaw Pact; a force of short- and medium-range bombers and attack aircraft; well-developed antiaircraft defenses, with missiles, artillery, and fighter aircraft; a limited deployment of antiballistic missiles; a growing fleet of nuclear-powered submarines armed with ballistic missiles; and a larger fleet of diesel-powered submarines, many possibly for coastal defense and use against U.S. strike fleets, some of them carrying cruise missiles armed with nuclear warheads.

The structure of the older part of these forces tends to indicate a preponderance of interest in deterring attack from Europe (historically the major threat to Russia) and defense in depth against such attack.

The major shifts in the Soviet force structure, the need for which may have been revealed by the Cuba and Vietnam crises, has been the buildup of ICBM's from a minimum deterrent to a force comparable with that of the United States, the introduction of some submarines with nuclear weapons—first with cruise missiles, probably with an antishipping role against the strike fleets, and more recently with ballistic missiles as an invulnerable second-strike force—deployment of naval forces into new areas, and development of an intervention capability with marines, helicopter carriers, and large transport aircraft.

These developments seem to indicate strategic concepts that are similar to those that have been discussed in American strategic writing over the past decade—deterrence of a general attack on the homeland, capability for limited war (including one with selected use of nuclear weapons), and a rapid intervention capability for seizing the initiative in a crisis.

On the other hand, the Soviets have always displayed an interest in and an advocacy of disarmament, although from the Western strategist's and arms controller's point of view it is difficult to know how far this is genuine and how far it is an attempt to gain international prestige as a peace-loving country while retaining the advantages conferred by military forces. Soviet experts no doubt have the same problem in gauging Western intentions.

Yields of Russian Warheads

Although the Soviets made rapid advances in missile and warhead technology, they did not develop a small, low-cost, reliable, solid-fueled missile available in reasonable numbers until several years after the United States had developed and deployed its Minuteman missiles. This apparent lack of interest in a highly sophisticated missile has often been attributed to a lower level of technology, but there is a rather simple technical explanation that is not often considered. The Soviets started their strategic nuclear weapons program after the United States and for a long time appeared to be pursuing a minimum deterrent policy based on land-based missiles (submarine ballistic missile systems were developed much later). Plant for the manufacture of fissile material was not built on anything like the scale in the United States.

The object of a minimum deterrent, that is, the smallest possible number of nuclear delivery vehicles, is to threaten retaliation against cities: the force would be too small to attack missile sites. For this strategy high-yield weapons will do the most damage and do not require high accuracy. With fission weapons a large increase in yield can be obtained for a relatively small increase in the amount of fissile material. In the case of fusion weapons, a large gain in yield can be gained from increasing the fusion component without any increase in the fissile core. In both cases the most efficient use of scarce fissile material is to produce a few very high-yield weapons. High yield will also compensate for low accuracy.

Strategic Interactions

Two extreme views are widely held on the influence each of the superpowers has on the other. On the one hand it is believed that each superpower alters its strategic posture and deployments only in response to some action by the other; on the other hand it is alleged that there is practically no interaction and the strategic posture is determined by internal forces, although these forces include perceptions and interpretations of the opponent. The real situation is most probably somewhere in between.

This is illustrated in the strategic policies of the United States and the Soviet Union. After initial defeats in World War II, the United States fought an attacking war in the Pacific with fleets organized around aircraft carriers; this was particularly suitable because their aircraft could reconnoiter wide areas of ocean, could protect troop transports, could attack enemy transports and land targets, and had great flexibility and speed of reaction. At the end of the war these carriers were available as launching platforms for the nuclear deterrent, so that the first available and continuing U.S. nuclear deterrent was attack carrier fleets.

To prevent the near approach of these fleets to the Russian homeland the Soviet Union appears to have built up a large fleet of submarines, many with comparatively short range, supported by naval aircraft eventually equipped with stand-off weapons. To cope with the U.S. carrier-borne strike aircraft, long-range aircraft from the United States and medium- and short-range aircraft stationed in Europe and elsewhere, the Soviet Union also deployed extensive air defenses. If these defenses seemed to be overelaborate to others, it must be remembered that even an attrition rate of, say, 25 percent would quickly blunt attacks armed with conventional weapons; but after even unrealistically high losses of, say, 75 percent an attacking air fleet armed with nuclear weapons would strike a devastating blow.

In retrospect it is possible to trace themes of interaction that appear quite plausible but may not be based on reality. For example, the development of Russian defenses may be so described: such an account may appear to be more logical than what is often considered as a more or less irrational or even ideological preoccupation with defense. This is not to discount that such a tendency does exist but indicates in what form it is manifested.

The Strategic Balance

The strategic balance that exists between the United States and the Soviet Union is not based on a simple equality; at present the former can claim superiority in that it has available more deliverable nuclear warheads; the latter can claim superiority because it could deliver a greater megatonnage. Neither is the most important criterion, which is the second-strike posture of each side.

The strategic balance is based on the weapons systems described above—that is, land-based intercontinental missiles, mostly deployed in underground silos; ballistic missiles carried in submarines as a second-strike force; bomber aircraft; and the U.S. strike fleets.

On both sides bomber aircraft have been extended in service by new weapons, electronic equipment, and different tactics, particularly low-level approach to the target, which reduces radar warning, the time within range of ground weapons, and vulnerability to interceptor fighters. Stand-off weapons enable air attack to be launched beyond the range of the active defenses around the target. There have also been important improvements in navigation systems and in electronic countermeasures.

The U.S. force of long-range bombers consists mostly of B-52's. This aircraft was first produced in 1952 and production was terminated in 1962.

Although a number of improvements have been introduced to extend the service life of the aircraft, there are no firm plans for replacement and the long-range bomber force is essentially a wasting asset. The decision yet to be made is whether, for the sake of diversification of strategic systems and for flexibility of manned aircraft, a replacement aircraft such as the advanced manned strategic aircraft should be proceeded with.

On the other hand it has been considered by some—including Robert McNamara—that the United States has consistently overestimated the threat from the Soviet long-range air force, which, despite possession of the formidable Tu-22 Blinder, can be seen more as a threat to Europe and areas contiguous to the Soviet Union. In spite of demonstrated skill in the development of civil and fighter aircraft, the Soviet Union does not appear to be contemplating the development of new long-range bombers.

A comparison of total numbers of strategic nuclear delivery systems in the existing balance is shown in Table 11. But the ratio

TABLE 11

Strategic Nuclear Balance, 1970

Weapons Systems	United States	Soviet Union
Land-Based Missiles		
ICBM	1,054	1,300
IRBM	—	100
MRB	—	600
Sea-Based Missiles		
SLBM	656	205
Cruise	—	362
Aircraft		
Long-Range Bombers	505	140
Medium-Range Bombers	35	500
Land-Based Strike	1,200	1,000
Carrier-Based Strike	900	—

Source: The Military Balance 1970-1971 (London: Institute for Strategic Studies, 1971).

between the superpowers in respect both of land- and sea-based missiles is changing in favor of the Soviet Union, which has more launchers in place and under construction than the United States has.

If, alternatively, a comparison is made of the numbers of warheads deployed by the two sides, the United States can claim superiority through being ahead in deployment of multiple warheads.

When total yields (megatonnage) that could be delivered are compared, the Soviet Union can claim superiority, partly because of the number of SS-9 (SCARP) missiles now deployed.

Another way of comparing the strategic nuclear armories of the superpowers is on the basis of area of the earth's surface that would be damaged in an attack. It is first necessary to specify certain parameters, the first of which is a minimum level of damage—say, severe damage to ordinary houses—and then to relate this to the appropriate weapons effect—say, 5-psi blast pressure. It is then necessary to specify the height at which the explosion shall take place, which could be ground level or at the optimum height appropriate to the yield that will damage the largest possible area. Such variables as type of target, its hardness, and the configuration of the terrain would be ignored. For blast the damaged area is proportional to yield to the two-thirds power. Damage from each of a salvo of warheads is not assumed to overlap, and the total damage is obtained by adding together the calculated areas for each of the individual explosions.

This may be expressed thus:

$$D \text{ (damage) } \alpha \Sigma(\text{yield})^{2/3}.$$

This method of calculation is often quite satisfactory for assessing damage to urban targets that are so large that accuracy of delivery is not important. In assessing relative first-strike capabilities accuracy plays an important part because the targets would be hardened missile silos. J. J. Holst has advanced a more useful formula:*

$$K \alpha \Sigma(\text{yield})^{2/3} / (\text{CEP})^2.$$

In this formula K is a measure of the kill, that is first-strike, capability, and CEP is the circular error probability, which in physical terms is the radius of a circle centered on the target, such that a shot aimed at the target would have equal chances of falling inside or outside the circle. This is numerically equivalent to a single shot probability of 0.5 for impact within the circle.

The formula put forward by Holst is very simple and therefore easy to use. Other, more elaborate models that can be employed are based on a large number of detailed calculations carried out on a computer. An advantage of the formula is that it illustrates very clearly the importance of accuracy as compared with yield. To double the yield would increase the value of K by a factor of 1.6, a 60 percent increase, while to double the accuracy—that is, reduce the CEP to half its original value—would increase K by a factor of four, a 300 percent improvement. This explains the interest in high-quality ballistic and terminal guidance as the emphasis has shifted from a "city-busting" to a counter-force option.

With this and similar formulas it is possible to compare existing deployments on the two sides; present with planned or anticipated

---

*J. J. Holst and W. Schneider, Why ABM? (London: Pergamon, 1969).

deployments; and the relative advantages, in terms of cost, of sacrificing yield in favor of more sophisticated guidance. For some total that might be the subject of an arms control agreement, it might be possible to calculate the optimum number of warheads per missile and pattern of attack to achieve some particular objective. Ian Bellamy has published a formula by which this can be done.*

The question of whether and when the Soviet Union will achieve a first-strike option against the United States will be returned to later. For the present it is sufficient to note that the roles of submarines and of bombers as second-strike weapons are difficult to quantify in simple terms and are often ignored in discussions of the future balance.

Submarine Second-Strike Forces

The United States has 41 Polaris-type submarines; most of them, it is planned, will be modified to carry the larger Poseidon missile, with multiple warheads and longer range, while older boats that cannot be so refitted will carry improved Polaris missiles. The United States also has 33 hunter-killer boats, whose duties include protection of the Polaris submarines.

The Soviet Union has fewer nuclear-powered submarines than the United States and those equipped with missiles, except for the latest to be launched, carry fewer nuclear-tipped missiles. However, in addition the Soviet Union has a number of diesel-powered boats that carry ballistic or cruise missiles and some nuclear-powered hunter-killer and other long-range diesel-powered submarines.

British and French Nuclear Deterrents

Until 1969 the British nuclear deterrent was based on the remaining aircraft of the V force, intended to attack below the level of radar interception and where ground and fighter aircraft defenses are at some disadvantage, and a small number of submarines carrying ballistic missiles. The submarines themselves are now of all-British manufacture but draw on a considerable amount of U.S. experience;

---

*Ian Bellamy, "MIRVs and the Strategic Balance," Nature (May 2, 1970).

the missiles are entirely American, and test firing takes place in American waters; and the nuclear warheads are of British design. Britain has production facilities for plutonium and for uranium-235. Because a number of British military nuclear reactors were dual-purpose and were designed for the production of electricity and plutonium, and natural uranium fuel was used in the first civil power programs, the cost of plutonium tends to be low. In the United States water-cooled reactors require enriched uranium and costs for electricity used in its manufacture are low, so there is plenty of capacity for U-235 separation. A barter agreement of economic benefit to both parties was made (July 1958) by which U.S. uranium-235 and British plutonium are exchanged.

The French nuclear deterrent was developed after the British and in comparison owes little to the United States. It was originally designed to be fully developed in three stages, but the second and third stages have been telescoped and will overlap more than originally intended. The first stage is a small force of Mirage aircraft armed with fission bombs, intended for a low-level attack. The second stage is to be MRBM's installed in silos in southern France; and the third stage, SLBM's, in nuclear-powered submarines. The French missiles are developed and manufactured in France.

It used to be argued that Britain should unilaterally give up nuclear weapons. While their possession may well have been one factor in encouraging the French and Chinese governments to develop strategic nuclear weapons, now that they have done so the argument for unilateral disarmament appears to have lost much of its validity; indeed, there are good arguments why Britain and France should retain their strategic nuclear weapons, at least until the superpowers have agreed on inspected reductions. But, from other viewpoints, it can be argued that there appears to be little reason why France and Britain should have separate systems. In some ways they are complementary, for France has experience in constructing missiles and Britain in manufacturing warheads, each experience being limited in the other country. Pooling would provide some financial saving and would reduce the French need for atmospheric nuclear tests. More important, cooperation could be a step toward an integrated European defense system that would perhaps reduce the pressure in individual countries for national strategic forces. Prolonged discussion of this point is beyond the scope of this book; the issue is mentioned because it may have important technical arms control implications in the future.

French and Chinese Attitudes Toward Disarmament

The policy of the French government toward arms control is difficult for an outsider, particularly a pragmatist, to understand. It appears to be based on two principles. The first is that France will not in any way restrict her ability to defend herself until there is genuine and inspected disarmament by the superpowers, that is, a reduction in the level of armament. The other side of the policy is that the possession of nuclear weapons capable of attacking any part of the world deters attack on the vital interests of France by making resultant losses exceed any possible gains. France has very few overseas possessions and there are no other easily understood reasons for mounting an attack, nor has France much to gain from mounting a nuclear attack; hence the French strategic forces can be limited in size.

Although the Chinese strategic nuclear forces are at an early stage of development, the pace at which they have been constructed has been astounding and beyond that thought possible by most expert observers. This is particularly so when cognizance is taken of the very small number of trained scientists at the start of the program, many of whom were abroad and had to be persuaded to return, while laboratories and manufacturing plants had to be built, assistant scientists and laboratory and industrial workers trained, and the whole program integrated. A very high level of scientific and managerial skill is indicated.

Because of its exclusion from the United Nations until October 1971, China has so far not had an opportunity to join in discussion on arms control. Government pronouncements appear to be slightly inconsistent: nuclear weapons by themselves would not be decisive in a war, and China is arming with nuclear weapons to be able to negotiate from strength on disarmament.

CHAPTER

11

STRATEGIC DEFENSES

TARGETS AND METHODS OF DEFENSE

Targets for strategic nuclear weapons range from cities to underground missile silos. Cities are large, soft targets much of which can be destroyed by relatively low blast pressures, by warheads in the tens of kiloton yield upward and of not particularly high accuracy. Missile silos can be destroyed only by blast pressures in the hundreds or thousands of pounds per square inch or by being so accurately attacked that the crater extends as far as the silo, which is literally dug out.

There are standard military procedures for preserving targets under attack: passive defense, such as mobility, dispersion, concealment, and hardening, and active defense, such as preemptive attack and ABM's. Which of these is used depends on the target, the expected form of attack, cost of defense, military dogma, and other factors.

Given sufficient warning, cities could be evacuated some days or even weeks in advance of an attack and the inhabitants dispersed into the countryside. The Russians have elaborate plans for the protection of their citizens in this way and carry out exercises in many of their cities. However, although at least some of the public may be saved, buildings of all kinds and their contents would be destroyed, for it is impossible to disguise the locations of cities, particularly now that satellites can be used for mapping. (Civil defense will be considered in more detail later in this chapter.)

Strategic nuclear missile systems may be defended by several methods. They may be dispersed and concealed in underground concrete silos and in submarines. Dispersal ensures that several weapons will not be destroyed by explosion of a single warhead. It is reported that the Russians have gone to the length of grassing over some of their missile silos, even building dummy villages and constructing dummy missiles.[1] Wide dispersal of targets has other advantages—for example, causing the attacker also to disperse his forces, with a reduction in the effectiveness of command and control.

Military aircraft may be dispersed to a number of airfields and to overseas bases. On each field they could be dispersed round the perimeter and protected by earth or concrete walls. Some aircraft may be kept in a state of airborne alert and others on ground alert, prepared to take off on receipt of warning.

Other military systems have appropriate defenses. Strategic radars would be as much as possible below ground level; but since the aerials could be damaged by blast, active defenses would also be required. Ground troops could be dispersed and dug in. Active defense against attack with strategic nuclear weapons with ABM's has been one of the most discussed topics of strategy and arms control of the past few years; and, for this reason, the amount of information, and the importance of weapons systems and issues, the discussion is carried out in a separate chapter. The remainder of this chapter will deal in more detail with damage limitation and passive defense.

DAMAGE LIMITATION

One form of active defense is to counterattack nuclear delivery systems before they can be launched. The United States for some years pursued a policy of damage limitation. That is, there was such an excess of nuclear delivery vehicles over parity that, even after absorbing a first strike, there would be enough of these vehicles surviving to attack not only cities but also such targets as submarine bases, airfields, and missile relaunch sites.

With the approach to nuclear delivery parity over the past few years, the ratios between the opposed forces of the superpowers have now so changed that this "spare" capacity does not exist. Instead, with the introduction of multiple individually targeted reentry vehicles of high accuracy, damage limitation can be considered only in terms of a first strike.

CIVIL DEFENSE

Civil defense is intended primarily to protect persons from becoming casualties and, second, to protect property. The main targets for a so-called counter-value strike are densely inhabited cities. The protection of individuals may be by shelters or by dispersion.

Dispersion of population could be carried out, as was mentioned above, as a long-term peacetime operation, given policies aimed at preventing and reducing very high urban densities. It is unlikely that governments will choose specifically to prevent the growth of cities, since such policies would interfere with the economic life of a nation. However, the growing congestion of city centers, the development of personal transport by automobile, and the great improvement in communications by telephone, teleprinter, and data transmission links have induced a movement of both dwellings and places of work to suburban and semirural areas.

It is difficult to conceive, however, of wholesale emergency evacuation of cities in a time of crisis that would not produce more problems than would be solved; and it is unlikely that it would be possible to organize more than the dispersal to safer areas of special groups, such as children, unless there has been sufficient time for an orderly evacuation to be carried out.

While, as we have seen, the Russians have stressed the importance of evacuation, the West has generally thought of nuclear war in terms of an attack with little warning, which would make attempts at evacuation likely only to add to the confusion.

In addition to redistribution of population and emergency evacuation, further protection would be necessary for the population. Some of those remaining in cities could be saved if they were in shelters capable of withstanding the prompt effects of the burst of a nuclear weapon, principally blast. For most purposes protection from blast also affords some protection against other prompt effects. Since it is unlikely that people in blast shelters could be rapidly evacuated because of blockage of routes and damage to vehicles, these survivors would also have to be protected against fallout that would return to the surface several hours after the attack. This means that shelters would have to be provided with airlocks to prevent the ingress of contaminated air, air filters, and facilities—in the case of larger shelters, at least—for decontamination of survey and foraging parties and those caught in the open or transferred from other shelters and rescue teams. Elsewhere, away from ground zero, where the prompt effects of the explosion of nuclear weapons were insufficient to cause serious and widespread casualties, fallout shelters would be required to reduce the exposure of their inhabitants to radioactivity deposited on surfaces or carried by the wind. These shelters would not require the physical strength of blast shelters but would have to have facilities for supporting human life for up to several days, since rapid evacuation of large numbers of people would be made extremely difficult by the prevailing conditions.

It is obvious from what has been said above that a shelter program of substantial size would involve the provision on a large scale of equipment such as air pumps and filters, water filters, gas masks, food, drink, medical and toilet requisites, sanitary arrangements, and mechanical and hand tools for the rescue of survivors and recovery of stores. In anticipation of an attack, stocks of materials for temporary buildings, food, medical supplies, and emergency transport would have to be stored away from the areas of likely damage.

However, a shelter program is designed to save lives but not property of all kinds: buildings, homes, factories, shops, stores, warehouses and their goods, railways, roads, power stations, and all artifacts would be destroyed or damaged over a wide area. The formidable nature of a passive defense has been one of the factors in encouraging an interest in active defenses.

Before ABM came under really serious consideration, the most cost-effective means for saving lives appeared to be, in order of preference, strengthening existing basements and similar areas and providing training, monitors for fallout, warning systems, fire protection, medical and rescue facilities, fallout refuges outside cities, and blast shelters in major cities.

ANTIAIRCRAFT DEFENSES

In the past, defense against high-level aircraft was provided by antiaircraft guns and interceptor aircraft, now integrated with radars (for early warning and control of the battle) and the command and control system. The attack would have been expected at a high altitude, to reduce the accuracy of the guns and increase the time and difficulty for the fighters to make an interception. With the introduction of surface-to-air missiles (SAM) and interceptor aircraft with a higher rate of climb and a loiter capability, the rate of expected loss to attacking bombers has so increased that new tactics have had to be developed. A low-level dash through the main defended belt, even as far as the target, is now included in the flight profile. By this means radar detection and warning, and the time available for defense batteries to acquire (i.e., locate and track), predict the flight path, and engage the target aircraft may be reduced.

A form of defense against low-flying aircraft is now being developed in which a few very high-flying aircraft are equipped with radars that can detect objects moving at high speed against the reflections from the landscape; standing patrols or interceptor aircraft equipped with long-range radars and air-to-air missiles can be directed to engage the intruders. The U.S. government is considering a new antibomber defense of this type built around the airborne warning and control system. In view of the present relatively limited threat from Soviet or other bombers, it is difficult to see a justification for this system on any grounds other than economy compared with the existing defenses. According to Secretary of Defense McNamara in 1967:

> The U.S. has consistently over-estimated the long range bomber strength of the Soviets, the ability to put bombers over the U.S. on a two-way mission (i.e. the aircraft will be able to return to their bases) is small and there is little experience or emphasis in training, nor are new aircraft being developed.[2]

However, if an ABM defense can be introduced that would very greatly lessen the Soviet missile threat, then it might well become important also to provide defenses of similar effectiveness against bombers.[3]

ARMS CONTROL OF ANTIAIRCRAFT

An agreement to limit antiaircraft defenses would be difficult to design and to administer. The actual defense weapons—interceptor aircraft, guns, and SAM—are only part of complicated integrated total systems and depend on radars, communications, and command and control to such an extent that the total effectiveness of the system depends on a large number of factors, many not subject to external scrutiny and regulation. Mere limitation of numbers of "teeth" units would be a very crude control. Other problems arise from the numbers and geographical dispersion of the different kinds of units and the consequent numbers of inspection personnel and the depth of intrusion into the inspected country. There could be difficulties in separating antiaircraft units for the defense of the homeland from those intended for the air defense of the field armies; indeed, many units could have dual roles. A trend in the defense of field forces is to provide a self-defense capability against low-flying aircraft; the instruments of such a defense are cheap, simple, short-range homing missiles. Extension of such a philosophy of defense to urban targets can be visualized should a low-level bomber threat develop. Finally, advanced SAM defenses may have some capability against missiles, including ICBM's.

In view of the gradual reduction in the long range bomber fleets, it seems that antiaircraft defenses themselves will have decreasing importance and might be left to wither quietly on the vine. In a comprehensive agreement attention would have to be given to the possibility of such systems being developed with more than a marginal effectiveness against ICBM, but this should not be difficult. (What may be a suitable means for limiting the roles will be described in Chapter 15.)

A factor against attempting to limit antiaircraft defenses might be the difficulty in justifying this part of an agreement to the legislature and public. On the other hand, experience in the United States shows that the public tends to resist deployment of ABM's in their own neighborhood.

ANTISUBMARINE WARFARE

In a strategy based upon deterrence by threat of inescapable retaliatory destruction, nuclear-powered submarines, armed with submarine-launched ballistic missiles (SLBM) with nuclear warheads, play a key role as a powerful second-strike force that it would be difficult to detect, locate, and counterattack effectively before the missiles could be launched.

The primary importance of antisubmarine warfare is its impact on the degree of invulnerability of the second strike from attack by submarines; its secondary significance lies in protecting convoys or other surface naval forces and in combating submarines on reconnaissance missions.

Submarine hunting can be carried out from the air, from the surface, and underwater but often is done by a combination of systems in these environments. The interaction between systems is complex.

Surface vessels can attack and be attacked by submarines; aircraft can attack submarines but the latter are to a great extent invulnerable unless they remain on the surface and so lose the advantages of concealment and mobility; the carriers, floating bases for aircraft, are themselves subject to attack. Submarines can also cooperate with aircraft in both offensive and defensive operations. The attractiveness of aircraft is their freedom from counterattack and their speed of search, but speed may reduce the fineness of search and attack. Helicopters have the ability to remain in close contact with a target but have limited range, cannot carry a very large payload of munitions, and are very expensive to operate because they generally require floating bases.

For searching from the air, sensor systems must be available that can detect submarines on the surface or partly or fully submerged. Possible sensors, which have been described in some detail in American technical journals, include the eye—aided, where necessary, by searchlights and binoculars—low-light television, the laser, radar, and electronic devices for the detection of radar and communications emissions from the submarine. The most important devices for detecting submerged submarines are sonar buoys, which are supplemented by the "sniffer," which can detect faint traces of exhaust fumes and of humans; by infrared detection—which, it is claimed, can distinguish temperature differences of 0.001°C and thus trace the "thermal scar" from the discharge of cooling water; and by magnetic anomaly detection, which is installed in an extension of the aircraft tail. In projected antisubmarine aircraft, sensor outputs will be integrated and printed out by computers, so that fewer crew members are required to watch.

Passive sonars depend upon the detection of noise from submarines, which might be from propulsion machinery or from water movement. Active sonars emit signals and detect reflections. The time interval between the emitted and received pulses can be used to measure the range of the target, and returns from the ocean floor that arrive later can be ignored.

Active sonars can, of course, be detected by the submarine, which can then take evasive action. Sonars may be carried by surface vessels or they may be laid as fixed detection boundaries, allowed to drift with the ocean currents, or dropped in patterns near locations where there have been indications of a submarine. Compared with radar, sonar is much more limited in range and its technique is more difficult, in that there is always reflection from the seabed, whereas the majority of radar scans are from the ground into the featureless sky. Relative speed of movement between the target and the background can be used to detect targets; in the case of radar the Doppler shift is high, while in the case of sonar the target is traveling relatively slowly and can even be stationary, using a thermal layer to confuse the return signals, or can rest on the seabed.

Sonar detectors themselves may be moving, and this adds not only to the difficulties of detection but also to interpretation of the returned signals.

Surface ships that may be used for submarine hunting include aircraft and helicopter carriers, destroyers, frigates, and fast, small vessels (in coastal waters). Weapons used are depth charges and torpedoes.

Because of the high speed of nuclear-powered submarines carrying ballistic missiles, hunter-killer submarines intended to attack or defend them must have similar speeds and endurance. Hunter-killer submarines may be equipped with homing torpedoes, short-range ballistic missiles, and a rocket weapon that has a mid-course in air but reenters the water to home on its target.

Mines can also be used as an antisubmarine warfare weapon, both by sowing mines by air or from submarines at harbor entrances and along trade routes, and by laying defensive screens to protect ports and sea-lanes.

The total effectiveness of an antisubmarine warfare system can be calculated from the effectiveness at each of several stages—that is, expressed in more formal language, the probability of a weapon platform (i.e., a ship) killing a submarine depends on its fractional statement of probabilities. Thus, if P stands for probability of success,

$$P_K = P_D \times P_C \times P_L \times P_S \times P_W,$$

where K is kill, D is detection, C is classification, L is location and attack, S is survival of the weapon platform and weapon, and W is the effectiveness of the weapon.[4]

Effective antisubmarine warfare depends upon improving these factors, and the greatest potential gain is from improving the lowest values. One possible ploy would be to decoy submarines within range of waiting homing torpedoes.

A possible future advance in antisubmarine warfare is the Delos platform, which is carried by vertical columns from catamaran-like hulls beneath the water. Movement of the platform is thus largely independent of wave motion, and compensation can be made for the smaller amplitude of motion below the surface. A first use for such a stable platform could be missile and satellite observation and tracking; but other possible uses include acting as a base for antisubmarine warfare, such as a pad and ferry station for helicopters and vertical takeoff aircraft, or a harbor for hovercraft and other light patrol vessels and for monitoring sonar and seismic signals.

The importance of antisubmarine warfare lies, we have seen, in its threat to the SLBM second-strike forces. If it continues to be considered that second-strike forces add to stability between the superpowers, then the threat to these forces by antisubmarine warfare must be assessed. For a first strike to be successful against the SLBM fleet, most of the ships at sea would have to be destroyed before they could launch their missiles; with the number of SLBM's now deployed by the superpowers, there is little probability that this could be done without warning the opponent. While advances are constantly being made in antisubmarine warfare, there appears to be none, nor any combination, that would give the kind of probability of success necessary for rational initiation of a first strike.

Nevertheless, and in view of any possible advances, it might be necessary to curb by agreement some kinds of antisubmarine warfare.

NOTES

1. J. J. Holst and W. Schneider, _Why ABM_? (London: Pergamon, 1969).

2. Robert McNamara, _The Essence of Security: Reflections in Office_ (London: Hodder and Stoughton, 1968), Chap. 9. (Speech at San Francisco, September 18, 1966).

3. For a description of Soviet systems, see Holst and Schneider, _op. cit_. For Western systems, see _Flight International_ (April 17, 1969).

4. Frank Leary. "Man in Space: Stations and Bases," _Space/Aeronautics_ (September 1969).

CHAPTER

12

ANTIBALLISTIC MISSILES

THE NATURE OF THE PROBLEM

Concurrent with the development of ICBM over many years, methods for reducing the damage that could be caused have also been studied. Dispersal of population, evacuation, and provision of shelters were considered in the previous chapter, as were hardening, mobility, and other means for protecting second-strike forces; counterattack was discussed in terms of countervalue damage-limitation strikes and antisubmarine warfare.

None of the passive methods so far considered is likely to be highly effective in reducing the damage from an attack. ICBM launch sites and underground silos are widely separated, so that several cannot be destroyed by the same warhead. The latest underground silos are immensely strong and are not vulnerable except to effects of powerful weapons. If a counter-force strike is likely to be ineffective or for political reasons cannot be countenanced, then the only way that appears to have the potential for containing an attack is an active defense capable of destroying, damaging, or otherwise reducing the effectiveness of an ICBM after it has been launched.

Technically the most favorable opportunity for destruction of an ICBM is in the launch phase, that is, directly after it has emerged from the silo or the pad and while the motors are still firing, because at this stage the missile is undergoing course and range corrections and some thousands of components have to operate satisfactorily; missile perturbations in this part of the trajectory would interfere with overall performance. The launch phase lasts only a few minutes and is terminated when the final stage motor is turned off and is detached from the reentry vehicle.

During the next phase, the midcourse, which is the longest part of the flight and lasts some twenty minutes, the reentry vehicle flies freely in a trajectory outside the earth's atmosphere, reaching a height of 700 miles and a speed of roughly four miles per second.

In the terminal phase the vehicle reenters the earth's atmosphere at a few hundred thousand feet, and it is only during the last 50,000 feet or so that it begins to slow down.

An ABM defense has to carry out and integrate a number of highly complex operations: warning, detection, identification, tracking, discrimination of warheads from decoys, launch of interceptors, guidance to target and control of engagement. It could also, in theory, be designed to counterattack ICBM in the launch, midcourse, or terminal phase. A defense based on counterattacking ICBM's during the launch phase is attractive because of the vulnerability of missiles at this stage and unattractive because of the scale of such a counterattack and the brief time for receipt of warning, acquiring targets, deciding to attack them, launching the defense missiles, and general command and control of the battle, not to mention the high risk of inadvertent release of some of the defense weapons, which might respond to any large source of heat, such as a forest fire.

A midcourse defense, in friendly territory or at sea, would require a close grouping of ABM installations on the main threat corridor for counterattack before the ICBM's diverge toward their individual targets. However, in this portion of the trajectory the ICBM's could release many lightweight decoys that the defense radars could not easily differentiate from warheads; in the absence of atmosphere these decoys would travel at the same speed as the reentry vehicle.

Defense in the terminal phase would be facilitated by the separation of reentry vehicles from decoys as the latter are slowed down or burned up by contact with air. Although the warning would generally be longer than for a launch-phase system, all of the other operations of the defense would have a similarly brief time in which to come into action. To carry out all of these operations at the necessary speed requires large and complex radars and computers, and very rapid response from the ABM's. Since the ICBM targets would not be known in advance, it would be necessary to defend all of the more important cities, military bases, airfields, submarine bases, missile farms, radars, and command and control posts.

THE ARMS CONTROL DEBATE—THE EFFECT ON DETERRENCE

Over the past few years the subject of ABM's has aroused passionate controversy among arms controllers in the West. The question is whether the United States should respond to the limited deployment in the Soviet Union, known as the Moscow system, by itself deploying ABM's. A second question that follows from a negative answer is whether the United States should take actions, such as the deployment of a greater number or more sophisticated missiles and payloads, to overcome the Moscow defense and any subsequent extensions, thus maintaining an assured destruction capability at or near the present high level.

Although both the original question and the derivative question appear to be simple, to answer them with any degree of knowledge and assurance is very difficult. The subject reaches to the roots of national strategic policy and raises questions about the dogma that has built up to support this policy, particularly that of deterrence, and thus about the level of deterrence that must be maintained. Because of the extent of the policy problems, the technical aspects of ABM defense have received comparatively little attention compared with the political, diplomatic, and other facets—and yet they have deep implications. It is interesting that no such problems have appeared to worry the Russians, who have very different basic concepts of national defense.

A fascinating aspect of the debate in the United States has been that the great majority of arms controllers, particularly those in academic circles, have been opposed to the deployment of ABM's in the United States while, with far less publicity, many of those more directly engaged in studying the problems have been in favor of an ABM deployment and have been supported, perhaps not surprisingly, by the military and technical personnel engaged in assessing the effectiveness of possible systems. The military and its supporters have been represented as being shortsighted in attempting hardware solutions to problems that are basically political. Because of the rather one-sided nature of published material, the countercharges have been less heard—that the academics are prepared to take risks with national security, are not in possession of the facts, and in any case do not have the responsibilities of officeholders.[1]

However, the major discrepancy between the attitudes of the two parties is in the emphasis given to defense and deterrence. On the one hand an effective ABM defense would reduce the number of casualties in a nuclear exchange, and as such would have the approval of arms controllers; on the other hand introduction of ABM's might be a stage in a developing arms race (the usual argument) or (particularly with concurrent deployment of multiple, independently targeted reentry vehicles) might reintroduce an unstable first-strike option for one or both sides. The choice of whether to deploy ABM's depends, therefore, upon perceptions of the relative importance of deterrence of war and the need to preserve deterrence at the highest possible level and of the duty to preserve lives if war should break out.

An extreme view is that if the United States has a capability to gain an advantage, including saving millions of U.S. citizens, then it should do all in its capability to do so. At the other end of the spectrum is the view that deployment of any ABM's in the United States would be the breaching of a barrier and would be followed by an arms race of unpredictable cost and danger.

A more temperate attitude would be to inquire into the technical performance of the systems, their limitations, and their possible counters, and to attempt to make the decision on the overall balance of advantage. A number of factors would be considered in reaching this balance, including arms control objectives (such as avoidance of an arms race and the saving of lives by deterrence as well as by defense), the possibility of an agreement involving ABM deployment, and the usefulness of the system as a policy instrument.

In contrast with the voluminous debate in the United States, there does not appear to have been any debate in the Soviet Union. A statement typical of the rather rare expressions of opinion is that of M. Talensky, published in 1965:

> It is said that the international strategic situation cannot be stable where both sides simultaneously strive towards deterrence through nuclear-rocket power and the creation of defensive anti-missile systems. I cannot agree with this view either. From the standpoint of strategy, powerful deterrent forces and effective anti-missile defense system, when taken together, substantially increase the stability of mutual deterrence, any partial shifts in the quantitative and qualitative balance of these two component elements of mutual deterrence tend to be correspondingly compensated and equalized.[2]

The acquisition of nuclear weapons by China has intensified pressures toward ABM defense by both of the superpowers, and an element of justification for deployment comes from this threat and from the threats posed by the other nuclear powers. However, response by deployment of ABM's by the superpowers may introduce pressures for other countries, which perceive threats, to be similarly defended.

Of more fundamental importance is the question of whether deterrence will decrease in any large measure as the threat of mutual destruction is replaced by the threat of facing a heavily damaged and vindictive but still surviving enemy, with the prospects of continuing hostilities and little opportunity of recovery from the initial onslaught.

The two aims of arms control—to prevent the outbreak of war and, if it does break out, to minimize the consequent casualties and destruction of property—may at times, as in the ABM debate, be opposed. Unwise preoccupation with reducing losses may reduce a major inhibition on war as a policy option.

The system of deterrence, that is, of maintaining the balance of terror, depends upon decision makers exhibiting a high degree of rationality at times of such high stress that they are least likely to act rationally. Provision of ABM's could reduce the catastrophic nature of such decisions and perhaps reduce the tensions under which they would be made.

THE ENGAGEMENT BETWEEN ABM'S AND ICBM'S

The warning time that a defense system will receive varies over a wide range, depending on the circumstances and the characteristics of the attacking weapons systems. Strategic warning of the possibility of an attack may be gained from political indicators—that is, a general deterioration in the international climate, with evidence that the government of the opponent has become increasingly bellicose, aggressive, and unstable, and is under such pressure that irrational action becomes more and more possible. On the other hand, the chances that a first strike will be successful depend upon the absence of such a warning; and a rational decision to make a first strike (if such a decision has any connection with rationality) would be at a time of relative concord and agreement.

Tactical warning depends on the effectiveness of surveillance and early warning systems. Present and certainly future satellite systems should be able to alert the defenses to a mass launch by a superpower within a few seconds of its occurrence.

This would give the defenses of a superpower some 30 minutes to prepare to make intercepts. As the ICBM group approached the mainland of the victim of the attack, it would come within range of the long range defense radars. Shorter-range radars would take over and acquire the incoming reentry vehicles and direct the ABM's to an engagement. The battle may be joined outside the atmosphere at a range of several hundred miles from the ABM site, or close to the target at an altitude of up to 100,000 feet. Different missiles would be required for these two tasks; both would carry nuclear warheads, but those for the long range missiles are in the megaton range, while those for short-range missiles are in the kiloton range to avoid damage to the defended area.

In addition to missiles and radars, computers and communications systems are needed to integrate and analyze the data and to command and control the battle. Important developments have been made in large computers, data transmission, and other essential technologies.

ABM KILL MECHANISMS

During the encounter the reentry vehicle would be traveling at about five miles per second and the ABM at a similar speed on an opposing course. Thus the timing of the explosion of the ABM would have to be extremely accurate if the ICBM is not to escape destruction.

Beyond the atmosphere or within the upper reaches there is insufficient air to transmit a blast wave; and shrapnel (solid particles, not necessarily metallic) would have limited range, so that warheads with high explosive charges would have only a limited kill radius and be unlikely to be effective.

Because of the high speeds of the approaching warheads and other difficulties of interception, weapons effects are required that operate to great range. The explosion of a nuclear warhead would release blast, neutron, and electromagnetic energy, the ratios of these different effects depending on the air density—that is, the altitude of the explosion. Blast would be effective only within the atmosphere and could slow or deflect the reentry vehicle and put it off course—or even, if sufficiently strong, produce physical damage.

The explosion of a nuclear warhead would vaporize all of the materials to a plasma with a surface temperature of 10,000,000°C. The lethal effects could be the fireball itself or the radiations emitted by it: soft X rays carry about two-thirds of the energy of the yield.

Neutrons have a very long range because they do not carry an electrical charge and are not deflected or attracted to other matter; and are slowed down or absorbed only in rare collisions with atomic nuclei. Neutrons could lead to failure of incoming reentry vehicles by causing premature fission, heating, and destruction of weapons components.

The kinds and effects of damage from X rays emitted by the fireball have been of considerable interest. The lethal radius, the distance from the point of explosion within which a reentry vehicle would be destroyed or made unserviceable, increases with altitude as a result of lower air density. The behavior of the fireball also varies with altitude.

It is not known how much these problems are understood, but it is fairly certain that they are more complex in regard to the Sprint missiles, which explode at about 100,000 feet. A few microseconds after the explosion the fireball temperature will drop to 1,000,000°C, and it will be expanding at 300 miles per second and rising with an initial acceleration of 50,000-g. These values are uncertain and vary with time. The mechanism by which the fireball rises varies with altitude; in the atmosphere it is the buoyancy of heated air, and beyond the atmosphere it is repulsion by the earth's magnetic field. The altitude of a Sprint detonation would be in a region of transition between these effects, and prediction would be particularly difficult.

Reentry vehicles can be protected to some extent from the effects of X rays by hardening; this can be done most easily by using materials that are immune to X rays of a specific energy. As a counter to reentry vehicles protected in this way the Spectrum ABM warhead is being developed; it will emit X rays over a wide range of energies, against which providing hardening would be difficult.

Nuclear explosions could damage incoming reentry vehicles by other mechanisms than the fireball or heating by X rays. Defects could be caused in the materials of electronic components, such as ionization, causing breakdown of insulation and stray currents; some defects may self-repair but may still be sufficient to put the missile off course or cause mechanisms to trigger. Heavy stray currents could burn out circuits. It has been calculated that, in space, neutrons could damage unhardened circuits to a 20 mile radius and that transient damage could extend to 100 miles. In the atmosphere, blast and thermal radiation would probably be the damaging mechanisms. (Protection of reentry vehicles against ABM is examined in Chapter 13.)

RADAR BLACKOUT

Weapons effects can also be used to aid the attacker. The plasma and radiations from the fireball produce an expanding sphere of ionization. The degree of ionization depends upon the probability for recombining of electrons and positive ions released by interactions of radioactive substances and air—that is, upon air density, which is related to altitude. Thus, after a high-level burst ionization may take several days to return to normal; at lower altitudes duration is much shorter. Ionization will absorb, attenuate, or reflect radar waves and also disupt long-distance communications. The effect is most marked for very long and very short wavelengths, and the effects of a nuclear burst may be focused by the lines of magnetic force onto another area on the surface.

POSSIBLE STRATEGIES WITH ABM's

The defense can attempt to destroy all enemy warheads that enter the defended area or only those that might cause significant military damage. This leads to three defense strategies: area, city, and point defenses. An area defense would deploy long range ABM's only, with the radars sited as near the enemy as possible and very few ABM sites. All incoming warheads would be attacked. A point defense, to protect a missile silo (for example), would consist of short-range missiles deployed near the target and intended to counter only those warheads that appeared to be jeopardizing the target. A city defense would be for a target area a few miles across that could be fairly readily damaged by low-pressure blast—for example, by a burst of a megaton weapon some miles from the center of the target. Similar targets would be airfields and troop assembly areas. This type of target would be vulnerable not only to low-pressure blast but also to a bypass attack by a surface burst upwind from it, which could scatter intense fallout over the target. For city defense a mixture of long- and short-range weapons would be required or a large deployment of short-range missiles around major cities, to the detriment of the protection of smaller urban areas.

The duration of an attack would vary. City targets might have to be defended against a sustained attack over a long period, whereas airfields might have to be defended only until their bombers were airborne for attack or dispersal. Troops might be sheltered to an extent not possible for civilians. Radars, control posts, and communications systems could be specially subject to attack and may be vulnerable, but they could be defended at least until missiles under their control had been launched. ABM radars are very tall (130 feet) and thus would be vulnerable to low-blast pressure and would require sustained protection.

The choice of a particular deployment of ABM's, therefore, depends to a large extent on the estimate of the opponent's intentions. If it is assumed that the other superpower is bent on unleashing a nuclear war at the first convenient opportunity, then a policy of maximum civil defense, damage limitation, ABM's, and even preventative strikes would be appropriate. Since the superpowers have not shown any wish to initiate a nuclear exchange, it is reasonable to suggest that any deployment of ABM should be made so as not to disturb existing deterrence or to aggravate the arms race.

JUSTIFICATION FOR AN ABM DEFENSE

If it is assumed that every possible opponent likely to have strategic nuclear delivery systems will always be subject to deterrence and has infallible systems to prevent accidental misfirings of weapons, then no ABM system is justified.

However, these conditions can be expected to be valid only to some particular level of probability. Estimating this probability and the various outcomes in costs of installation of ABM's, and in casualties and damage, is at the core of strategic decisions.

Justifications for an ABM deployment, and objections to it, are listed in Table 12.

RATIONALE OF DEPLOYMENTS

From the point of view of the superpowers, the threat is either from a massive and sophisticated assault or from a small and possibly unsophisticated attack. Unsophisticated, in this connection, means that ICBM fleets are fairly vulnerable to counterattack. If these two forms of attack are examined in conjunction with the three defense strategies from the point of view of the attacker, the matrix in Table 13 expresses in a general way the different possibilities.

The technical status of offensive and defensive systems must also be taken into account. Protection of a superpower against a lesser nuclear power or accidental attack would be obtained at lowest

TABLE 12

Summary of the Arguments on Deployment of Antiballistic Missiles by Superpowers

Justifications
May reduce the chances of war between the superpowers by emphasizing defense
May reduce the casualties in such a war
Enhances the probability of survival as a nation and reduction in the period of recovery
Provides protection against small-scale attack and so reduces chances and consequences of war between a superpower and other nuclear powers
Minimizes the possibilities of war between the superpowers catalyzed by a third power
Reduces chances of war by accident
Improves the protection of second-strike forces and so reduces the first-strike option of an opponent armed with highly accurate MIRV
Raises the cost to other powers of going nuclear
Reinforces nuclear guarantees given by a superpower
Complicates planning of opponent's attack and may provoke transfer of resources to compensate
Increases the number of options for action at a time of crisis and a reduction in the tension during confrontations
Alternative policy is countervalue, i.e., destruction of cities
A prudent government must make contingency preparations to protect its citizens
Some items of equipment require very long lead times and must be ordered well in advance of requirements
Deployment of this system would give experience and training

Objections
An increase in U.S./Soviet tensions
Could increase a first-strike option, in that the retaliatory strike could be contained

Objections (Continued)
ABM would be most effective against a disorganized retaliatory second strike and thus tend to incite a first strike
Deployment is not likely to lead to limitation of nuclear weapons—indeed, the reverse, provoking increases in offensive weapons
Increases the requirements for nuclear warheads and thus causes vertical proliferation
Leads to continuation of underground testing
Generates demands for atmospheric testing
Emphasizes the importance of nuclear weapons
Apparently enhances the Chinese threat to the superpowers and hence the apparent importance of the threats to India and Japan
While costs of systems are high, but not insupportable, they may be less cost-effective than other ways of allocating funds
Any defense offered could be nullified at less cost by improvements in opposing offensive forces
A defensive/offensive arms race could be started that would increase costs without any change in the balance
If offensive was not improved, deterrence would be undermined
Political attitudes could change, perhaps reversing multipolar trends and producing tighter, more antagonistic groupings round the superpowers
Alternatively, the superpowers could withdraw and become more self-contained
The superpowers would feel able to take greater risks in their foreign policy
Allies and friends would compare their vulnerability with the comparative safety of the populations of the superpowers
Extension of system to protect allies would cause jockeying for position and resentment among other powers

cost and smallest effect on relations with the other superpower by strategy IIA in the table. However, ICBM's of the superpowers are continuously being improved in accuracy, partly as a result of experience gained in launching test and space vehicles, including better knowledge of gravitational perturbations and other physical parameters of the environment.

ABM's compete with shelters as a means for protecting the public, but they have the advantage that they will also protect property. From the point of view of defense, the population of a superpower can be divided into broad categories, each with an optimum type of defense:

Nonurban: too expensive to attack directly with nuclear delivery vehicles—fallout shelters provide protection

Suburban: could be attacked with low-pressure blast—protection by blast shelters, followed by rapid evacuation before the arrival of fallout

Urban: subject to high blast pressure, heavy local fallout; some protection from blast and fallout shelters equipped for long stay, but difficult to protect and rescue survivors—case for ABM defense.

ABM's AND THE FIRST-STRIKE OPTION

Improvement in accuracy of ICBM's together with the possibility that each missile can carry several warheads, may provide a first-strike option—that is, an initial attack could destroy so many missiles in their silos that not enough would survive to present a real threat to the attacker, particularly if he were also equipped with ABM's to defend against this second strike.

There are various ways in which this enhanced threat can be countered: by increasing the number of missiles in hardened silos, so that enough will survive to threaten retaliation; by concealment and mobility in submarines and land-based systems; and by ABM defense of missile silos. This last policy is shown as IC in Table 12; and its adoption could cause the opponent to abandon his first-strike strategy and to retarget his missiles against cities, that is, adopt a deterrent strategy.

Having decided upon a strategy, the next important problem is to ensure that it is understood by the opponent and cannot be misinterpreted. One way in which this information can be conveyed is by

TABLE 13

Interaction of Offense and Defense: The Effect of Deployment of ABM's on the Threat from ICBM Attack

Defense	Offense	
	I Massive and Sophisticated	II Small and/or Unsophisticated
A. Area		
Few long range ABM sites	Damage reduced somewhat; any compensating increase in ICBM's likely to be cost-effective in favor of attack	Damage much reduced
B. City		
Combination of long- and short-range ABM's	Damage much reduced, but defense can be overcome in various ways, including deployment of more ICBM's but this may lead to arms race	Damage to main population centers almost eliminated and attack deterred, but at high cost; some risk of damage from defender's own ABM's on bypass attacks
C. Point		
Short-range ABM's to protect missile silos, etc.	First-strike option further reduced; attacker will retarget missiles against cities and rely on deterrence	Pattern of attack against cities unaffected

policy statements intended to reach a wide audience, not only the opponent's highest levels of government but also those levels in both adminstrations where policy is studied—and the general public. However, such statements may be accepted with reserve and even suspicion; and, furthermore, those involved in national defense prefer to base their calculations on the opponent's capabilities rather than on intentions, which may change rapidly. Hence a more unambiguous signal is the number and locations of radar stations and missile sites, which will indicate the direction, nature, and intensity of the attack against which the system provides a defense. Long- and short-range missiles are sufficiently different to avoid confusion. The problem of conveying this reassurance as to intentions is easier in the case of the Soviet Union than it is for the United States, which could be attacked from the same general direction by the Soviet Union and China and also has two long coastlines to be defended.

Employment of short-range ABM's to defend missile silos is technically much more attractive than for the defense of cities, for the following reasons:

Silos are located in only a few places, so that only a few ABM batteries and radars would be required

At first it would be essential to defend only a few second-strike missiles, and a small initial deployment could be increased in step with a growing threat

While penetration by a single warhead would devastate a city, only one silo would be destroyed and the remainder of the flight would still be available for retaliation

Hard point silos could withstand more severe effects from defensive weapons, so that counterattack could be delayed until better discrimination against decoys is possible and only those reentry vehicles likely to damage a silo would be intercepted

Since the counterattack would be short-range, radar blackout would be of less importance

A point defense could be supported by an area defense, which would force the attacker to spread out his attack, to carry decoys, and generally to solve more problems.

In attempting the local defense of cities, as was pointed out above, not only must the defense remain operative over a longer time but it may have to sustain a very heavy attack if the attacker decides to concentrate all his efforts on only a few targets. Hence, all possible targets may have to be overdefended with ABM's. A concentrated attack on a missile site, on the other hand, would be at the expense of leaving other sites unattacked and their missiles available for retaliation. An area defense would offer the possibility of support for hard-pressed targets; this would be more important in the case of cities, where, as has been shown, the attack could be switched between targets.

COST-EXCHANGE RATIO

A central factor that can be used to determine whether ABM's should be deployed is the cost-exchange ratio, which is the cost of nullifying the advantage gained by the opponent per unit expenditure. An example will make this clear. If the cost of an ICBM to the attacker is $1 million and it costs the defender $1.5 million to provide ABM's to destroy it, then the cost ratio is 1.5 in favor of the attacker—that is, the attacker can overcome the defense at less cost. If the cost ratio were 0.8, this would indicate that it would be unprofitable to continue to extend the deployment of offensive weapons because a defense could be provided at less cost.

The question of cost-effectiveness of ABM's versus ICBM's has been a direct or implicit problem in the more sophisticated arguments over the deployment of ABM's in the United States. D. G. Brennan, for example, who earlier opposed the proposed deployment of ABM's, changed his mind after analyzing official estimates of the casualties from various deployments.[3] He came to the conclusion that the cost-exchange ratio was about unity in terms of lives saved, rather than money; that is, the defense offered by an ABM system could be offset by a similar expenditure on more offensive weapons. Actual figures on monetary costs that have been released in the United States have put the price of a reentry vehicle at $10 million, but this is expected to reduce to about $3 million within a few years. An intercepter missile, together with its portion of the costs of the radar and associated systems, would have a price tag in the range $2.5-$7 million each. These costs are not directly comparable, since the effectiveness of the ABM's must also be known.

If this analysis is correct and the cost of extra defense and equivalent extra offense are approximately equal, then the decision as to whether to buy either will depend upon other factors. The most important of these is the value placed on the saving of lives and, in some circumstances, the balancing of compatriots who could be saved against enemy citizens who could be destroyed for the same amount of money. Another decision, which has already been mentioned, is how the threat of retaliatory destruction compares as a deterrent with the threat of continued survival of the opponent.

An example of the kind of reasoning employed in this macabre cost accounting will now be considered. The cost-exchange ratio of ABM's to ICBM's depends on the level of damage that it is considered necessary to inflict to achieve deterrence. It has been calculated that the cost of a life saved by ABM may be in the wide range of $2,000 to $250, depending on circumstances, but also saved would be property, such as production resources, housing, transport facilities, and all the other requirements of urban life. Thus, as insurance ABM does not appear to be unduly expensive. The total cost of some proposed ABM systems has varied from $8 to $20 billion—large sums of money, but they should be compared with $50 billion for antiaircraft defense of the continental United States. One of the weaknesses of this line of argument is that it takes little or no account of any effect on allies; and it tends to assume that the opponent is susceptible to the same style of argument, will understand the other's point of view, and, in fact, come to the same conclusions.

Another argument that can be made in favor of ABM defense is that its value is not only that of targets successfully defended (which may not be very high if the opponent switches his attack) but also of those targets not attacked. This argument is based on the alleged likelihood that military targeting specialists allocate weapons to targets solely on a crude "assured destruction capability," that is, they target enough weapons to ensure 95 percent probability of destroying each target attacked. This can be very wasteful. Suppose that four warheads are required for 95 percent probability for destroying a single city. Yet they could be reallocated with the probability of 50 percent of hitting each of four separate target cities; on average two of these cities would be destroyed, and thus the total amount of damage would be doubled. The only reason for concentrating on particular targets is that they have some other military value, such as command posts, or will play a role in postwar recovery. In subjective terms a 50 percent or even 25 percent probability of losing a capital or major city may not be very different, as a deterrent, from a 95 percent probability of such a loss.

"THICK" AND "THIN" DEPLOYMENTS

The costs of an ABM deployment to cover the whole of the territory of a superpower would be very great, and it would be difficult to assess its effectiveness against a sophisticated and massive attack. For this reason there has been opposition to a "thick" (or "heavy") deployment even by those who support a "thin" (or "light") ABM deployment. A thin deployment, which would be ineffective against an attack by a superpower, might, for a number of years, provide a defense against a small-scale or unsophisticated attack, such as could be mounted by one of the lesser nuclear powers, and could also prevent damage from an accidently launched ICBM.

THE SOVIET ABM SYSTEM

The Soviet Union has deployed an ABM system around Moscow. During the construction there appear to have been several delays due, it is thought, to technical problems; and its present status (i.e., at the end of 1971) is uncertain. Little is known about the components of the system. There appears to be only one missile, Galosh, with a range of about 200 miles—that is, for interception at the end of the midcourse and beginning of the terminal phase. There has been no evidence that a similar system is being deployed elsewhere, although it would be reasonable to expect new deployments to start when the present system approaches completion.

The Soviet Union has to face possible threats from China, France, and Great Britain, in addition to the main threat from the United States; this will undoubtedly be a factor in increasing pressure for an ABM deployment.

U.S. ABM SYSTEMS

Much more is known about U.S. development of ABM's and plans for deployment; considerable detail has been revealed in official pronouncements and evidence presented to Congress. This is not the place to attempt to review this vast volume of literature or to give a history of the development of ABM's in the United States except in sufficient detail to bring out the interaction with arms control.

U.S. development of ABM's like that in the Soviet Union, has also been prolonged by the immense technical difficulties to be overcome. The problem, to recapitulate briefly, is to respond to a warning of what could well be a nuclear warhead approaching at 15,000 mph, at several hundred miles above the earth, and possibly carrying electronic countermeasures and surrounded by decoys.

The first substantial development in the United States was the Nike-Zeus missile for terminal-phase interception. In addition to the threat of missiles launched from the Soviet Union and coming by the main threat corridor over the polar regions, U.S. planners had also to take into account a possible growing threat to many densely inhabited areas from missiles launched from submarines. The radars available for Nike-Zeus were of the mechanical scanning type with limited speed of operation, particularly for several targets. To avoid damage to home territory, interception was intended to take place at a high altitude; but discrimination against decoys was poor, so that each incoming object had to be attacked by several simultaneously launched ABM's, each with its own target-tracking and command radars.

Inability to solve these complex problems with existing equipment led to a complete reassessment and the decision to develop the Nike-X system. There were several features that embodied much more advanced technology than had been available before. Two missiles were developed for different functions. Sprint was developed as a rapid-response and high-speed interception missile that would permit the defense to delay launch until atmospheric sorting had slowed or destroyed the decoys. Zeus was later replaced by Spartan, a larger missile with longer range, intended for area defense.

Parallel developments were made in the radar system. The speed of operation of conventional radars for scanning large volumes of space is limited by the mechanical inertia of the great dishes, even though dishes are very adequate for tracking single objects with a low angular velocity. The new radars were of the phased-array type, with a very large number of transmitter/receiver elements in each of the fixed flat operating faces of the installation. Each face of the installation so equipped points in a different direction.

When all of the individual transmitters emit a pulse at the same time, a wave front is generated parallel to the axis of the face (i.e., perpendicular to the face). If a small variable time delay is introduced, so that pulses are emitted from one element of the face and then by the next, like a ripple spreading across the face, the resulting wave front is deflected to an angle with the axis of the face. The timing delays are readily changed according to programs; and the beam can be made to sweep in essentially the same way as the mechanical dish, except, of course, that each face of the phase-array radar will subtend only part of a circle. Thus, for full all-round cover, three or four faces may be required. Electronic switching is much faster than mechanical movement, so a phased-array radar can scan more rapidly and can handle more information, simultaneously observing a number of targets by slipping quickly between them without the necessity to examine the areas between. Control of the phased-array radar can be by a computer, so that its response can be determined by the type of signal being returned without further human interference. Thus a quick overall scan for new targets can alternate with detailed examination of identified targets. The effect is of constant surveillance of both the whole field and particular objects.

Several radars with different functions would be required in any system. The first requirement is to acquire targets (i.e., reentry vehicles) at the maximum range, so that the targets may be identified and their courses plotted to provide data for computing interception trajectories. In U.S. systems perimeter acquisition radars are designed for this purpose. They would be sited along the Canadian border and on the seaboards to provide flank protection. Two other radars would be required in a thick deployment: missile acquisition radars and missile site radars. The function of these radars is to take over tracking of the incoming reentry vehicles, to complete identification and discrimination from decoys, and to guide ABM to make an intercept. TACMAR is a tactical version of missile acquisition radars with half the capabilities.

THREATS TO CONTINENTAL UNITED STATES

In essence the four threats to the United States to which ABM systems can offer a defense, in order of increasing damage intensity, are the following:

One or a few missiles released by accident or fired as a warning to show determination

A relatively small-scale attack of, at the most, a few tens of missiles, aimed at urban centers and originating from one of the lesser nuclear powers

A counterforce first strike against missile silos intended to destroy power of retaliation but to hold the cities as hostages under threat

A massive all-out attack by the Soviet Union aimed at destroying as much of the United States as possible, including cities, missile silos, and other military targets.

The first two threats aimed at urban centers pose similar problems to the defense: the target area is large—virtually the whole country—and within the area there are a number of alternative targets. The prime requirement is for an area defense covering all, or most, of the country.

It is for the last threat—an all-out attack against all targets—that it may appear to be possible to reduce the casualties and damage, at about the same cost as to the offensive to restore the situation, i.e., a cost-exchange ratio of about one.

The third of the threats listed above, that of a first-strike option against ICBM silos, was made possible by improvements in missile technology, particularly in accuracy, resulting, in part at least, from experience of orbiting of satellites and space shots, from high-yield warheads that can be carried by the relatively large reentry vehicles that can be borne by Russian missiles, and from multiple individually guided warheads, which increase the number of attacks that can be made.

A great many estimates have been made as to the level of the threat presented by the new Soviet missiles. At one extreme it has been calculated that as many as 20 warheads would be required to destroy each silo to a high level of probability.[4] Other calculations have shown that only a few Minuteman silos would escape from an attack.

There is general agreement as to what formula should be used in making these calculations, which are widely used for computing the effectiveness of weapons. The debate hinges mainly on the data input and some of the methods for handling it. Suppose, for example, that the attacker allocates one warhead per silo, but 20 percent of his missiles abort; then at least 20 percent of the silos will survive. But most missile aborts occur in the launch phase, and the loss can be replaced within minutes by a second, retargeted missile. Other missile failures would occur at warhead separation, and a system is believed to be under development in the United States for signaling successful separation, so that a replacement could be fired for any defective missiles.

However, the ratio of Soviet warheads to Minuteman silos could be greater than one to one; official estimates in the United States are that 600 SS-9 SCARP ICBM's could be deployed by 1974-76, and each could carry three warheads, so that there would be 1,800 warheads of this type alone to attack 1,000 silos.

The most crucial discrepancy in the calculations is in the numerical value given to the accuracy of ICBM. Modern ballistic missiles have a CEP of less than one mile, and values as low as a quarter of a mile have been quoted. This means that for warheads of high yield and a large radius of destruction, very few impacting warheads would fail to damage the target seriously. A further advance that could improve missile accuracy is under investigation in the United States: reentry vehicles would have terminal guidance using a stored radar picture taken earlier by a reconnaisance satellite; this would be compared with the target viewed on a television scanner in the nose of the reentry vehicle.

PROPOSED DEPLOYMENT OF ABM's IN THE UNITED STATES

Land-Based Systems

Proposals for deployment of ABM's in the United States have varied from the extreme of a full deployment to provide a defense against all possible threats to deployments specifically tailored to a particular lesser threat. Two systems that have been sanctioned to cope with lower-level threats are Sentinel and Safeguard.

Sentinel was designed as a thin system to provide some national protection against a small-scale attack or the accidental release of a weapon, together with thickened local defense of some key urban areas using Sprint missiles. The development of Spartan long-range ABM's with a range of 400 miles (compared with 200 miles for Nike-Zeus), enabled an overall cover to be provided by relatively few batteries.

An entirely unexpected outcome of the first construction work on sites near cities was the volume of public protest. The basis for public doubts appears to be the presence of nuclear warheads, with the concomitant danger, at least in the view of the public, of nuclear accidents. It has been estimated that a ground-level accident to a warhead in the kiloton range could cause fallout capable of fatal doses as far away as 50 miles, in addition to blast damage over a radius of several miles. Sprint warheads would be comparable in yield to the Hiroshima and Nagasaki weapons, while the warhead for Spartan would have a yield of about one megaton, some 50 times greater. Other causes of concern were the possible danger to the public from bursts of defense missiles in the atmosphere at a range of a few miles and the effects of fallout. Finally, the public was concerned that provision of a defensive battery would draw attention to the military value of the locality and make it a prime target.

Local campaigns against Sentinel coincided with a change in the U.S. administration in 1968, and they may have been a factor in a reappraisal of ABM defense that was carried out. As a result the Sentinel system was replaced by Safeguard, using essentially the same components but in different proportions. The emphasis in strategy of the Safeguard system is away from attempts to defend populations from heavy attacks—which would appear to be difficult if not impossible to achieve, and could well start an arms race with the Soviet Union—and toward an overall defense against a comparatively light attack, together with defense of some Minuteman silos, some bomber bases, and other military targets.

There are certain advantages in the Safeguard deployment as compared with Sentinel. The first is that whereas Sentinel had to be more or less complete before it could achieve all its objectives (although of course it would be effective in some circumstances with only partial deployment), with Safeguard's more limited objectives deployments can be made more or less in step with growing threats. Thus the deployment of long-range Spartan missiles can match the buildup of the Chinese ICBM force, while the number of Minuteman sites protected by Sprint missiles can be extended in step with the growth of the threat from Russian ICBM's. Thus, while Safeguard will cost some 30 percent more than Sentinel, the costs can be spread over a longer period and halted at any time should the threat cease to grow, or should an agreement be reached that limits deployment of nuclear delivery systems. Other advantages of a slower deployment include the opportunity to incorporate new technical developments and to modify deployment in accordance with changing assessment of the threat, and extension of the time for troop training and operational experience in order to use skilled manpower more efficiently.

In both cases initial costs are to a large extent determined by the very high costs of the radars. A full deployment of perimeter acquisition radars would be required at an early stage with either system.

Siting missile farms and radar installations near cities, as in the Sentinel deployment, would have some advantages. Public services such as electricity and water would be available, as would rail transport, housing, and recreational facilities for the construction gangs and operating personnel. On the other hand, in the concept of Safeguard as area defense there is no need for location of sites near cities. Remote sites would have the following advantages:

Cheaper land

Better site security

Possibility of overlapping defenses for important targets

Wide spacing of missile site radars will reduce effects of radar blackout

Less risk to public through accidents

If the sites themselves were attacked, there would be less collateral damage to the public

Intercepts with enemy reentry vehicles would be less likely to take place above or near cities

The initial deployment of short-range missiles is intended to protect U.S. Air Force missile sites at Malmstrom, Montana, and Grand Forks, North Dakota.

Seaborne ABM's

The United States has been investigating an ABM system, SABMIS, in which the missiles and radars would be carried in naval vessels. Generally the uses of such a system could be as a forward defense against the main threat corridors; as a flexible overseas deployment to protect Japan, India, and Europe; as a screen around China; as protection for the Polaris submarine fleet; and as flank protection against missiles launched by submarines.

There would be two important advantages for such a system. First, the vessels could be stationed forward of land-based defenses below the threat corridors, so that interception would take place before the lines of flight had diverged toward the separate targets and before wide separation of reentry vehicles and decoys had taken place; thus a smaller target would be presented, all of which could be destroyed without the need for discrimination of the warheads. Furthermore, the battle would be joined above the atmosphere and above largely uninhabited areas, so that other problems would be reduced.

A second advantage of a seaborne system is its mobility, which would enable it to be deployed toward a particular threat. For example, a seaborne system could be suitable for the defense of Japan and of Australia, and perhaps even of India.

A seaborne system, however, has many problems, including the high cost of the platforms—that is, the ships—as compared with land-based platforms. The instability of platforms would make control of the radars and of the launching of missiles much more difficult. Mobility would require more flexibility in this system than in systems with fixed positions in relationship to the threat corridors. Problems of command and control of a seaborne mobile system would be much greater, owing to the absence of secure land-surface communications, so that links would be less reliable and more subject to breakdown.

Another seaborne ABM system that has been proposed is forward area ballistic missile intercept system, in which the platforms would float but be moored as near as possible to the enemy launch sites.

Airborne ABM's

In the United States a two-stage intercepter missile is being considered that would be launched from the giant Lockheed C5A transport aircraft; this weapon is part of a proposed airborne ballistic missile intercept system and would have a maneuvering second stage. Target detection and tracking would be done by equipment carried by the C5A. The system is intended to intercept low-trajectory missiles attacking coastal cities.

SIDE EFFECTS OF ABM's

Explosion of ABM nuclear warheads would produce a number of problems for the defense: blackout, fallout, and injuries to the defended population.

Blackout of the defense radars results from their inability to penetrate the ionization surrounding a nuclear burst and to detect objects beyond the burst. Thus the attacker may launch his ICBM's one after the other along the same track, so that detonation of the first defense weapon will provide cover for the succeeding warheads to penetrate the defenses. The attacker could even arrange to use some of his own warheads to provide a blackout.

There are several blackout mechanisms. Beta blackout occurs at once at 200,000 feet; the problem can be overcome to some extent by defense radars of as high a frequency as is compatible with range. Gamma blackout occurs at 100,000-200,000 feet, and delayed gamma rays continue to ionize the surrounding air for perhaps tens of seconds. Fireball blackout will rise out of line of sight of the incoming radars in a fraction of a minute.

Considerable effort has been put into developing methods for penetrating radar blackout, and some degree of success has been achieved. Nevertheless, the problem is still probably of importance in relation to a massive attack, when there would be constantly regenerated ionization and possibly other deleterious effects on communications and other electronic systems.

DEPLOYMENT IN OTHER THEATERS

The possibility of deployment of ABM's by some of the other powers is superficially attractive. The threat from the nuclear powers would be removed or reduced, without the need to deter with a counter-threat. There are several areas where such possibilities exist: Europe, Japan, India, and perhaps more generally in East Asia and Australasia. In theory, at least, these defenses could be provided by the nations to be defended, or by the United States and the Soviet Union, or by some kind of arrangement between the parties.

For the nations mentioned to provide their own ABM cover would involve them not only in enormous expenditure but also in areas of technology in which they now lack expertise. The cost to the United States of developing an ABM system, with the concurrent need to study penetration in similar depth, has been very great; such sums could not easily be found even by a consortium of European powers. This being so, reliance might have to be placed on obtaining the system, or at least the know-how, from the United States or Soviet Union. Problems of sharing costs and the terms for supplying the information or hardware would present great difficulties in negotiations. Stationing of large numbers of nuclear-armed missiles would cause political uncertainties in many parts of the world, as would problems of ownership of warheads and authority to fire. Would it be necessary to refer to the United States (or Soviet Union) for permission to fire? Would there be any possibility of the host country converting the missiles for offensive purposes? How would it be possible to reassure neighboring countries that the weapons were in fact defensive? What would be the effects on the Non-Proliferation Treaty and the Comprehensive Test Ban Treaty? Would there be pressure for test explosions as demonstrations and for troop training?

Fallout from high-level bursts in or above the atmosphere will not produce the intensity of fallout from ground bursts and, by destroying incoming warheads before they impact, local fallout could be considerably reduced by an ABM defense. However, worldwide contamination by fallout might well be increased, since the total yield is increased by the explosion of ABM's.

At the height at which an ABM warhead would be exploded, much of the energy would be released as a very large incandescent mass that could, depending on the height of the explosion, cause damage to eyes, second-degree burns, or fires in easily ignitable materials. The defense would to some extent be constrained in trying to avoid these effects on the defended population.

ABM's AND ARMS CONTROL

Very little comment has appeared from the Soviet Union about their own or the U.S. ABM systems, and none has taken the line that introduction of ABM's could be destabilizing. On the other hand, opinion has been sharply divided in the United States as to the advisability of deploying an ABM system. Generally, support for proposed systems has come from the military and associated systems analysts, and opposition has come mainly from the academic community and some politicians. Arguments in favor have been centered mainly on the possibility of saving millions of lives in the event of a nuclear war, although there have been supporting arguments of various kinds, including those of political advantages. The gravamen of the argument against deployment has been that an arms race between offensive and defensive weapons could follow in which the advantages in cost appeared, at least until recently, to be in favor of the offensive. This kind of analysis of cost-effectiveness appears to be to some degree a product of American business management procedures and of a concept of "assured destruction capability" for causing some stated millions of casualties. It is certain that policy makers in the Soviet Union do not share this style of logic. Statements of Soviet policy do not specify the number of casualties and are couched in more general and national terms; what appears to be a traditional emphasis on defense has led to the deployment of weapons systems of high cost but, as far as it has been possible to judge, not of commensurate effectiveness. Neither has the possibility of destabilizing mutual deterrence by deployment of the Moscow system been considered in the same way as the matter has caused concern in the United States. Ironically, at the Eighteen Nations Disarmament Conference it was the Soviet Union that defended the United States when the latter was attacked by its allies for considering making a deployment of ABM's.

Arguments for deploying ABM's are not, from the arms controllers' point of view, quite as one-sided as they sometimes appear. Saving in lives has to be balanced against some increase in the chances of a nuclear war. The vast cost of the system turns out, on closer examination, to be a fraction of the present annual defense expenditure in the United States and about 0.50 percent of the GNP. The cost of an ABM in the United States is equivalent to $250-$2,000 per life saved—which is only a small fraction of the average cost of killing an individual in battle in modern war. Reduction of casualties from 50 percent to 10 percent of the population and protection of property would reduce the devastation and misery, and would make economic recovery possible in a much shorter time.

Arms control objections to ABM's include the possibility that a comprehensive test ban would not be signed and the Limited Nuclear Test Ban and the Non-Proliferation Treaty would both be jeopardized. These risks come from the requirement to develop nuclear warheads for the ABM's; it is unlikely that a large and expensive deployment would be made without a considerable body of data, such as the rate of expansion and rise of the fireball at different altitudes and the effects on the warhead under attack. Underground testing alone is unlikely to give sufficient confidence for extrapolation and, in any case, may not be suitable for the highest-yield devices and will give no information on the performance of radars, communications, and other parts of the system when nuclear explosions are taking place.

One of the objections to an ABM defense is that it could provoke an increase in the offense; and if the defense should then fail, the level of damage would be greater than if ABM's had not been deployed. Another problem is that, once begun, an ABM system would have to be continuously improved to ensure that the effectiveness was not impaired by improvements in offensive forces.

Perhaps the most telling argument against a deployment of ABM's rather than some other policy is that the whole of the immensely complex system would have to function almost perfectly on the very first occasion on which it was used, without any possibility of full system trials.

NOTES

1. See W. T. Gumston, "The Controversial ABM, "Science Journal (July 1969).

2. M. Talensky, "Anti-Missile Systems and Disarmament," Bulletin of the Atomic Scientists (February 1965), p. 195.

3. D. G. Brennan, "The Case for Missile Defense," Foreign Affairs (April 1969).

4. In Donald C. Winston, "SS-9 Seen Spurring Nixon ABM Effort," Aviation Week and Space Technology (March 31, 1969).

CHAPTER

13

ADVANCES IN STRATEGIC NUCLEAR DELIVERY SYSTEMS

The three previous chapters were concerned with a description of the types of weapons systems and the nature of the deployments of the nuclear powers, particularly those of the superpowers, the United States and the Soviet Union. The present chapter will describe improvements in strategic nuclear systems that are already deployed or are at some development stage, or have been considered and show some promise.

The arrangement of the chapters might be seen as implying a chronological order in the development of systems—that is, offensive systems, then defenses to counter the offensive systems, then various improvements and new offensive systems to overcome the defenses. This has been the general pattern of arms races; but it is not, under present conditions, entirely accurate. Because of the tempo of advances in technology, combined with the long lead-time for procurement of numbers of sophisticated weapons, the whole process tends to be telescoped in time. Two other factors tend to accelerate the process of development: those technologists who develop a new system are more likely to appreciate its shortcomings and be in a position to develop a counter system, so that the arms race often tends to appear to be between different groups in the same country; and this situation can be made worse by the lack of real information about the intentions of the opponent as far as procurement goes. The cautious reaction is to overinsure and to assume that the opponent's future capability will be greater than it may in fact prove to be. Counter deployments are made and themselves become reasons for concern by the opponent.

ADVANCES IN TACTICAL USE OF STRATEGIC NUCLEAR DELIVERY VEHICLES

At the start of the ballistic missile program the US planned to install 20 to 40 ICBM's to support the long range bomber fleet. After assessment of the threat of a "missile gap" the Eisenhower administration decided to reschedule the procurement for a deployment of 200 missiles, and under the Kennedy administration it was planned further to expand the force to 1,000 Minuteman (a fraction of the number requested by the military) and 656 Polaris missiles. Since then plans have included replacement of older missiles by others with multiple warheads: Minuteman-3 and Poseidon.

Deployment of ICBM by the Soviet Union, although it started earlier than in the United States, appeared for many years to be limited to a minimum deterrent; the current large-scale deployment in the Soviet Union might derive from an effort to counter the earlier U.S. expansion, which, with the addition of MIRV's, may appear to have a growing first-strike potential.

Introduction of ABM's has led to development of new strategies, tactics, and weapons systems. An attacker has a choice of responses that can be made to overcome an improved ABM defense. Among the tactics that can be used with existing missiles are the following:

Decoy attacks to split the defenses

Blackout attacks, in which the defense radars are deprived of warning of following missiles

Overwhelming the defense by massive saturation attacks on a few important targets

Overextending the defense by an attack in which the missiles follow each other so rapidly that the defense does not have time to recover

Evading the defense by attacking less well defended targets

A bypass attack, from which ground bursts upwind would scatter heavy fallout over the target

Outflanking the defense by attacks from the sea.

Bomber aircraft can employ some of these tactics, as well as low-level attacks and standoff bombs.

ADVANCES IN DESIGN OF STRATEGIC MISSILE SYSTEMS

There have been a number of qualitative advances in strategic missiles that would enable the new tactics to be employed and may affect the strategic balance, including the following:

ABM's (discussed in Chapter 12)

Fractional orbit ballistic systems

Multiple reentry vehicles

Multiple individually targeted reentry vehicles

submarine-launched strategic missiles with longer range

Increased accuracy of reentry vehicles

Armed satellites (banned by treaty).

A number of corresponding advances have been made in the design and operation of strategic bomber aircraft and their weapons systems, to equip them for the new tactics mentioned above and for new roles:

Improved command and control, particularly in the deployment of aircraft as airborne command posts for both missiles and bombers that could survive in first strikes

Long range standoff missiles, which would allow bombers to attack without the need to penetrate the heavy defenses around the target

Development of terrain-following and navigation equipment for low-level attacks

Improved bombsights, such as lasers, television, infrared, and radar homing devices

Before examining possible new systems, some counters will be outlined, since these may take the same or similar form. Also, the possibility of a counter may influence the decision on deployment of an offensive system.

COUNTERS TO INCREASED THREAT

Faced with numerical and qualitative improvements in strategic nuclear delivery vehicles, the defense has a number of options to restore the balance, some of which are technically the same as the advances that they are intended to counter. Some of these options are shown in Table 14.

With a wide choice of response, the defender may be able to counter the increased threat to his assured destruction level at costs that may be less than that incurred by the attacker. While any of these systems now under discussion could probably maintain a capacity for assured destruction, they would have very different implications for the other superpower and for damage limitation, and hence on the eventual size and costs of the new strategic strike forces.

The U.S. policy of qualitative improvements in penetrability of U.S. warheads and the increase in numbers of warheads may be seen as an attempt to penetrate the Soviet defenses; these steps can be viewed as less threatening than an increase in the number of missiles. Alternative policies of overwhelming, overextending, or evading the Soviet defenses would have involved a greatly expanded U.S. missile force. Had this been done, with the already existing U.S. advantage in numbers of ICBM's, then the Soviet retaliating forces would have been threatened and the Soviets would have been forced to increase their own missile armory, to be followed by a similar step by the United States.

A system is not viable until tested, deployed, and operational in the required quantities; for most of the systems listed in the table, quantities required may well be in the hundreds of individual systems—that is, warheads, missiles, launchers, guidance, command and control radars—so that, given good intelligence, there should be a lengthy warning that new deployments were in hand.

Some of the more important developments in the technology of strategic nuclear delivery systems will now be described, with attention first to methods to protect strike forces and then an examination of improvements in strike forces.

TABLE 14

Possible Improvements in Strategic Nuclear Delivery Vehicles for Attack or Retaliation

---

Increased inventory, so that more are likely to survive a first strike
Diversification, such as missiles, bombers, and submarines, to complicate planning by the attacker
Dispersion to widely separated launch sites, airfields, and patrol areas, so that a single attack cannot destroy several at once
Mobility, so that enough cannot be located with sufficient accuracy for a disarming strike
Concealment
Decoy targets
Hardening of missile launch sites and airfields
ABM defense
Multiple warheads to increase effectiveness of surviving delivery vehicles
Improved command and control to survive attack
Improved early warning to alert defenses or to permit aircraft to be airborne before arrival of attack, or to permit ICBM to be launched before being destroyed
Penetration aids to improve effectiveness of first strike or second strike by surviving vehicles
Multiple reentry vehicles (MRV)
Multiple individually targeted reentry vehicles (MIRV)
New aircraft
Nothing, on assumption that deterrence is not seriously undermined
Longer-range SLBM for greater range of outflanking attack
Development of fast surface ship launcher
Development of an ocean bottom launch system
Development of a long-range submarine that does not require overseas ports and bases

---

DUMMY SILOS

Drawing the fire of the enemy by providing simulations of targets is an ancient military strategem, but there do not appear to have been any considerable attempts to build dummy silos. A major problem of constructing dummy silos would be the cost. Real silos are very costly and take months to build; during this time they could be observed from satellites, so any difference in effort exerted between constructing a dummy silo and a real silo might be obvious and reveal which were dummies.

The position could change in the United States if it were decided to develop and deploy the WS-120 or other more advanced and larger missile to replace or supplement Minuteman. The cost of these advanced missiles would be so much greater than the cost of the silo that it might be worth building spare silos and rotating the missiles.

HARDENED SILOS

With increasing missile accuracy, silos are much more vulnerable to attack, so that silo hardness has become of greater importance. The U.S. Air Force has been interested in the development of a hard rock silo, heavily reinforced to withstand an overpressure of 3,000 psi and large enough to accommodate not only Minuteman-3 missiles but also the proposed WS-120A advanced missile.

An alternative program, Brimstone, has also been investigated. Missiles would be housed deep below the surface in copper and brimstone mines in which there are hundreds of miles of underground galleries.

Also being studied in connection with these programs are arrangements for power supplies and launch facility processors to maintain the state of readiness of missiles, to provide for their upkeep, and to control the launch. The processor could take over some of the duties performed by the missile's own computer, which, freed from these tasks, could be used for more flexible targeting.

High blast pressure alone may not be effective in damaging silos to the extent that the missile cannot be launched. Excavating a crater by a ground burst may be more effective in displacing or cracking a silo; another effect that may damage the control mechanisms is an electromagnetic pulse, but silos can be protected against this by electrical screening. The energy from a ground burst tends to partition with a higher fraction of energy to the atmosphere. A much bigger crater and deformed zone can be obtained with a warhead that explodes below the surface: warheads to do this are under development in the United States.

INCREASED MISSILE ACCURACY

Hardening of silos can be seen as a response to increased missile accuracy, and vice versa. Improved accuracy may be seen as an attempt to secure a first-strike option, as a means of limiting damage, and as a way to economize on the number of missiles required for this purpose.

It can be said in a general way that improvements in accuracy indicate a move away from a deterrent posture, for which low-accuracy weapons capable of destroying cities are adequate, to a first-strike posture, with increased possibility of success in a sudden attack on missile silos. However, there are no obvious means, except a ban on testing, that would prevent improvements in accuracy.

Long range missiles follow a ballistic path to their targets—that is, after the motor is cut off within the first few minutes, the missile is not further guided. Improvements have come from finer control of the thrust, greater accuracy in setting the missile on course, better knowledge of allowances to be made for variations in gravity, and more accurate location of targets and corrections for wind and air pressure at the target. Some improvements have followed from observations made from earth-orbiting satellites.

Even greater improvements in accuracy could be achieved with terminal guidance. One system that is known to have been under investigation would depend on matching a picture from a television camera in the nose of the reentry vehicle with a picture of the silo taken from a satellite. These improvements could, in theory, confer a first-strike option; but it is much more likely that it would be assumed that the enemy had achieved this advantage and countermeasures would be adopted.

PENETRATION AIDS

Reentry vehicles may be defended against counterattack by ABM in two ways: by hardening and by penetration aids. One example of penetration aids is the metalized balloon capable of reflecting radar and thus resembling a reentry vehicle. During the midcourse part of the trajectory, balloons would travel at the same speed as a warhead; but on contact with air on reentry into the atmosphere, they would be slowed and heated by friction, and destroyed—this process is known as atmospheric sorting.

Heavier decoys could be designed with reentry shields that could survive frictional heating, but it may become more cost-effective to provide additional warheads, MRV's or MIRV's.

Other penetration aids include fragments of the rocket motor that have been disintegrated by an explosive charge after separation and chaff (metalized strips), which, dispensed in quantities, produces a general radar reflection in which it would be difficult to identify a reentry vehicle. A similar generalized reflection can be obtained with dipoles (short pieces of metal wire or metalized plastic), the wire being of various lengths to secure maximum radar reflection. It may be possible to distinguish reentry vehicles from decoys by examining the radar reflections from the wake of ionization that follows reentry vehicles. Methods for simulating the wake have been suggested, and it would be possible to release reflecting decoys equipped with rocket motors to simulate the reentry vehicle. Another method for disguising reentry vehicles is to make them nonreflecting to radar by special coatings; a device that is being tested is a small aerial that emits a signal neutralizing an incident radar. Electronic counter-measure devices could also be carried to jam the defense radars, which would then be unable to analyze any returned signals.

HARDENING OF REENTRY VEHICLES

Which weapons effects from a nuclear explosion would destroy an incoming reentry vehicle would depend upon the range from the point of the explosion. The fireball would consume all within it; a strong pulse of X rays could be absorbed in the outer layer of the reentry vehicle and be released as heat, causing cracking and exfoliation of the ablative shielding, so that the vehicle would burn up on entering the atmosphere. The flux of neutrons could damage electronic components, particularly solid-state devices, which could be rendered conducting, so that stray currents could cause premature action of some of the mechanisms; neutrons could also lead to some premature fission and distortion in the fissile material.

Protection against X rays may be provided by using layers of material that will absorb X rays of a particular wavelength and underlying layers that absorb and conduct away the heat released.

Electronic devices may be permanently damaged, or the damage may be transitory. Some circuits may not be in operation when subjected to the neutron flux, and self-repair of the damage may take place before the circuit is required to operate. Desirable characteristics of electronic components in reentry vehicles are resistance to damage and rapid recovery.

MULTIPLE REENTRY VEHICLES

Light decoys would be delayed or burned up in the atmosphere, but heavy decoys could be designed to reenter the atmosphere by providing a reentry shield. However, the weight of shielding required would be at the expense of payload available for the warhead. A decoy with reentry capability would approach the weight of one carrying a warhead; an alternative combination for the payload could be several smaller warheads. This system is now known as MRV (Multiple Reentry Vehicle), and the number of warheads that can be carried has been said to be three, six, and even ten.

It is obvious that taking into account the extra reentry shields and structural and other components, the total weight of fissile material to be shared between the warheads in an MRV is less, possibly much less, than for a single warhead; and the total yield would also be less. However, the total area of damage from several small warheads can be as great as or even greater than from a single large warhead. This is illustrated in Table 15, which lists the number and yields of warheads required to produce equal areas of damage.

TABLE 15

Payloads Needed to Damage Similar Areas

Original Missile Designed for			
Megaton-Range Warhead		Multimegaton-Range Warhead	
Warheads	Yield	Warheads	Yield
1	1 mt	1	25 mt
3	190 kt	3	4.8 mt
6	69 kt	6	1.7 mt
12	24 kt	12	600 kt
		24	100 kt

Source: Calculated from data in Samuel Glasstone, The Effects of Nuclear Weapons (Washington, D.C.: U.S. Atomic Energy Commission, 1964).

Of course it is possible that the areas damaged by multiple warheads may overlap to some extent. On the other hand, increasing the number of warheads aimed at a single target—say a city—will increase the probability of its destruction. This is illustrated in Table 16, where it is assumed that the target is defended, so that there is only a low probability of a hit with a single warhead. It is also assumed that each of the warheads is large enough to destroy the target.

Besides increasing the probability of destruction of the target, another advantage that can be obtained from multiple warheads is that the pattern of impacts could be made to compensate for possible errors in aiming. Thus, if the greatest error was in range (rather than line, that is, direction), the impacts could be in a pattern elongated in the direction of range. This is normal practice with other weapons.

Table 15 shows the advantage of having large missiles that can be converted to MRV's. Full advantage of such conversion can be obtained only if there are extremely well developed skills in miniaturization of various components.

The original single warheads on both sides of Table 15 were of the fusion (hydrogen) type, using uranium-235 for the core. The maximum warhead size that can be made using fissile material only is probably about 500 kilotons, so that when multiple warheads of less than this yield are used, they may be all fissile and require only plutonium. Multiple reentry vehicles could, therefore, be built

TABLE 16

Probabilities of Destruction of Target

Number of Warheads	Probability of Destruction
1	20%
3	49%
6	74%
12	94%

Note: This table shows the vulnerability of a well-defended target to attack by one or more similar warheads.

without the need for U-235 and either the costly gaseous diffusion or the gas centrifuge process. These weapons could damage as large an area as a single multimegaton fusion warhead.

Multiple warheads have been developed, tested, and installed in some missiles, such as Polaris and Minuteman-3. Although MRV's would not necessarily greatly increase the first-strike option, once they had been deployed it would be impossible to know whether individual high-accuracy guidance had been added, thus giving a qualitative improvement in a first-strike weapon.

MULTIPLE INDIVIDUALLY TARGETED REENTRY VEHICLES

The individual warheads of MRV's will most likely be rather less accurate than the single warhead; and since accuracy is the most important quality for a counter-force strike, MRV's may not be much better than, and may even be inferior to, the single warhead for attacking missile silos, even when each silo can be attacked by more than one warhead.

However, if the warheads are each separately targeted or equipped with their own guidance systems, as in MIRV's, there could be an appreciable increase in threat to missile silos. Deployment of MIRV's could thus introduce a first-strike option. The option would be further enhanced if ABM's were also deployed by the attacker, since he would then have a defense against the retaliatory second strike.

The number of MIRV's that would confer a first-strike option against an opponent's land-based ICBM's will depend upon a number of factors; including the yield and accuracy of the impacts, the hardness of the silos, and any ABM screen that must be penetrated. Independent guidance implies that in addition to guidance for the assembled payload, after separation each reentry vehicle would have some form of maneuvrability and guidance to enable it to seek a specific target. Weapons systems of this type are under development but may not be deployed in quantity. One that has been described is the "space bus." J. S. Foster made the first official reference in public to MIRV's as a major breakthrough when combined with the space bus, the post boost control system, in these words:

> . . . contains individual reentry vehicles with thermonuclear warheads. After the main booster has cut-off,

> the bus keeps making minute adjustments to its speed and direction and after each adjustment it ejects another warhead. Thus each warhead is delivered on a trajectory to a different city, or if desired, all can be delivered within the same city.*

He also said that the space bus/MIRV combination would be carried by both Poseidon and Minuteman-3 missiles.

Details that have been published of different packages that could be carried by U.S. missiles include the following:

Mk 11, a single high-yield warhead to be used against cities

Mk 12, three multiple independently guided missiles of intermediate yield

Mk 18, a large number of small-yield warheads together with decoys and other penetration aids.

Various estimates have been made of the date by which the Soviet Union could have large numbers of highly accurate SS-9 missiles. The possibility that it could, in a few years, have a first-strike option, has been advanced as an argument in favor of a deployment of ABM's in the United States.** Arguments advanced on the other side have included alternative calculations that have shown that a first-strike option could not be achieved in the same time period.*** Many calculations on both sides can be faulted on methodology. A common error is to assume that the abortion rate for ICBM's, estimated at about 20 percent, would leave this number of targets unattacked. However, most missile failures are during the launch phase, and those losses could easily be replaced. Other missiles would fail on separation of the reentry vehicles; a signaling system is under development in the United States that would report any failure at this stage. Most missile failures could, therefore, be replaced.

---

*John S. Foster, "Options for Strategic Systems," Astronautics and Aeronautics (August 1970).

**Donald C. Winston, "SS-9 Seen Spurring Nixon ABM Effort," Aviation Week and Space Technology (March 31, 1969).

***See Aviation Week (April 14, 1969), which quotes the conclusions of a report by Ralph Lapp; see also Space/Aeronautics (September 1969).

From the point of view of inspection, it would be impossible to guess accurately how many of the opponent's missiles had been converted to MIRV's, even though the number of warheads carried in each MIRV might be known from monitoring of tests—but only if one type has been tested. If a number of types of MIRV's had been tested, it would be more difficult to know which type or types were being installed in missile warheads. In order to achieve and prove high accuracy, many tests would be necessary; and at least some of the tests could be monitored from outside the country conducting the tests. Even so, estimating the accuracy of an opponent's weapons could be more difficult, and the defense is likely to overinsure.

Because deployment of MIRV's might be destabilizing, it has been proposed as an arms control measure that deployment of MIRV's be prohibited. The main problem in such an agreement would be verification. Direct inspection would have to be extremely detailed, in that all payloads would have to be opened and examined; and it is difficult to imagine that this would be permitted. A ban on testing of MIRV's would hinder development and deployment, in that it would make reliability difficult to estimate, but would not be certain to prevent deployment. Since MRV's are to be deployed in some recently developed U.S. missiles, it would be difficult to ensure that these were not replaced by MIRV's, unless the ban was applied to all forms of multiple warhead missiles. A ban on MRV's might be resisted on the grounds that these were necessary to maintain an assured destruction capability against a deployment of ABM's.

For a first strike to be successful, it would be necessary not only to destroy a large proportion of the opponent's ICBM's before they could be launched but also to neutralize retaliation from nuclear-armed missiles from submarines, long range bombers, strike fleets, and tactical aircraft. These various deterrent systems could be defeated only by other separate and elaborate systems, all coordinated to effect almost complete destruction without warning.

Apart from the difficulties in organizing a first strike on this scale to achieve the requisite amount of damage, it would be impossible to make a first strike against land-based missiles without the mass launch being detected by at least one of the early warning systems: satellites, over-the-horizon radars, and ballistic missile early warning systems. Any of these systems would give up to half an hour's warning, which would be more than ample time to launch the land-based missiles under attack. If the power expecting attack is prepared to launch its retaliation on warning, rather than waiting to have the attack confirmed by actual impacts, then there is really little prospect of successful first strike against land-based missile silos—and even less against the whole panoply of deterrent forces.

However, a "fire on warning" policy would very much increase the risks of war by accident. Furthermore, there would be the suspicion in the mind of the opponent that such instructions had been issued secretly.

The measures taken by a prudent policymaker when he is designing an attack are very different from those taken in designing a defense. Thus all of the factors are considered as they favor attack or defense (that is, probabilities are weighted differently), and the number of silos containing missiles that the attacker would feel he could leave undestroyed would be less than the defender would feel it essential to retain.

It may be considerations such as these that have drawn the United States and the Soviet Union into discussing strategic arms limitation, rather than the high costs of developing and deploying such systems.

Some of the advantages and disadvantages of multiple reentry vehicles are listed in Table 17.

TABLE 17

Military Advantages and Disadvantages of MRV's/MIRV's

First Strike
- A large number of targets could be attacked
- The total area of damage could be greater
- Defenses could be confused and stretched
- If highly accurate, there could be a first-strike potential against silos

Retaliatory Second Strike
- More warheads would survive

Destabilizing Effects
- Numbers and accuracy of those deployed by the other side would not be known, leading to overinsurance
- Counter might be "fire on warning," leading to tension
- Premium on first strike would be enhanced

Note: Although it is argued in the text that MRV's and MIRV's can serve different purposes, in practice there would be an overlap; and in any case it would be difficult for an opponent to be sure which of the two systems or which mixture was deployed and to know details of performance. The opponent would have to assume a high level of threat in designing countermeasures.

TABLE 18

Possible Military Activities in Space

Direct	Indirect
Weapons of mass destruction in orbit	Support
Weapons for use against space vehicles	Reconnaissance
Missile launchers	Surveillance
Weather control	Targeting
	Transportation of men and materials

MILITARY USES OF SPACE

Possible military activities in space can be direct or indirect: direct activities are those which include weapons. The main areas of activities are shown in Table 18.

Vehicles armed with nuclear weapons could be placed in earth orbit as a more or less permanent threat. Two orbits have advantages: a near-earth polar orbit at about 100 miles above the surface and, at 22,300 miles above the surface, a geostationary orbit, that is, remaining stationary above the same spot on the earth's surface. Nuclear-armed bombardment satellites would have to be large and heavy and carry, in addition to one or more reentry vehicles with warheads, a retrorocket to bring the vehicle out of orbit. Putting the vehicle into orbit would need a launch vehicle of the size of the Saturn rocket, costing some £50 million (approximately $131 million).

The near-earth orbit system would require on the order of 100 nuclear-armed bombardment satellites to have a first-strike potential, and it would be difficult to see any military justification for such a system otherwise. Apart from the technical difficulties, the cost would be very high and the orbiting of the first vehicles, if recognized as such, would be likely construed as an intention to achieve a first-strike option and thus upset the existing balance of deterrence.

Nuclear-armed bombardment satellites in synchronous orbit

would take a minimum of 3.5 hours and probably 7.5 hours to be brought down onto the target, which would give ample time for the launching of, and interception by, a defensive missile.

Satellites of either of the types described would be vulnerable to antimissile missiles of existing types armed with nuclear warheads, and it is known that the United States has a small number of missiles available for this task. Both superpowers have demonstrated a capability to rendezvous in space with manned spaceships and for crews to transfer between vehicles. The possibility therefore exists for direct inspections to be carried out in space.

There could be a requirement in the future for unmanned maintenance vehicles using remote-controlled manipulators and television to carry out repairs and replace defective or exhausted components, with the aim of extending the useful life of satellites in orbit. With such vehicles in orbit it would be possible to carry out remote-controlled inspections very quickly and, if necessary, dismantle suspicious vehicles.

The possibility of inspection and vigorous counteraction, and also the certainty of causing international tension without any military advantage, were no doubt some of the factors that led to successful negotiation of the Outer Space Treaty in 1967. This treaty prohibits weapons of mass destruction in space and includes rights of access to nationally owned satellites.

Other direct uses of orbiting satellites are not of such immediate importance as the orbiting of nuclear weapons and will not be discussed further. Although the direct use of space for military systems appears to be limited both by treaty and by practical difficulties, satellites are highly advantageous for indirect military purposes, such as photographic reconnaissance, communications, and navigation of naval vessels and aircraft. Some of these tasks are obviously of value in inspection for arms control and will be examined more closely later in this study.

FRACTIONAL ORBIT BOMBARDMENT SYSTEMS

The Soviet Union is at present deploying the SS-9 missile, an advanced design, powered with storable liquid fuel and capable of carrying several warheads in the megaton range of yield. It is believed that most of those deployed would be intended for attacking via the normal direct ICBM threat corridors. However, trials have shown that this missile has other capabilities, as the launcher for fractional orbit bombardment systems and depressed trajectory intercontinental ballistic missiles.

The reentry vehicle for a fractional orbit bombardment system would be injected into a near-earth orbit at about 100 miles above the earth, from which the system would be deorbited by the firing of retrorockets. Its track could be in a reverse direction from the main threat, and in this way it would travel about three-quarters of the way round the earth before descending on the target.

An orbital weapon in as low an orbit as would not impose too great a drag from the atmosphere would be above the horizon for only three to four minutes; an ICBM would be visible to direct radars for 12 minutes. There would thus be much less time to detect, track, and intercept a fractional orbit system. Furthermore, firing of the retrorocket would put the reentry vehicle on a different trajectory and thus confuse the defenses. Until the retrorockets were fired, it would be impossible to predict which target was under attack. The requirement of a higher orbital velocity and inclusion of a retro-rocket would be penalties on the weight of the payload, although there would be some gain from an eastward launch. The accuracy of a fractional orbit system is likely to be relatively low because of the longer range and also because launching errors would affect an orbital body more than a ballistic body and further errors would be introduced from the retrorocket. It is possible that the average miss-distance (CEP) might be about seven miles, as compared with one - two miles or even less for ballistic missiles.

Although the warning time from objects in a reverse orbit to radars in the United States would be only the few minutes mentioned above, the corridors that the fractional orbit system would follow would still be known from the location of the launch sites and most likely targets, because the trajectories must be on a plane through the center of the earth. Early warning could be obtained from long range radars installed in Australia. Any militarily significant strike with a fractional orbit system would require a mass launch of a large number of vehicles, and this could be detected by several surveillance systems.

In view of the lower payload and reduced accuracy, it is difficult to see a clear role for fractional orbit systems. Intense speculation has been aroused in the United States, and it may be that the weapon is intended to attack airfields before the bombers could be airborne or dispersed. The United States has already taken precautions to reduce the effects of such an attack by dispersing aircraft more widely.

DEPRESSED-TRAJECTORY INTERCONTINENTAL BALLISTIC MISSILES

The SS-9 missile has also been used for test launches of depressed-trajectory missiles. Although not orbital weapons, the latter are discussed at this stage because the launcher is the same as that for fractional orbit systems; and as far as can be seen, the purposes of the two systems are generally similar. The depressed-trajectory reentry vehicle follows a direct track to the target in a near-earth ballistic trajectory, rising to not much more than 100 miles. This weapon also would give very much reduced warning to radars in the United States, as compared with normal ICBM's; and although the reentry vehicles would almost certainly pass sufficiently close to one or other of the Ballistic Missile Early Warning Systems (BMEWS) radars in England, Greenland, and Alaska to be detected, the time within range would be short and perhaps not sufficient for accurate identification. The defense radars in the United States would also have less time for tracking. Depressed-trajectory missiles, like fractional orbit systems, would have to be launched in large numbers to carry out strategically significant tasks.

While it is plainly of importance to try to identify the role of fractional orbit systems and depressed-trajectory missiles in order to design a counter, it is possible that they have no specific functions and that the purpose of these developments is to exploit the full range of possibilities of an existing missile, thus adding to the tasks of the defense and increasing or maintaining deterrence, rather in the same way that the different multiple reentry vehicle packages for Minuteman would complicate Soviet defenses.

NUCLEAR-POWERED ROCKETS

The United States has carried out research into nuclear-powered propulsion for rockets in Project Nerva. No immediate military tasks have been proposed, but a nuclear rocket motor in a third stage would provide some maneuverability that could be valuable for inspection and verification purposes. Nuclear-powered rockets present great technical difficulties in development because of the possibility that an accident would release quantities of radioactivity.

It is likely that for some time nuclear power in space will be confined to isotope generators to supply electrical power to manned and unmanned satellites, but in the longer term it will be used for vehicles for interplanetary and other long voyages.

EXPLOITATION AND MILITARIZATION OF THE OCEANS

The vast areas of the oceans, as compared with the land masses, and their potential for commercial exploitation have increased the interest in and attention being paid to a number of aspects of oceanography. The oceans provide three environments: the surface, beneath the surface, and the ocean floor. Of these only the first is exploited to any degree at present, and that almost exclusively for transport, naval activities, and means of supporting and increasing the safety of vessels. Apart from fishing, undersea developments have been almost exclusively concerned with military activities such as submarines and mines. The range of operations has been increased with the development of nuclear-powered submarines able to remain on patrol for extended periods. (The development of antisubmarine warfare was considered in Chapter 11.) Use of the seabed has been confined largely to the laying of communication cables.

Problems of an increasing world population and the need for more food (particularly more protein), the possible recovery of valuable minerals, the advent of advanced life-support systems for exploration (deriving in part from space technology), and, of course, the military potential have considerably increased the interest being paid to a number of aspects of oceanographic research and exploration in recent years. The first areas to come under scrutiny have been on the continental shelf, on which oil has been found in several locations. Mining for other minerals may also be economically worthwhile. A major change may take place in the fishing industry as it moves from hunting to farming, a revolution made many thousands of years ago on the land surface. Since the oceans are, compared with the land surface, a more uniform environment, it could be that once the necessary techniques are available, worldwide exploitation could proceed very rapidly.

Proliferation of civilian activities in the seas and on the ocean floor will have an impact on military activities. Military interests in the oceans can be considered to fall under the following headings:

Enhancement of performance of present systems, in particular nuclear-powered submarines, by provision of undersea bases and communication networks

Threats to present systems by the establishment of sensor networks and generally improved antisubmarine warfare

Introduction of new offensive strategic systems

Requirements to protect national civilian projects

Observation and monitoring of other nations' activities, both as to their technological status and to ensure that they are not a cover for clandestine weapons systems.

In the paragraphs below, some of the new possibilities for weapons systems will be examined in a little more detail. Since it is unlikely that several of these systems will be fully developed, consideration of specific arms control measures is premature; a general agreement reached in the near future could restrict these activities and so reduce the problems.

ADVANCES IN MARITIME MISSILE LAUNCH SYSTEMS

The United States has extensive coastlines, and it is not unexpected that American sources have presented the most proposals for new missile systems. The U.S. Navy has been considering plans for deterrent systems to follow the updating with new missiles of the present fleet of 41 Polaris submarines. Systems that had been considered include the following:

A force of long-range surface ships equipped with missiles

A class of fleet ballistic missile submarines that would be larger than the existing vessels

A missile improved beyond Poseidon, to fit the present launch tubes

Development of a small missile, several of which could fit into existing launch tubes

A fixed seabed ICBM launch platform

A mobile seabed ICBM launch platform

A larger force of the existing type of fleet ballistic missile submarines.

High-speed, long-range, missile-bearing surface ships could be produced in quantity, rapidly and relatively inexpensively. Speeds would be 80-100 knots, achieved by using technologies that could be developed within the next few years and by introducing aircraft firms into the shipbuilding industry. While more vulnerable than submarines to a preemptive attack, because of their mobility they would be less vulnerable than land-based silos, would require considerable effort in tracking, and would be too fast to be shadowed by surface craft or submarines. Even satellite observation would be hard put to locate each of a force of such vessels accurately. These vessels could also be used to convey a warning and have good cost-effectiveness.

Development of a larger fleet ballistic missile submarine would have as its aim putting to sea vessels that could remain on station for a longer time and would not require logistic support and crew recreational facilities overseas. These large submarines could be based entirely in U.S. ports and thus avoid political problems that might arise from the present need to use friendly harbors for replenishment of supplies, etc. Increasing the number of fleet ballistic missile submarines of the present type would not have the advantages outlined above, but the cost of development and testing of a new system would be avoided and it would be possible to maintain a larger number of vessels on station, thus reducing the chances of preempting the entire fleet.

The undersea long range missile, which it has been proposed should follow from the Polaris and Poseidon missiles, would enable the submarines to be stationed in much wider regions of the ocean and to be available for action for a longer period in each patrol, since targets would be within range of stations much nearer the home port.

MILITARY SYSTEMS ON THE SEABED

There are a number of ways in which the seabed may be exploited for military purposes. ABM's could be installed on the ocean mountain ranges to increase the opportunities to intercept ICBM's in midcourse and before separation of reentry vehicles. Bottom crawlers and mobile seabed weapon systems could be installed, as well as mobile seabed systems for detection of military installations, anchored sonar systems to detect and track submarines, anchored beacons and other navigation aids, communication systems, underwater submarine bases and missile silos and other fixed installations, which may be excavated into the ocean floor.

The advantages of seabed systems (except those for detection and tracking) derive from the opacity of seawater, the relatively short range for sonar detection (as compared with radar), and the low noise level from fixed installations as compared with that from the propulsion machinery and water movement of submarines.

In the United States some consideration has been given to installation of ABM's on the mid-Atlantic ridge of underwater mountains. This would be a formidable technical operation but could show some advantages in bringing an ICBM within range at an earlier stage of its trajectory.

Bottom crawlers are a proposed type of undersea tractor that could carry ICBM's. They would be difficult to locate, could move to new positions, and could be fully automatic and serviced by submarines carrying divers or equipped with remote handling equipment.

Nuclear mines would have a much greater radius of damage than conventional mines. They could be used to provide fixed defenses but, in view of the range of weapons systems, are more likely to be used offensively against the exits from submarine bases. It is difficult to see any military role for nuclear mines that could not be as readily performed by missiles.

Submarines and other craft could be armed with torpedos with nuclear warheads. Because of the range of destruction of these weapons, which could endanger the vessel making the attack, the military advantage of covering a wide sweep of ocean, and their speed in making an attack and the limited range of torpedos, new weapons have been developed, such as SUBROC, that combine the advantages of airborne missile and a terminal phase as a torpedo.

DRAFT TREATY PROHIBITING WEAPONS OF MASS DESTRUCTION ON THE SEABED

Because it seems to follow naturally from the context of this chapter, the question of a limited treaty on arms control on the seabed is dealt with here. The following chapter deals with limited arms control in a more general context and includes a more detailed consideration of a ban of weapons of mass destruction on the seabed.

The United States and Soviet Union both presented draft treaties on the prohibition of mass destruction weapons on the seabed to the Conference of the Committee on Disarmament at Geneva. These drafts had quite different approaches to the problem. The essential difference was that the United States proposed to ban only weapons of mass destruction—in practice, nuclear weapons—and the Soviet Union proposed a complete prohibition of all military activity on the ocean floor. The opposed views can be seen to be related to the different geopolitical problems of the two superpowers. The United States has long coastlines and a large fleet of nuclear submarines; there would be important advantages in being able to deploy warning and defense systems. The Soviet Union has more limited access to the oceans, and it would be advantageous to be able to deploy nuclear submarines without detection.

The technical arguments advanced by the United States are that only the large engineering projects for installing nuclear weapons could be readily detected. Many smaller projects would be difficult to detect, there would be constant suspicion about clandestine activities, and it would be difficult to differentiate prohibited military operations from permitted civil activities. An additional complication is that many civil activities will undoubtedly be carried out by military personnel, for the same reason that most astronauts are active officers—that is, because military personnel have a combination of the appropriate technical qualifications, physical fitness, dedication to duty, experience with the type of equipment, and familiarity with the environment.

The Soviet Union and other countries made the case for complete demilitarization of the ocean floor. A powerful argument, although one which does not appear to have been made at Geneva, is that prohibition of all military activity on the ocean floor would reduce the threat to the retaliatory second-strike submarines and so prevent attrition of deterrence.

Eventually the United States and Soviet Union were able to submit a joint draft treaty, based generally on the U.S. model; this treaty, after receiving wider scrutiny, was signed by 37 nations in February 1971.

CHAPTER

14

LIMITED ARMS CONTROL OF STRATEGIC NUCLEAR DELIVERY VEHICLES

This chapter is concerned with various arms control procedures that could be applied unilaterally by one or both of the superpowers and also by the other nuclear powers, or could be the subject of an agreement between two or more of the nuclear powers. The object in each case is to reduce either the risks of war or the damage and casualties if war should break out.

Some of the arms control measures to be discussed were proposed at various times in the past but, for various reasons, including some technical difficulties, have not come to fruition, although the ideas contained in these proposals may be combined with more recent ideas. Arms control on the seabed, which was referred to in the previous chapter, will be considered in more detail.

SAFEGUARDS

Ownership of nuclear weapons imposes a need to prevent accidents. Accidents can occur at different levels:

Those which do not release any form of radioactivity

Those which release some of the radioactive material and may involve the high-explosive trigger, but do not result in criticality

Those in which there is a nuclear explosion, but the results, however devastating to the immediate vicinity, do not lead to explosion of other weapons

Accidents in which the first explosion, because of its nature, the place where it occurs, or misinterpretation, triggers a nuclear exchange.

The problem of designing safety systems for nuclear weapons is in striking a balance between the need to take precautions to prevent an accident with nuclear weapons and not imposing such precautions that the weapons could not be launched on command when this is required. The military tends to prefer a high degree of readiness, whereas arms controllers would probably prefer a much higher degree of restraint; but the point of balance does not depend only on individual opinions. The final decision rests with political directives and depends to some extent on the contemporary international situation. Thus, at times when the likelihood of use of nuclear weapons is low, greater precautions will be acceptable. Technical requirements that determine the level of safeguards depend largely on the vulnerability of strategic and tactical nuclear forces to a first strike.

Both physical and administrative safeguards are used. A physical safeguard is one that prevents an unsafe action, while an administrative safeguard is a procedure in which personnel are trained. The first known safety procedure with an operational nuclear weapon was Capt. William S. Parsons' request and receipt of permission to assemble in the air the nuclear weapon intended to be dropped on Hiroshima, rather than risk a collision or other accident during takeoff.

When fissile material became more plentiful, the United States engaged in a number of experiments aimed at discovering whether nuclear weapons would detonate under a variety of accident conditions, such as aircraft crashes or fires at missile launchers, in storage, and during transport.

Safety precautions that would be introduced in weapons could include switches to prevent an electric current from firing the detonators on the high-explosive segments; these switches could be controlled remotely from a superior level of command, so that the crew or even the base commander could not take the final steps for arming the weapons. Another type of precaution would be incomplete assembly of a weapon until the last moment, so that even if the high-explosive charges were fired, a high-yield nuclear explosion would not be achieved, although the explosion of the charges could scatter fissile material from the core. If one or more of the high-explosive charges were omitted until the last moment, inadvertent firing of the remaining charges would not compress the fissile material into the shape required or keep the mass intact for the requisite time for a high-yield explosion. With many of these safeguards further precautions are possible by requiring simultaneous actions, designed to be sufficiently far apart that they could not be carried out by one man, and requiring these actions to be performed by officers (preferably) of the same rank, so that no question of local precedence could countermand orders from above. These requirements are the basis of what is known as the "two-man rule."

Other precautions prevent the throwing of switches, pressing of buttons, removal of obstructions, or placing of components in position unless a series of operations is carried out first, such as the breaking of a seal, removal of a padlock or dialing of a number, as deliberate nonroutine actions. In addition, switches may be incorporated in the weapon in such a way that they will close only some time after launch or at a predetermined altitude. Precautions such as these are more particularly designed to safeguard the launch system, whether it be a bomber or a missile.

It is of course more than probable that men will think of ways to circumvent these systems, and it is essential that physical safeguards systems should be inspected from time to time by an independent authority and misuse of precautionary systems discouraged.

A well-known administrative procedure is "fail safe." This safeguard ensures that U.S. bombers carrying nuclear weapons not approach the Soviet Union closer than a certain geographical line unless positively instructed to do so by an order from the U.S. president. The term "fail safe" is used widely in technology to denote a precaution by which, when a component fails, the system reverts to a safer condition—for example, the "dead man's hand" on systems to shut down a nuclear reactor automatically if instruments fail that are essential to safe operation. The safeguard just described for U.S. bombers has therefore been renamed "positive control" and probably would not allow a closer approach than some hours of flying time from Soviet territory and would require the collaboration of three crewmen to accept a "go" message; only then would the procedures be started for arming the weapons by a team, each at a different location in the aircraft and carrying out simultaneous operations.

With the introduction of long-range missiles new procedures had to be introduced, since those designed for bombers were not adequate. The liquid-fuel missiles, which at one time constituted the main strategic striking forces, had an inherent safety system—the time taken to prepare for launching, which could be up to ten hours.

On the other hand, the missile forces were vulnerable to a first strike, so that for the deterrent to be effective some of the missiles had to be held at a higher state of readiness. With the introduction of more stable liquid fuels, more missiles could be held in immediate readiness. Generally, however, only a few missiles could be held in this state. With the introduction of solid-fuel missiles in the United States an even larger fraction of the force—indeed, all those missiles not under maintenance—could be in immediate readiness with a reaction time of only 30 seconds. Only two men are required to launch a flight of ten missiles, but in each command post the two have to cooperate by turning keys that are too far apart to be simultaneously operated by one man; a further safety precaution requires the cooperation of another crew several miles away. The warhead becomes armed only after launch. At the same time that physical controls and administrative procedures were being devised in the United States, attention was also given to the psychological stability of personnel associated with nuclear weapons. On assignment to a unit a man is interviewed by his new commanding officer and then referred, if necessary, for medical examination.

The United States has deployed tactical nuclear warheads in Europe for the support of NATO forces. The warheads are stored and guarded by U.S. troops. A "two-key system" operated—one key was held by a U.S. officer and one by an allied officer subject to a different chain of command; both keys were necessary for the launching of the missile. This system was objected to partly because of doubts as to the legal position under the U.S. Atomic Energy Act and also because there was the possibility of an officer being overpowered and his key taken. A new system, the "permissive action lock," was devised; it depends upon a signal being received from a higher level.

Despite the kinds of precautions discussed above, there have been several incidents involving nuclear weapons, including the dropping of nuclear bombs and aircraft crashes, that have led to the release of radioactive material and local contamination. These accidents have been serious not only in themselves, because of the hazard to the public, but also because of their international repercussions.

PRECAUTIONS AGAINST SURPRISE ATTACK

In 1958 the Surprise Attack Conference was held with the intention of finding whether arrangements, including an agreement, could be reached to reduce the chances of a nuclear war by providing precautions against a surprise attack. At that time there was little experience in conducting international negotiations in which scientists were deeply concerned, and preparation and consultation to achieve a national point of view were lacking.

J. J. Holst has given a brief account of the conference: in his opinion there was an essential discrepancy between the objectives of the United States and of the Soviet Union and their respective allies.[1] Both sides advanced proposals for aerial surveillance, and other suggestions were for ground observation posts. The U.S. representatives entered the negotiations prepared to explore the "technical" problem with alternative surveillance systems to guard against surprise attack. The Soviet delegation and those of their allies, however, appeared to have the intention of entering into political negotiations about experts' proposals. The U.S. emphasis, then, was on exposing the "technical facts," so that when this was done, a suitable solution would be apparent and acceptable to both sides. The Russians saw the problem as basically political, arising from the different policies and national objectives of the two sides. Until some understanding of the opposed points of view could be reached, there was no possibility of agreeing on the technical means for control unless, at the same time, steps in disarmament were also taking place. With this dichotomy between a technical approach and a political approach, it is not surprising that even an agenda could not be agreed upon. Another difference existed between the delegations: those from East Europe consisted of 42 experts and advisers but did not include scientists; the Western delegations had 108 advisers and experts, including particularly strong scientific contingents.

Despite the disappointments at the failure of the conference and the fact that the arms race was not halted, the exchange of views affected the unilateral technical controls applied by both sides and may have helped to clarify the notions held by either side regarding the other.

THE BOMBER BONFIRE

In 1964 proposals were made for the destruction of some of the bomber forces in the United States and Soviet Union. The destruction would be carried out in each case under inspection by the other superpower. Remainders were not to be counted. This proposal, if it had been carried out, would have represented a genuine degree of disarmament and would have reduced the weight of a strategic attack and therefore the casualties. There would also have been a second advantage, in that these aircraft could not be sold to other nations.

The aircraft nominated to be destroyed were the U.S. B-47 and the Soviet Tu-16. At the time of the proposal these aircraft were toward the end of their operational life, and they have since become obsolescent and have been phased out. The aim of the proposal has therefore been largely achieved and the original conditions are now out of date. The present interest in these proposals is more in their form than in their substance, since similar arrangements would be possible for other weapons systems.

NONUSE OF NUCLEAR WEAPONS

Several proposals have been made for agreements not to employ nuclear weapons in specified circumstances. These proposals can be classified into three groups:

Non-use, that is, a complete ban on the employment of nuclear weapons in any circumstances

Nonfirst use, that is, an agreement not to be the first to launch an attack with nuclear weapons

Nonuse against nonnuclear powers, that is, nuclear weapons would be resorted to only against the nuclear powers and their allies who have nuclear weapons on their territory.

Agreements of this nature are plainly almost purely political, with little technical content and without any steps in disarmament or other aspects in which technical control could be applied. This, indeed, is the principal objection to them: that without controls an agreement is little more than a scrap of paper and does nothing to change present policies, which are based on a second-strike philosophy, while the same time perhaps inducing euphoria.

Because this type of proposal has so little technical content, the problem will not be discussed further.

BANS ON DEPLOYMENT OF NUCLEAR WEAPONS

It will be recalled that the two major aspects of arms control are limitation on types of weapon and limitation on deployment. The bomber bonfire was an attempt to limit a particular type of system; what will now be discussed are some means for limiting deployment of nuclear weapons in various geographical areas and environments.

Nuclear-Free Zones

Besides outer space, agreements have been reached to prohibit deployment of nuclear weapons in particular zones, such as Antarctica and Latin America. The Antarctica Treaty (1959) has been of great importance because it has served as a model for later agreements and also because it included provisions for inspection. The treaty of Tlatelolco (1967) banned nuclear weapons from an inhabited continent. One of the most difficult problems during negotiations was the interpretation of the treaty regarding whether it would permit the use of civil nuclear explosives. Some of the countries were concerned that they should not be denied civil engineering technique that could be valuable in underdeveloped and sparsely populated areas, while the opposite view was that granting the facility would open the way for the manufacture of nuclear weapons. A ban on the stationing of weapons of mass destruction on the seabed has already been considered in Chapter 13 and will be again dealt with later in this chapter.

Restrictions on Deployment of Bombers

A number of proposals have been made to restrict deployment of particular nuclear weapons systems. Because of the kinds of incidents referred to earlier, attempts to restrict bomber aircraft have received considerable attention. As far as is known, the Soviet Union does not deploy bomber aircraft carrying nuclear weapons beyond the national frontier. The United States, on the other hand, has worldwide deployment of bomber aircraft, some of them carrying nuclear weapons. It has stated that flights of nuclear-armed bombers were made necessary by the "threat posed by the Soviet forces." The Soviet Union has argued that these patrols are not necessary, particularly in view of the deployment of missiles, and has asked for immediate discontinuation of flights by aircraft carrying nuclear weapons beyond the limits of national borders.

Requests that the United States discontinue flights of bombers carrying nuclear weapons over their territory have been made or considered by a number of countries. Apart from nuclear weapons in aircraft of the deterrent forces on airborne alert, movement of weapons to dispersal stores may also be made by air.

Ban on Weapons of Mass Destruction in Space

The military possibilities of space were discussed in the previous chapter. The most important use of satellites at present is surveillance. Since both of the superpowers have similar capabilities and both derive immense benefits from these strategic warning systems, there has been little pressure to control military satellites. Furthermore, it would be difficult to distinguish satellites with military surveillance missions from others with the tasks of mapping earth resources, weather observation, and research. However, the possibility of putting nuclear weapons and other weapons of mass destruction into orbit caused some concern. This was not because the weapons system would confer a first-strike potential—the number of satellites required would have been too great—but because even a single nuclear-armed satellite could be used, or it might be thought it could be used, for blackmail: a threat, for example, to obliterate a single city as a deterrent or punishment for some limited transgression. The likelihood would be, therefore, that any satellite known or thought to be carrying a nuclear weapon would be destroyed or at least inspected. Since both sides had capabilities for destroying, and would soon have capabilities for inspecting satellites, it was comparatively easy for the superpowers to propose an agreement to prohibit the use of space for weapons of mass destruction, the so-called Outer Space Treaty formalized in United Nations Assembly Resolution 2222 (xxi), of January 27, 1967.

Unilateral Restrictions on Land-based Missiles

Both the United States and Soviet Union have withdrawn missiles from overseas deployment. The confrontation over Cuba in 1962 will be well remembered. Russia probably had two reasons for deploying medium-range ballistic missiles in Cuba: to provide a deterrent against an attack by the United States on Cuba and significantly to increase the Russian threat against U.S. cities, which at that time was from a limited force of ICBM's deployed in Russia.

Shortly after the Russian missiles had been removed from Cuba, the United States deactivated its first-generation IRBM's, the Thors and Jupiters based in Great Britain, Italy, and Turkey and its first-generation ICBM's, 13 Atlas and 14 Titan-1 missiles. (This step was actually ordered before the crisis.) A wide-ranging debate took place in the United States on the advisability of deploying ABM's and MIRV's: some saw this justified by existing and future Soviet deployments, while others considered that it would provoke deployments. In 1969 the U.S. government decided to replace the Sentinel ABM system with the Safeguard system, designed to protect the U.S. retaliatory capacity against a Soviet first strike and U.S. cities against Chinese attack.[2]

Limitation on the Deployment of Submarines

Control of the deployment of submarines armed with nuclear weapons has been suggested by Eric Crawford.[3] Submarines would not be permitted to patrol within launching range of the opponent's homeland, and a single submarine detected within the zone would constitute a violation. The fact that the submarines were not at their launch station would not seriously detract from their effectiveness as a second-strike force. The difficulties in such an agreement are those of detection, identification, and proof of violation. Such an agreement is less likely now that longer-range missiles are carried in submarines, and the introduction of even longer range missiles will in any event reduce the value of the agreement.

Ban on Stationing of Weapons of Mass Destruction on the Seabed

Since the late 1950's there has been an explosion of interest in the commercial exploitation of the oceans and the ocean floor. A number of international problems have arisen, such as the limits of the national sovereignty of the coastal states, and a convention on the rights of coastal states with regard to the continental shelf was agreed upon in the United Nations in 1958. The United Nations also agreed to submit to the disarmament conference at Geneva the task of examining the problem of reserving exclusively for peaceful purposes "the seabed and ocean floor" and of utilizing these resources in the interests of the people of the world. The U.N. Secretariat has produced a working paper on the subject of the military uses of these areas.[4]

When examination of the problem was taken up at Geneva in 1969, the Soviet Union and United States both submitted draft treaties. These treaties had somewhat different aims: the Soviet draft was for a complete ban on nuclear weapons and other types of weapon of mass destruction, and on military bases, structures, installations, fortifications, and other objects of a military nature. The U.S. draft would have banned fixed nuclear weapons and weapons of mass destruction and associated launching platforms, and the parties to the treaty would have rights of observation of the activities of others. Verification would be made easier by the fact that a large number of installations would be required to disturb the balance between the superpowers. As far as inspection is concerned, it was pointed out that the hostile environment under the sea would make access to facilities extremely difficult and even hazardous. On the other hand, the size of such installations would involve so much activity on the surface that there would be a very high probability of detection, and subsequent observation would reveal the nature of the undertaking.

The draft introduced by the Soviet Union would have prohibited all military activity on the ocean floor, and there would have been rights of inspection. Applying inspection would have been even more difficult than in the case of installations for weapons of mass destruction alone, since some military installations would be more numerous and on a smaller scale and hence difficult to detect and identify from operations on the surface; it is also likely that very specialized and even unique equipment would be required to carry out inspections of the different types of installations. Perhaps an even more intractable problem would be that of defining what were military and what were civil operations: communications systems that can serve both purposes would be one such problem, and military personnel are frequently employed in civil operations because of their specialized training and experience, their strong discipline, and their preparedness to serve in remote and arduous stations.

An intensive debate took place at the Eighteen Nations Disarmament Conference, with many nations making contributions and suggestions because of their concern with the arms race and their need for access to the resources of the seas.

Apart from nuclear weapons, other types of military installations on the seabed are likely to be confined to detection systems for some time in the future: in the United States no other possibilities appear to be under consideration. The Soviet Union, on the other hand, thought that unless installations of all weapons on the seabed were prohibited, the treaty would not meet all requirements because it would not prevent an arms race in weapons other than those specified, would not conform to the General Assembly resolution 2467A (xxiii) that had presented the problem to the Eighteen Nations Conference, and might involve a separation of "offensive" from "defensive" systems, a separation that could be difficult to maintain in practice. Finally, problems of definition of "military activity" and "military base" would arise: apart from the initial problem in forming a definition, changes in the future could make the definitions out of date and no longer relevant, leading to disputes. The Soviet Union, however, would not include in the ban underseas communications systems, including beacons and other peaceful installations, even if these were manned with military personnel.

Mrs. Myrdal, leader of the Swedish delegation, compared the U.S. and Soviet drafts; an analysis based on her observations is shown in Table 19.

TABLE 19

Comparison of U.S. and Soviet Drafts of Seabed Treaty

	Soviet	U.S.
Scope	All direct military uses of seabed	Installations for nuclear weapons and other weapons of mass destruction
Area	12 naut. mi. from coast	3 naut. mi. from coast
Control	Free access by all parties	Free observation (law of the seas): access after consultation

Source: Alva Myrdal, Swedish delegate, in Eighteen Nations Disarmament Conference, Paper PV 422 (July 1969).

Sweden suggested a policy of exemptions from the ban, rather than a listing of banned items, using a general heading of "purely passive defensive systems," with the details to be agreed upon during negotiations.

Concern was expressed by some of the delegates that the scope of the treaty would be confined to the superpowers; while many other powers were anxious to make a positive contribution to the debate and also to inspection. Several nonnuclear powers were also concerned to make the ban as comprehensive as possible, as in the Soviet draft. Various limits and special zones were proposed: Canada suggested a 200-mile zone in which each coastal state would have sole defensive rights. The problem of the limit of the extent of jurisdiction of the coastal states was made difficult by the various limits already claimed; a number of suggestions were made, but it was decided in principle that the treaty limits need not be related to limits determined for other purposes.

As a result of private negotiations the Soviet Union and United States were able, on October 7, 1969, to present to the Eighteen Nations Conference (which had now become CCD) a new joint draft that incorporated some of the proposals from other nations. The treaty was signed in February 1971 by 37 countries, including the Soviet Union, United States, and Great Britain, but not France or China.

The inspection problems appear to be fairly tractable. The resources for undersea inspection are limited; but it is believed that significant military installations would be observed because of the unusual engineering support activities involved, with large-scale deployments on the surface and the arrangements for defense, maintenance, command, and control. Surveillance of surface activities would not involve problems significantly worse than those met in land inspection.

NOTES

1. J. J. Holst and W. Schneider, *Why ABM*? (London: Pergamon, 1969).

2. *Ibid*.

3. Eric W. Crawford, "Withdraw Missile Submarines?" *Bulletin of the Atomic Scientists* (November 1967).

4. United Nations, "The Military Uses the Sea Bed and the Ocean Floor Beyond the Limits of Present National Jurisdiction," A/AC 135/28 (July 1968).

CHAPTER

15

COMPREHENSIVE ARMS CONTROL OF STRATEGIC NUCLEAR DELIVERY VEHICLES

Both of the superpowers have from time to time proposed limitation, destruction, and even abolition of strategic nuclear delivery vehicles. The Soviet Union suggested in November 1956 that all nuclear delivery vehicles should be destroyed in stage one of their general and complete disarmament proposals. The United States favored the retention of some nuclear delivery vehicles until a late stage of disarmament. The Soviet Union subsequently made similar proposals for a minimum nuclear deterrent to be retained by both of the superpowers until a late stage of disarmament; the purpose of this force would be to provide an insurance against clandestine retention of even only a few nuclear delivery vehicles by either side. These proposals relate mainly to the late stage of disarmament, and the more immediate problem is how to reach this late stage.

As an essential first step a freeze on further deployment of nuclear delivery vehicles has been advocated by, among others, former President Johnson. Many other powers besides the superpowers have advocated and encouraged discussion around the idea of a freeze, if only for the reason that they too would be severely damaged by a nuclear exchange between the superpowers.

These early proposals are now largely of academic interest, and attention is now concentrated on the private talks taking place between the United States and Soviet Union.

REASONS FOR SEEKING AN AGREEMENT

It has been widely agreed that an agreement between the superpowers is now opportune. Both of the nuclear powers have made large deployments of nuclear delivery vehicles and both have sufficient power not only largely to destroy the other in a first strike but also, if the victim of a first strike aimed at their nuclear forces, would still have sufficient weapons surviving to destroy approximately half of the opponent's population and industrial resources in a retaliatory second strike.

Damage caused in a nuclear exchange would not, however, be confined to the superpowers; it would also involve other countries by attacks made on overseas bases and allies and by worldwide fallout, the precise long-term effect of which is not known with certainty.

But this stable (perhaps a more scientific description would be metastable) situation is threatened by the deployment of ABM's and MIRV's. ABM's are highly efficient and, deployed alone, could so protect the population and resources that the value of the hostage could be reduced until the losses might become acceptable to the government when compared with some advantage gained. MIRV's, if deployed alone, could threaten destruction of a high proportion of land-based missiles; and although it does not provide a serious threat against submarine-launched ballistic missiles, it does offer a considerable damage-limitation capability. A combination of ABM's with MIRV's could be most dangerous in this way, since the MIRV's could reduce the retaliatory second strike to a level that could be largely coped with by the ABM defense.

Many commentators consider that now is the time to negotiate an agreement on the further limitation of strategic nuclear delivery systems. First, both the United States and Soviet Union have sufficient nuclear delivery vehicles to inflict unacceptable and assured destruction on each other, even in a second strike after most of their land-based missiles have been destroyed, so that a state of mutual deterrence exists. The opposed forces are roughly equal and, although qualitatively different, both sides can claim to hold the advantage, one in number of warheads that could be delivered and the other in the total megatonnage of explosive power that could be delivered. The technological gap is relatively small, and further technological advances threaten the basis of present security. Attempts to purchase security by further deployments are certain to be expensive, are not likely to be successful, may trigger an arms race, and could lead to technological advances of potential danger. Both superpowers have important problems of domestic development, and both may be more chary of extraterritorial commitments. The developing military threat from China makes desirable a clarification and simplification of the military and diplomatic situation between the superpowers. Finally, there may be the possibility of a controlled movement away from deterrence of war by "balance of terror," to another system in which populations would be defended and the deterrent to war would be the impossibility of destroying the opponent.

CRITERIA FOR AN AGREEMENT

There are several different criteria on which an agreement could be based. It is most unlikely that an agreement could be reached that obviously left one side in a position of inferiority. However, from what has been said, there is already a rough equality; and by selection of the criteria this equality could be emphasized. It can also be assumed that an agreement would be closely related to the nature of the deployment at the time, that is, it is unlikely that an agreement could be reached that would permit only one side to increase its deployment, or require only one side to destroy existing weapons. Thus, an agreement would in the first place be some kind of freeze, which would not involve reductions, and only after this had been shown to operate successfully for some time would bilateral reductions take place. Nevertheless, it would be very desirable that the first agreement be in a form suitable for extension to an agreement for reductions.

An early decision to be made is what strategic systems are to be included. Table 20 lists the most important systems that might be considered. The systems have been arranged from those that can be used only offensively and, in the present situation, provide deterrence, to those that are intended to counter the offensive systems and are defensive. There is, however, no clear demarcation between offensive and defensive systems. Offensive systems could be used solely in a counter-force strike to preempt a first strike that is being prepared; defensive systems could defend and add to the power of offensive forces. To give a specific illustration of different employments: submarine-launched cruise missiles could be used to attack coastal cities but are more likely to be used to attack aircraft carriers on offensive missions.

If there is to be a change from a policy of deterrence through a policy of partial defense to a policy of pure defense, it would be

TABLE 20

Existing Nuclear Delivery Vehicles and Other Systems

From Nominally Offensive/Deterrent

- Long-range bomber aircraft
- Strike fleets
- Land-based ICBM's
- Intermediate- and medium-range ballistic missiles
- Submarine-launched ballistic missiles
- Medium-range bomber aircraft
- Short-range tactical strike aircraft
- Submarine-launched cruise missiles
- Short-range coastal defense submarines
- Active antisubmarine warfare systems, such as long-range maritime aircraft, helicopter carriers, surface craft, nuclear-powered hunter-killer submarines
- Interceptor aircraft systems
- Surface-to-air and other antiaircraft defenses
- Passive antisubmarine warfare warning systems
- ABM systems

To Nominally Defensive

---

natural to assume that the emphasis might shift from systems near the top of the list to systems toward the bottom. However, the transition from one state to another could be fraught with danger. A reduction in the number of casualties with, at the same time, an increase in the probability of war (partly in consequence of the decrease in casualties) may not restore anything like the same situation. This can be illustrated as follows: suppose that a nuclear war would cause an unbearable 50 percent casualties and the probability of war was, say, one in 10,000 but in a new deployment of ABM casualties were reduced to 5 percent (i.e., within the range of casualties suffered by several countries in recent history and even anticipated by countries that have been prepared to take up arms to defend themselves against aggression). In this case, would not the chances of war be increased by more than a factor of 10? The difference lies between an absolutely unbearable outcome and one that, however painful, is within what nations have borne in the past. In such a case simple linear relationships are unreliable; the economists' notion of utilities, a kind of sliding scale, is more appropriate.

LIMITATION OF LAND-BASED ICBM's

A number of partial agreements controlling strategic nuclear delivery vehicles have been mentioned earlier, and others that could be incorporated in a more general agreement will be discussed later. The main concern in the control of strategic nuclear weapons is in preventing an increase in the possibilities of a first strike, and the burden of the argument is now concerned with the limitation of land-based ICBM's. The discussion will then be broadened to include other systems.

COMPARISON OF DEPLOYMENTS OF ICBM's

An analysis of means for comparing deployments of land-based ICBM's by the superpowers has been made by Col. Kent of the U.S. Air Force.* Our concern is to describe certain principles for the control of ICBM's and the difficulties that would limit the usefulness of some methods for control and to show in general how a solution advocated by Col. Kent could be extended to embrace bomber aircraft, submarine-launched ballistic missiles and intermediate-and medium-range ballistic missiles, and more recent developments. Unlike Col. Kent's, this is a nonmathematical treatment; however, a mathematical treatment would lead to the same conclusions.

The initial assumptions for this analysis are the following:

The purpose of an agreement to control ICBM is to retain or improve upon the present stability, that is, to ensure that neither of the superpowers can rationally contemplate a first strike

---

*Glenn A. Kent, On the Interaction of Opposing Forces Under Possible Arms Agreements (Cambridge, Mass.: Harvard University Center for International Affairs, 1963).

A desirable feature of an agreement would be to avoid a situation in which one or both sides would feel compelled to attempt urgent quantitative or qualitative improvements in its present forces, that is, the agreement should not start an arms race

The purpose of a first strike is counter-force and damage limitation, that is, to destroy as many of the opponent's missiles as possible before they can be launched

Sufficient missiles from the inventory must survive a first strike to be able to launch an unacceptable retaliatory blow against the cities of the aggressor

The agreement does not attempt control of such improvements as would be difficult to inspect, either because they would be easy to conceal or because they require intensive inspection, such as increasing missile accuracy, hardening of sites or reentry vehicles or addition of penetration aids.

To quantify the effectiveness of an attack with nuclear weapons there must be a criterion for assessing the damage from a single warhead and then totaling this damage.

How can the effectiveness of a single warhead be estimated? Nuclear explosives can cause casualties and damage in two ways: by primary effects—that is, blast and thermal radiation, the latter causing fires, body burns, and eye damage—and by secondary effects—neutron irradiation and radioactive fallout, both of which produce damage in body tissue. For attacks on silos, the important effects would be blast and cratering; a suitable criterion is the surface area that is subject to weapons effects sufficient to damage the targets to the required level, that is, subjected to a shock wave that damages the silo or missile so that the latter cannot be launched or function as required.

Assuming that the attacking warhead in each case is exploded at the appropriate height for the yield, the surface area subjected to damage is proportional to yield to the two-thirds power ($\alpha Y^{2/3}$). The total surface damage will be proportional to the sum of these terms for each weapon, expressed at $nY^{2/3}$ when the yields are different. It is assumed that damaged areas do not overlap—a reasonable assumption for attacks on silos. A useful measure of the effectiveness of a warhead against a silo is given by the expression $Y^{2/3}$ $(CEP)^2$. Since missile accuracy is not known or likely to be divulged, this expression is not suitable as a parameter for an agreement.

For collateral effects—thermal and neutron irradiation and radioactive fallout—the total yield is a rough measure; but it is good enough, since these effects are extremely variable and depend to some extent on the design of the weapon—that is, whether it is "clean," "ordinary," or "dirty"—the height of burst, type of terrain, proximity of population, weather conditions, and so on. The total yield is measured by nY (or ΣY).

Comparison of ICBM's could be based on one or more of the following criteria:

Total number of missiles

Total number of deliverable warheads

Total yield

Total deliverable payload

Some combination of these.

In designing an agreement, the following questions would have to be answered: what are the advantages, disadvantages, and implications of each agreement? what relative stability would be achieved? and in what form could an agreement be embodied in a treaty to avoid misinterpretation and prevent one side gaining an advantage? Stability in this context means that neither side has the incentive to change the characteristics of its deployment because the latter is sufficiently robust to be proof against the other side having an overdeployment (say 10 percent) not detectable with certainty by the proposed inspection procedures.

LIMITATION ON TOTAL NUMBER OF MISSILES

An agreement to limit the total number of missiles would be fairly easy to verify only within the limits that would not jeopardize the strategic balance. The form of the agreement would be N = K, where N is the total number of missiles and K is an agreed-upon constant number.

It is obvious that with this form of agreement each of the superpowers could attempt to increase the effectiveness of its warheads by increasing the yield or the number of warheads carried by each missile, and that this would add to the probability of destruction of the silos attacked. Calculations by Col. Kent show that increasing the yield of warheads available for second strike would not restore the balance; in other words, the situation would be destabilized and could be made worse by improvements in accuracy. Furthermore, collateral damage would be increased.

LIMITATION ON TOTAL NUMBER OF DELIVERABLE WARHEADS

A limit on the total number of warheads would be an insurance against a first-strike option. Other versions of this limitation have been advanced in the form of a ban on MRV/MIRV's.

Inspection must cover the total number of missiles deployed and the number of warheads carried by each missile. The difficulties of such an agreement are in the level of inspection required to ensure that multiple warheads are not carried by any missile and that no payloads with multiple warheads are available in stock to replace existing single warheads. An alternative approach would be checks on the complete inventory of all warheads in stock. It is probable that inspection methods could be developed to verify that payloads do not contain more than one warhead, but it is highly unlikely that such a level of intensive inspection would be permitted by either side.

In other words, technical solutions to the problem of control of the total number of warheads are possible, but there would be political and military objections; and it may seem wasteful to spend much time and effort when there is little chance of acceptance of such a scheme and while there are alternative methods of control that are more likely to be acceptable.

Apart from the problem of inspection, another objection to limitation of the total number of warheads is that attention would then be focused on providing warheads of larger yield, and this would increase the primary and collateral damage.

LIMITATION ON TOTAL DELIVERABLE YIELD

To attempt to limit total deliverable yield would require a knowledge not only of the numbers of each type of ICBM in the opponent's deployment but also details of the payload and of the yields of each warhead carried, and even of the design. Even if it is assumed that this highly secret information would be revealed, there are other problems associated with this solution.

The form of the agreement would be

$$NY = K$$

By dividing the total yield into many smaller packages, the total area damaged would be increased. In such an agreement there would thus be pressure to increase the number of warheads, while keeping total yield constant, by replacing existing warheads with multiple warheads or by replacing existing missiles by many with smaller warheads, or by a combination of these steps. This would increase the threat to silos and would force the other side to increase the number of its missiles in an attempt to ensure that enough could survive to produce a deterrent.

In practice N—the number of warheads—required by the attacker would have to exceed the number of targets, to allow for aborts and other exigencies and, possibly, multiple attacks on silos.

From the point of view of the defense, to ensure survival of a deterrent it would be necessary to deploy even more warheads. Thus, in whichever role—attacker or defender—each superpower would be in competition in deploying small warheads. It would be up to the system designer how the payload weight was to be allocated among warhead, heat shielding, structural materials, hardening, penetration aids, and avionics. With a limitation on yield only, there would be no restriction on improvements that would increase the effectiveness of the warheads.

Thus there would be pressure for both qualitative and quantitative improvements in weapons systems. The difficulties—indeed, for practical purposes, the impossibility—of inspecting for total yield must be stressed. It would be necessary closely to inspect not only warheads fitted to missiles but also those warheads in stores and to spot check deployed missiles, to ensure that warheads of increasing yield were not being substituted. Unless the inspection teams had access to all warheads in stores, it would be possible to replace the deployed warheads secretly at a convenient time. It is difficult to believe that either of the superpowers would agree to such intrusive inspection.

While splitting the total yield into smaller packages would increase the area subjected to damage, the total collateral damage would remain fairly constant. The situation would, therefore, be unstable, with both sides engaged in development and production of new smaller weapons systems. Furthermore, the final situation would be much worse, with a great increase in the total area of damage and thus in loss of life and property. A limit would be reached at the point at which missiles are so small that they cannot carry an effective warhead, or when providing each reentry vehicle with a missile, guidance system, launch pad, command and control, maintenance, etc. is no longer cost-effective.

LIMITATION ON TOTAL DELIVERABLE PAYLOAD

The next type of agreement, on total payload, appears at first sight to be almost as difficult to inspect as a limitation on total megatonnage. This examination is confined to hardened, fixed, land-based ICBM's only. Other systems will be considered later.

Leaving aside for the moment the mechanisms of enforcement, would an agreement based on the formula

$$\sum Y^{2/3} = K$$

be of value? Would an agreement of this kind have better "stability" than those just discussed? That is, would there be incentive either to carry out a complete change from the present force structures or to cheat?

Col. Kent has shown, using fairly reasonable values for CEP and lethal radius, that for missiles with single warheads, from both the attacker's and the defender's point of view, the optimum warhead would be about one megaton; this value is reasonable in that the yield could be within a fairly wide range on either side of the optimum value without affecting the situation. Furthermore, stability is not seriously affected by changes in accuracy of the attacker's warheads, within reasonable limits. Finally, cheating—either by small increases in the number of warheads above treaty limits or by introduction of warheads of somewhat higher yields—does not substantially affect the balance. Since the deployment tends to remain stable, collateral damage also remains constant.

Before proceeding beyond Col. Kent's discussion to consider the effects of MRV, MIRV, and ABM on this form of agreement, some attention will be paid to verification. It has already been said that verification that $\Sigma Y^{2/3}$ has not exceeded treaty limits appears to be a difficult problem. However, there is an indirect approach. It should be possible to estimate the numbers of each type of missile deployed, either by national (intelligence) means or by inspection against schedules provided by the opponent to sufficient (if not perfect) accuracy. Confirmatory calculations would be made as to the damage sustained should these numbers be underestimates, to the maximum extent that could not be detected. The verification team now has the number and type of each missile deployed. From the missile type an estimate can be made of the maximum damage that could be inflicted, by means of a chain of logic given below. The task of the inspectorate would then be to confirm the numbers and types of the deployed missiles, to ensure that no new missiles were being substituted illegally, and, when replacement has been permitted, that the replaced missiles are destroyed.

Since it is a maximum weight that is being controlled, changes that are made—for example, by introduction of MIRV's or PENAID's—would reduce the total yield and, hence, collateral damage. It is true that MIRV's would allow more targets to be attacked and increase the total area of damage, but only within certain practical limits.

The rationale for considering the total payload as a suitable parameter for control stems from the following steps: missile type is related to dimensions, dimensions are proportional to maximum weight of fuel, weight of fuel is proportional to thrust, thrust is proportional to weight of payload over a stated range, weight of payload is proportional to maximum weight of warhead, weight of warhead is related to maximum yield, and yield is related by the two-thirds power law to the area damaged.

Col. Kent has estimated that the relationship between weight of fuel and area damaged is fairly linear. In other words, it is not very important, within reason, how the total yield is distributed between large or small warheads, since the damage inflicted will be fairly constant. Furthermore, since there will be little incentive to change deployments, collateral damage would remain as it is now.

If the relationship between weight and damage is not sufficiently near linear, it might be sufficient to use, instead of weight, some function of missile weight. It might also be necessary to use different functions of weight between liquid-fuel and solid-fuel missiles.

In this study it is intended only to discuss principles: designing detailed proposals would require access to a great deal of secret information and would be the work of a team of specialists.

The problem that Col. Kent set himself was to discover the conditions for a stable agreement. An alternative approach is to assume conditions for an agreement and to check whether these are stable even when clandestine changes are made by one side.

Figure 2 shows the results of a first strike against 1,000 silos. Without going into the details of the method of calculation, it can be seen that there are two parallel curves. Below and to the left the defender would have more than 200 of his silos surviving and would be confident of delivering a second strike. Above and to the right the attacker would be faced with a retaliation from not more than 50 undamaged missiles. If we assume accurate missiles with a CEP of 0.5 nmi, then the attacker would have to fit five of the five-megaton warheads to each of his missiles to be confident of a successful first strike. Even if the CEP was reduced to 0.3 nmi, that is, was highly accurate, the attacker would have to fit an average of 2.5 warheads to each missile. It would be unlikely that fitting of warheads of high yield, in such numbers and of such accuracy, would escape inspection, particularly if missile type and size were controlled.

It is not claimed that this method is superior to the method of calculation used by Col. Kent; rather, it supplements it and gives results that are fairly easily understood by those who have to evaluate the effects of an agreement on force structures and national defense.

THE EFFECT OF MRV's, MIRV's, AND ABM's ON THE AGREEMENT

In the above discussion it was assumed that in each case the calculation was made as if the payload carried a warhead of maximum yield. Each superpower was free to design his payload in any way he liked within the limits of the weight that could be covered by the missile. This freedom could extend to MRV's, MIRV's, PENAIDS, hardening, and maneuverability, since we have seen that these would be at the expense of weight available for warheads.

One way of dealing with ABM's would be a complete ban; but it is unlikely that, in view of the threats from other nuclear powers, the superpowers would agree to giving up their ABM defense. ABM's could also be excluded from the agreement, but this could lead to an arms race in ABM's. Another way would be to include ABM's in the agreement in the same way as ICBM's—that is, by numbers, types, and weight, with use of a factor if necessary, in the same way that was suggested for equating solid- and liquid-fuel missiles.

FIGURE 2

Stability of an Arms Control Agreement

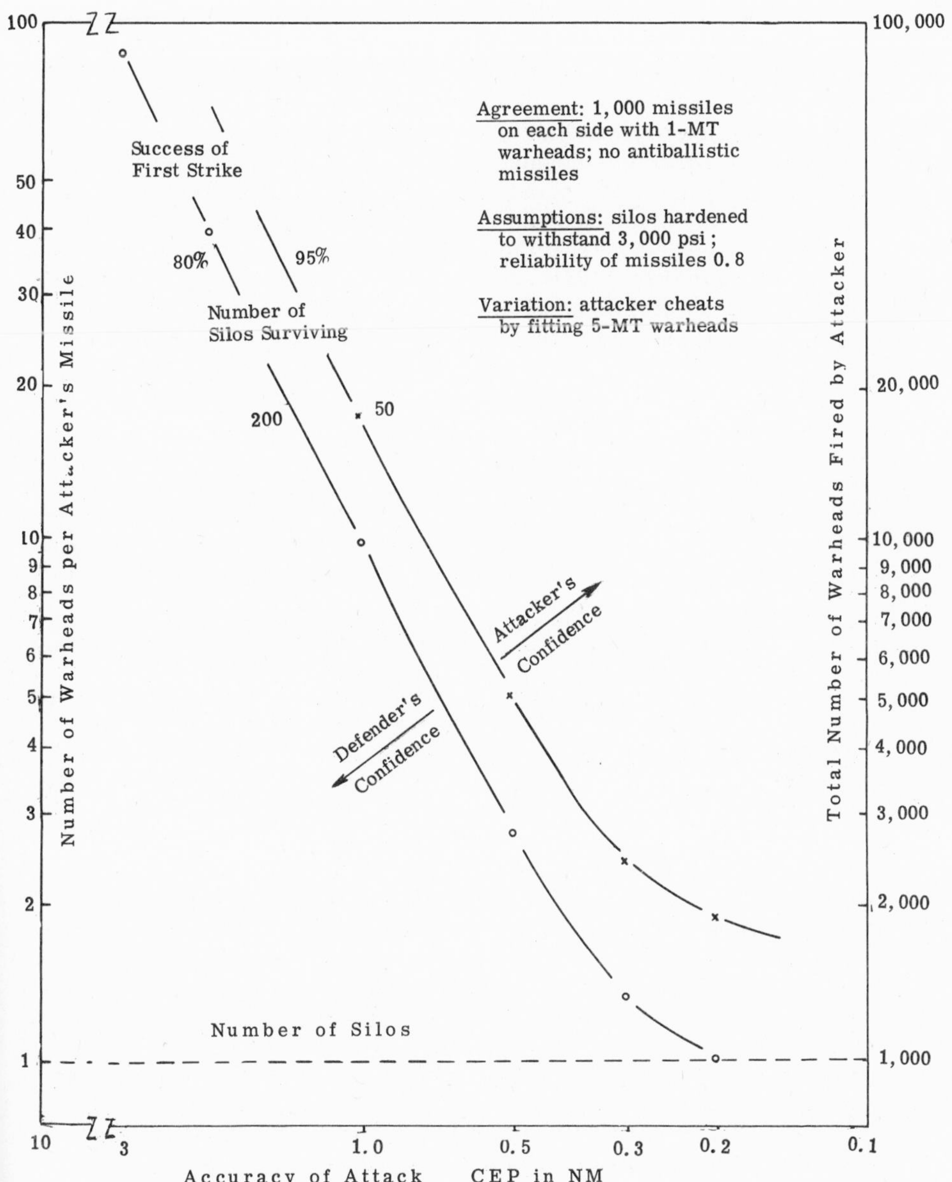

The main advantage arising from including ABM's with ICBM's is that ABM's would be included in the total permitted weight of missiles, that is, would be deployed at the expense of ICBM's. Each of the superpowers would then have to make its own decision as to the ratio between ICBM's and ABM's in the armory.

What would be the effects of deployment of ABM's on an agreement? It is possible, even likely, if the agreement had been well designed and appropriate factors chosen, that at first there would be little change. Initial deployments might be made mainly to gain experience of the system and to defend populations or missile sites according to the priorities and reading of the situation by the superpower concerned. Later, if the balance of cost-effectiveness were to change in favor of ABM's, deployments might be made to defend other targets. Deterrence by assured destruction could become, by degrees, deterrence by assured survival of the opponents.

An agreement on limitation of strategic missiles should aim at the preservation of the second-strike capability. One way of doing this is by having several different offensive systems that are independent and not vulnerable to the same counter-force system and therefore unlikely to be jeopardized by improvements in the counter force.

LAND-BASED INTERMEDIATE- AND MEDIUM-RANGE BALLISTIC MISSILES IN A GENERAL AGREEMENT

The United States no longer has intermediate- and medium-range ballistic missiles deployed, but the Soviet Union has a large number on launch pads in Russia: most of the missiles can be presumed to be targeted on Europe. Should these missiles be included in an agreement?

The purpose of these forces is to hold hostage the population of Western Europe against an attack on the Warsaw Pact countries by NATO. They are therefore strategic forces in the same way as ICBM's.

There seems to be no reason why the intermediate- and medium-range ballistic missile forces should not be included with ICBM's on exactly the same basis, that is, by missile weight. Because of the short range, compared with that for intercontinental missiles, a larger warhead could be carried for the same total weight; and it might seem desirable to introduce a weighting factor.

SUBMARINE-LAUNCHED BALLISTIC MISSILES IN A GENERAL AGREEMENT

Submarine-launched ballistic missiles are similar in size to intermediate- and medium-range ballistic missiles and could be treated in exactly the same way. Indeed, as far as verification is concerned, they could probably be easier to verify, since only the submarines would have to be counted. There would be many opportunities for doing this during building in the limited number of shipyards and in the basins of their home ports.

LONG-RANGE BOMBERS IN A GENERAL AGREEMENT

Both of the superpowers have fleets of long range bombers that are nearing the end of what would be normal expected service life. These bombers have been updated for carrying long-range stand-off weapons and, in the case of the U.S. aircraft, by training and fitting of special equipment, for low-level attack below the radar screens. In this mode the aircraft would be only briefly within range of individual batteries of surface-to-air missiles (SAM), which would have little time to respond.

Long-range bombers could be included in a general agreement by taking into account their maximum payload for the range, with a suitable conversion factor to the same base as for ICBM's.

Since neither the United States nor the Soviet Union has definite plans for follow-up long-range heavy bombers, it might be worth considering a total ban on this type of aircraft after the normal or accelerated phasing out of present types. This would mean that the U.S. advanced manned strategic aircraft that is being investigated would not be built. In view of the variety and power of U.S. offensive strategic systems at present deployed, it is difficult to see the rationale for another offensive strategic system.

Demise of the strategic bomber might be encouraged, from the arms control point of view, since bombers are flexible in use and increase the options for an attacker, are more vulnerable than missiles to a first strike, and encourage expenditure on defensive systems and improvements in the aggressive potential that would be difficult, if not impossible, to control.

At the same time, use of aircraft in reconnaissance or surveillance should not be excessively discouraged because factual information so gained can be reassuring; and it is often lack of information that is alarming.

TACTICAL NUCLEAR DELIVERY SYSTEMS

It has to be borne in mind that while the United States can be reached only by long range aircraft of the Soviet long-range air force, western Russia is within the range not only of the long-range aircraft of the U.S. Air Force based in the United States and in some of the overseas bases but also of NATO tactical aircraft. At the same time, of course, Western Europe is under threat of some 700 intermediate- and medium-range ballistic missiles in western Russia and Warsaw Pact tactical aircraft.

Since tactical aircraft that could be armed with nuclear weapons are deployed on both sides, they could be considered as outside the agreement; but some kind of maximum payload and range might have to be stipulated to prevent larger aircraft from being introduced as replacements.

Other tactical nuclear delivery systems deployed in Europe include short-range missiles and tube artillery; there are believed to be about 7,000 U.S. tactical nuclear warheads on the NATO side and probably a similar but smaller deployment of Russian weapons on the Warsaw Pact side.

A major difference between tactical nuclear weapons and strategic nuclear weapons is that the former are likely to be fission weapons in the kiloton range of yield, while the strategic weapons are more likely to contain a fusion component and to be in the megaton or even the multimegaton range. The yield-to-weight ratios would be different, which would make warhead weight, or some related parameter, of little value for comparison. It would be impossible to verify the numbers of these warheads and the characteristics of the delivery systems.

The only practical solution is to exclude tactical weapons from a general agreement, at least in the first versions, although it might be possible later to conclude a supplementary agreement or to restrain tactical nuclear weapons as part of an agreement relating to conventional forces in Europe. Until such a stage could be reached, restriction on deployment of systems over a particular range would be necessary to avoid a creeping deployment of higher-yield and longer range weapons.

PROBLEMS OF REPLACEMENT

A constant and irksome problem in most forms of agreement is that of replacements of equipment. It is not likely that either side would be content to allow elements of its strategic armory gradually to wither away from neglect. In addition to replacement of components and subsystems that routine checks or planned maintenance have shown to be necessary, from time to time it would be more economic to ensure a quick return to service if a whole missile were replaced. Replacement of a missile or of a major component could be used to improve the quality of a missile system. It would not be necessary under the type of agreement outlined above to be concerned about replacement by a larger missile. A single replacement, while it would break the agreement, would not upset the strategic balance; this would be upset only by replacement on such a scale that it would become known to the other superpower.

STRATEGIC ARMS LIMITATION TALKS

After both sides had expressed willingness to join in discussions on limitations of strategic nuclear weapons, the United States and Soviet Union held preliminary discussions in Helsinki in the autumn of 1969 and at subsequent meetings in Vienna. While it is of course impossible to predict the scope of these talks, an eventual agreement could include any of the subjects listed in Table 21.

Some of the more important bases for an agreement have already been discussed, and it is not possible to consider in detail each of the criteria in Table 21. However, some general problems that arise are worth examining a little more. Some of the criteria would be difficult, or almost impossible, to apply without intense and very intrusive inspection, for example, of all possible manufacturing facilities, research and development laboratories, payloads, etc. Other criteria may be applied fairly successfully without on-site inspection: flight testing of long range missiles can be detected from outside national territory—although, of course, it would be more difficult to determine whether the missile was of a standard type and whether it was being fired for troop training, or proof testing of stocks, or was of a new type. It would be easier to detect the latter if the differences were considerable; for example, multiple reentry

TABLE 21

Possible Topics for Discussion and Agreement at Strategic Arms Limitation Talks

Numbers of strategic nuclear delivery vehicles
Maximum yield of warheads
Maximum weight of warheads
Total weight of warheads
Total weight of payloads
Numbers of reentry vehicles
Total weight of missiles
Total yield of warheads
Total area of destruction
Ban or limitation on flight testing of strategic nuclear delivery vehicles
Ban or limitation on flight testing of new types of strategic nuclear delivery vehicles
Ban or limitation on deployment of particular types of strategic nuclear delivery vehicles
Ban or limitation on manufacturing facilities
Ban or limitation on research and development
Freeze at present level of deployment
Limited total of missiles, unlimited replacement
Limited replacement of missiles by numbers
Limited replacement by type
Limitation on budget

vehicles, if these had not been flight tested before or had been tested only on a different trajectory. Other technical improvements could be tested in space vehicles; indeed, control and guidance systems could probably be thoroughly tested in this way without any test firing of military missiles. However, some safeguard exists against upsetting stability by a technical breakthrough because of the time required to produce, modify, or replace the several hundred missiles necessary to gain a strategic advantage.

Any agreement between the United States (and its allies) and the Soviet Union (and its allies) must not increase the risk of a first-strike option by either side. The agreement must not unduly favor one side with present deployments because this would reduce the chances of acceptance and, even if accepted, would induce expenditure in the attempt to equalize the position. This expenditure alone would be an unsettling factor, leading to doubt as to what technical advances were being made at the same time.

In other words, the agreement should freeze present deployments as far as possible. But neither side is likely to agree to a halt on research and development and other activities; and it would be difficult to verify both any advances made and which, if any, are being incorporated into weapons.

Given that ICBM's and ABM's are available to both superpowers, there is considerable freedom for technical improvement, changes in force posture, and strategic dogma that can be used by either side to gain an advantage or restore equilibrium; in other words, it is not essential to copy exactly the move made by the other side. Some of the options that are open are listed in Table 22, which shows those that are more particularly suited to first and second strike—although this allocation could be disputed.

In addition to the type of agreement between the United States and Soviet Union, there are a number of other possible collateral agreements, some of which are listed in Table 23.

MINIMUM DETERRENT

If some kind of freeze can be arranged between the superpowers by which deployments of about the present magnitude can be stabilized, then, if the agreement is well designed, it should be possible later to progress to a gradual reduction in strategic systems. Such a reduction would raise the question of how far disarmament could be carried out before deterrence ceased to operate.

An attraction of a minimum deterrent to many writers on strategy has been the possibility of reducing the casualties and damage that would result from a nuclear exchange. The amount of assumed

TABLE 22

Possible Improvements in Strategic Nuclear Delivery Vehicle Systems

For First Strike	For Second Strike
Greater accuracy	Increase in yield
Improved reliability	ABM defense of missile sites
Increased availability	Dispersion of launch platforms
Multiple warheads	Increase in variety of nuclear delivery vehicles
Greater payload	Survivability of command and control
Nonoptimum flight path	Hardening of silos
Coordination of attack to reduce warning	Concealment of silos
Postattack surveillance	Penetration aids
ABM defense of cities	Hardening against ABM
antisubmarine warfare	Mobility of launch platform
developments of strike fleets	Rapid retargeting
tactical strike aircraft	Peacetime surveillance
intermediate/medium-range ballistic missiles	Improved warning
	Continental-based strategic aircraft
	Interceptor aircraft
	Surface-to-air missiles
	Tactical nuclear systems

destruction that could be inflicted by a second strike of a superpower after it absorbed a first strike is about one-third to one-half of the population and equivalent damage to property. It is clear that a superpower would be deterred by a much smaller amount of damage.

MINIMUM STABLE DETERRENT

New problems arise from deployments of ABM's and MIRV's. For a second-strike force with sufficient magnitude for deterrence to survive, the total forces might have to be larger than under a minimum deterrent, to take into account a rapid technical breakthrough by the opponent. When the question of how many missiles are required to provide a minimum stable deterrent is put to those who design strategic systems, the answer given by cautious military strategists tends to be in favor of much larger forces than the arms controller would believe necessary.

It is of course likely that the level of assumed destruction that is now considered to be a deterrent against any kind of attack is already out of date, and that in the evolving politicoeconomic situation a much smaller threat would be sufficient to deter. If not now, this will almost certainly be true in the future; but how far and how quickly present trends in the concept of deterrence can reverse is a matter of conjecture, as is the possibility of present deployments themselves having an adverse effect on international politics.

THE NUCLEAR UMBRELLA

The number of nuclear weapons held by the nuclear powers is very great and, even with elaborate and detailed inspection, many weapons could be retained and hidden, probably justified by the possibility that the opponent would do likewise. If only one nuclear power had clandestine weapons, then when all other weapons had been destroyed, it would be in a position to blackmail the world. To guard against this possibility (for which the temptation would be very great), it has

TABLE 23

Possible Collateral Agreements for Strategic Arms Control

Limitation on strategic weapons of allies, e.g., by including British and French strategic nuclear forces in totals permitted to United States, separate ceilings, safeguards to prevent proliferation to allies on either side
Restriction on research and development (very difficult to apply without intrinsic inspection)
Further limitation on testing of nuclear warheads
Limitation on testing of nuclear delivery vehicles (difficult to apply to aircraft)
Restriction on testing of MRV and MIRV and other detectable developments
Prohibition on deployment of ABM
Moratorium on ABM
Moratorium on ICBM, no restriction on ABM

been suggested that the superpowers should retain a small stock of nuclear weapons.

NUCLEAR ARMS FOR UNITED NATIONS FORCES

At this point it would seem that an impasse had been reached and further disarmament would be impossible. To provide a deterrent that would permit the superpowers to disarm completely, apart from internal security forces, it has been proposed that international forces should be backed with deterrent forces armed with nuclear weapons. This eventuality is so far away, in a future that cannot be imagined clearly, that consideration at this stage is unreal.

CHAPTER

16

SURVEILLANCE AND UNILATERAL VERIFICATION

"Unilateral verification" or "verification by national means" will remain of importance until international means of verification are accepted as sufficiently reliable, both technically and politically, to ensure national security. For obvious reasons this confidence will not be easily attained, and it is certain that national means for verification will continue to provide the main effort for many years. Verification by national means is generally understood not to include cooperation between the parties.

"Adversary inspection" is used to describe systems in which there is some cooperation between the parties, that is, visiting inspectors would be accepted, subject to the constraints detailed in the agreement—for example, access might be limited to the emplacing and servicing of unmanned sensors. Such verification systems are more likely to be acceptable if there is the minimum of intrusion into the affairs of the host nation.

There are a number of methods and systems that can be used for off-site inspection: these include satellite reconnaissance, high-level surveillance by aircraft, offshore surveillance, long-range radars, and seismography. It would also be possible to install unmanned systems in the territory of an opponent, either as a clandestine operation or when some form of duress could be exerted. Unmanned on-site systems, with or without the knowledge of the opponent, would require tamper-proof and shockproof sensors.

All arms control verification systems will require means, preferably near the source, to process the data and eliminate non-essential information. Another general requirement is for sensors of small size and weight: this is either to make them inconspicuous if used for on-site inspection, or because of the high cost of transportation in satellites or aircraft. Reliability and low power consumption are also important because of the difficulties or even impossibility of servicing and replacing defective equipment. These constraints are essentially similar to those for other military equipment for which microelectronic circuits are finding increasing uses. A sensor contains some form of transducer that converts the incoming signal from the event to be detected into a form that can be transmitted, stored, and analyzed. The incoming signal usually requires conversion to an electrical signal, in either analog or digital form, suitable for dispatching to the data processing center.

SURVEILLANCE BY AIRCRAFT

Attention was drawn to the possibility of aircraft for arms control surveillance by President Eisenhower's proposed open-skies agreement, put forward at the summit conference of July 1955, under which aerial patrols would be flown by either side over the territory of the opponent for the purpose of ensuring that no preparations were being made for an armed attack.

Although no agreement was reached, some special aircraft have been used to overfly the territory of an opponent. Although reconnaissance flights over the Soviet Union by U.S. aircraft have been banned, aircraft are widely used by both sides in overseas reconnaissance for shipping and for border patrols for a number of purposes.

Aircraft carry several types of sensors: the modern approach is the multiple-sensor system in which the inputs from all the sensors are integrated through a computer to give a single output that is an analysis of all of the information. Many of the systems that are used are similar to those used in satellites and include photography, infrared sensors, radars, lasers, and in some cases means for detecting the radioactivity from nuclear explosions.

Lasers, the most recently introduced technique, have already found specific uses in surveillance and reconnaissance systems, although the initial military uses have been in laser-aided weapons delivery. Laser cameras have been developed on the line-scan principle and rapidly examine the target area, by day or by night, with a good chance of not disclosing that surveillance is being carried out. Real-time displays are also under development—that is, the picture can be seen immediately, without the delays caused by development and printing. Similar systems are being explored for surveillance satellites.

Aircraft surveillance is made difficult in many parts of the world, including Northern Europe, by weather conditions, particularly cloud cover. Difficulties with weather would be particularly important in an adversary inspection system, because it is likely that each flight would have to be given authorization some time in advance, with little or no possibility, when the weather was unsuitable for making observations of scheduling a replacement flight.

The presence of aircraft flying at high altitudes is not obvious to the general public but can be detected by military radars and poses a problem for antiaircraft defense systems.

The introduction of surveillance satellites has reduced the need for aircraft on these missions. It is certain that satellites do not appear to produce so much tension, if only for the reason that both the United States and Soviet Union operate similar systems.

SEA-BASED AND UNDERSEA SURVEILLANCE SYSTEMS

Because of its worldwide system of bases the United States has concentrated mostly on overseas surveillance by aircraft and has expended less effort on naval vessels for surveillance purposes. The Soviet Union, on the other hand, lacks overseas bases and has therefore developed seagoing trawlers that have been deployed in large numbers throughout the world. These have been used, for example, to monitor the activities of NATO naval vessels and for observing missile test firings.

It is presumed that seagoing surveillance systems are equipped with radars for detecting surface and aerial objects and with a wide range of electronic receiving, monitoring, and decoding systems for determining the location of the opponent's radars and for analyzing his communications, particularly new patterns that might imply a change in the state of preparedness.

Seagoing surveillance vessels could also be used offshore to watch for the putting to sea of nuclear submarines and other capital ships and as picket ships to provide early warning of aircraft or of missiles. They could also be used to monitor missile ranges, particularly when the target area is in the sea.

Increasing use is being made of sonar for detecting the movement of submarines. Sonar is used in antisubmarine warfare, both from vessels and dropped from aircraft. Sonars may be fixed in position by being moored to the seabed or sown to float with the ocean currents.

Other systems suitable for surveillance of undersea traffic were described in the discussion on defense against submarine-launched missiles (in Chapter 13).

SATELLITE SURVEILLANCE

Satellite reconnaissance involves some of the most advanced sensor techniques and is at the same time the most useful and unobtrusive means by which objects down to a few feet in diameter may be observed from vehicles in orbit 200 or 300 miles above the surface. Both superpowers have this facility; the United States has orbited satellites in the Discoverer, Samos, Midas, Tiros/Nimbus and Vela H series, while the Soviet Union has had Proton and Cosmos satellites. Many satellites have civilian missions on which information has been fully published. Undoubtedly military systems have benefited from this experience, and what follows is based on the open literature on both civil and military satellites. Satellites designed for military surveillance could be equipped with a number of different types of sensors but, for reasons of weight and operational purposes, only one or two may be carried by the same satellite. It is probable that there will be a tendency to develop heavier satellites with a multiple array of sensors, as has been done for aircraft systems.

Sensors that are used include color and black-and-white photography, television, and infrared detectors. The atmosphere is opaque to many wavelengths from the electromagnetic spectrum but will transmit wavelengths in the visible spectrum, a limited number of wavelengths in the near and far infrared, and a wide range of radio wavelengths. Photography has the finest resolution and is essential for identifying most objects. The film used has to be of a grade specially selected for use in space. It is likely that procedures are used similar to those for film carried by manned vehicles used in space exploration; samples of this material are tested from the batches before approval, and other samples are developed from the exposed stock before bulk processing, to ensure that the processes are matched to the film.

The important requirement of a sensor system is the ability to detect significant objects. Resolution of camera systems is defined as the ability to distinguish between sets of parallel lines of various spacings. This is rather different from the ability to distinguish and identify specific objects, say parked aircraft, for which a high level of skill as a photo interpreter is essential. When this skill is combined with experience and knowledge of the kind of object being searched for, it becomes possible to identify military and commercial installations and even individual vehicles. Restrictions on the amount of film that can be carried means that only selected areas can be photographed to high resolution, these areas probably having been identified in previous surveys by photographs of lower magnification.

Orbits of earth satellites are always in a plane that passes through the center of the earth. The orbit swept by the satellite may extend over both poles, but for maximum useful coverage the orbit will not generally extend so far. The minimum range to which the orbit may extend north and south of the equator is the latitude from which the launch was made. Due to rotation of the earth, successive parallel traces on the surface are offset; by selection of the launch trajectory it is possible to maintain the same angle of lighting from the sun on identical traces, so that shadows from similar objects will look alike—this considerably facilitates photo interpretation. To conserve photographic film the cameras are operated only over target areas, according to a prearranged program or on command from the ground. It may also be possible to avoid photography when cloud cover is too dense; information gathered by U.S. and Soviet weather satellites is valuable for this purpose.

Photographic information can be returned to the earth in three ways. It can be stored for several days and recovered when the satellite is brought back to the earth's surface. A more advanced system depends on the release of capsules of exposed film that, after reentry, are slowed by parachute and can be recovered in midair by specially equipped aircraft. These reentry capsules are elaborate devices with retrorockets, stabilizers, and ablative shields. Even after the pack of negatives has been recovered, it has to be rushed to a processing laboratory. With these various delays it may be several days after the photograph was taken that a print becomes available for examination by the photo interpreters. The third system involves the digital encoding and transmission of the photograph to earth by means essentially similar to that employed in distributing newspaper photographs. The digital transmissions may be subject to direct interpretation on computer. There are essential limitations in this system that may make the recovered pictures relatively crude and lacking in detail but, of course, available much sooner.

Direct interpretation of photographs has been mentioned. It might seem well worthwhile to hand over this task to a computer. The straight comparison of two almost identical pictures does not present too difficult a problem, for the computer can be programmed to carry out a parallel scan and report differences. But examination of individual pictures is much more difficult because the computer must be told in minute detail what to look for, such as the shapes of aircraft, silos, vehicles, or even only the visible parts of these objects, of variable contrast, size, and orientation. Pattern recognition is a higher ability of the human mind; enormous effort is required to dissect this ability into simple discrete tasks, and may require so much computer memory or operating time as to be impracticable.

By what can be seen as an extension of photographic techniques there is also the possibility of relaying television pictures to earth receivers. In fact, this procedure was used at an early stage of the satellite program, but it also suffers from some of the problems of transmitting photographs from space to earth.

PERFORMANCE OF SATELLITE SURVEILLANCE SYSTEMS

In order to establish the value of data and filter out unwanted detail, an examination of the "signature" from the emitter should, if possible, be carried out in the satellite to ensure that only relevant information is transmitted to the earth station. By use of films and filters suitable for particular wavelengths, photographs can be taken both within the visible spectrum and in those parts of the infrared spectrum that are not absorbed by the atmosphere. Examining the emission in a narrow wave band may identify particular phenomena—for example, the small difference in water temperature in the wake of a nuclear submarine from discharge of cooling water. Other phenomena may be identified by combining two or more photographs taken in different parts of the spectrum. Multiple photography has been widely used in earth resources investigations, and it is likely that similar techniques are used for military surveillance. Photography and sensors in the infrared wave bands can be used to search for heat emissions such as those from rocket, tank, and aircraft engines.

No photographs taken from military surveillance satellites have been shown in the open literature; but many photographs have been published that were taken from civilian spacecraft, often with hand-held cameras. Estimating from these photographs, it would be expected that military systems would be capable of recording, at the very least, the larger military objects, such as launch sites, submarine yards, and atomic energy plants.

No reliable estimate has appeared on the resolution that can be achieved by photo reconnaissance, although it has been guessed that there is an improvement by a factor of 100 over those seen for civilian purposes. Improvements in photographic film, particularly in the fineness of grain and in sensitivity and in lenses, which have benefited from computer design, will make it possible to obtain resolution approaching theoretical limits. The maximum resolution by photography depends largely on the design of camera lenses. The first limitation is on the diameter of the glass elements that can be ground to the required accuracy and freedom from aberrations. The next limitation is the resolution of the film, in which fine grain is achieved at the expense of speed. A suitable compromise of speed and resolution, together with lens aperture, will fix the focal length and thus the size of objects which can be distinguished. There are in addition those other factors that affect the photographic image: lack of contrast at the target, air turbulence, and clouds, which make it difficult to identify objects. If some reasonable assumptions are made as to the resolution of the film and the focal length of lens, a rough calculation suggests a theoretical maximum resolution of perhaps 5-10 feet, but this would be further degraded by imperfections in the lens system and those arising from atmospheric effects.

Early U.S. satellites of the Midas and Samos series carried infrared sensors to detect missile exhausts. The system, however, was uncertain in operation, often reported signals from sunlight reflected from clouds, and in some instances did not detect actual exhaust emissions. Improved infrared sensors can now be employed, and the information can be stored and repeated to the ground base later in the satellite's orbit. Electronic information obtained from monitoring could be processed in the same way, and the delays at present associated with the photographic process could be avoided. However, photography offers such a wealth of information that it is most unlikely to be superseded by any other process.

One solution of the problem of real-time operation is in having several satellites in synchronous orbit—that is, apparently stationary over one part of the earth. Synchronous orbit is at 22,300 miles above the earth's surface, which is too remote for close observation of the surface. Another way of obtaining real-time observations would be to have a number of satellites in low earth orbit relaying their data through synchronous satellites to earth stations.

Besides earth observation, satellites are also used to monitor for nuclear explosions on the surface, in the atmosphere, and in space. (Procedures for the detection of nuclear explosions were discussed earlier.)

The most recent U.S. Air Force satellite system uses the Agena spacecraft for reconnaissance and surveillance. The information gathered is highly classified, but some of the conclusions appearing either directly in reports and statements or in annual posture statements could have been obtained only in this way.

President Johnson once stated that space reconnaissance, by providing firmer appreciations, had saved enough in military expenditure to pay for the entire military and space programs. The Soviet systems must also have yielded a similar wealth of information about U.S. deployments. Thus, by any criterion, surveillance by satellite is a most powerful arms control device.

MANNED ORBITING SURVEILLANCE SYSTEMS

Considerable research and development has taken place in both the United States and Soviet Union on earth-orbiting manned stations. These stations could have several civilian missions, particularly for earth resource surveying and also in the development of way stations as a stage in the exploration of space. Manned stations could also be used for arms control and military surveillance. It has been claimed that manned systems would be much more flexible than unmanned systems, would be able to respond to unusual situations, and could be adjusted or repaired while still in orbit. However, there must be doubts as to the watch-keeping abilities of astronauts over long periods. The high cost of replacing crews and providing life support systems has to be compared with the demonstrated reliability and effectiveness of present systems. It is probably because the comparison is unfavorable that the manned orbiting laboratory was canceled in June 1969.

In this system pairs of astronauts would have a 30-day watch. Much more ambitious projects are under active examination both in the United States and Soviet Union. These space stations would be put into orbit in sections and then assembled in space. The interest shown by the Russian space program in an ability to rendezvous and in welding in space is related to the problems that must be solved. In the United States there has been revived interest in reentry vehicles of aerodynamic shape, so-called lifting bodies. Two or three of these would be strapped together at launch, with the intention of putting one, containing the space station relief crew, into orbit. All of the bodies could return to the surface and land as aircraft and could be reused. This would save on costs as compared with expendable stages, and relatively few individuals would have to undergo the full rigorous training as astronauts.

LAND-BASED SURVEILLANCE SYSTEMS

Land-based long-range radars have a number of surveillance functions: to monitor earth-orbiting objects, to monitor tests of long-range missiles, and to act as an early warning system of launch of nuclear delivery vehicles.

With increasing numbers of earth-orbiting satellites, together with debris from their motors, there are now some hundreds of objects circling the earth. It is necessary to keep a watch on new additions and to distinguish them from those which have been in orbit for some time. The long-range radars are used to track objects and feed information to computers that calculate orbits and predict possible trajectories and warning time.

Monitoring of launches of missiles by radars and other means will yield information on the state of act and indicate possible future deployments.

Long-range early warning radars are sited in England, Greenland, and Alaska. Radar picket lines to protect the continental United States lie across northern Canada. Other long-range radars have been sited to cover missile launches in the Soviet Union. A recent innovation has been over-the-horizon radars, from which the emission follows a series of reflections between the upper atmosphere and the earth. (Seismic systems for the detection of underground weapons tests were discussed earlier.)

The ability to carry out surveillance from space, and to a lesser extent by other long-range systems, is available only to the superpowers. These countries are becoming able to observe military and other activities of other powers and thus to warn possible victims, and even to take steps to provide assistance and in general to control or influence behavior worldwide. The implications of these developments in terms of world government do not appear to have been considered in any detail by experts in international relations.

CHAPTER

17 TACTICAL NUCLEAR WEAPONS

YIELDS AND DELIVERY SYSTEMS

Now that fission-fusion-fission weapons have been developed, there is virtually no upper limit to the yield of a single weapon. The Soviets have exploded a test weapon of 65 megatons—that is, 50,000 times the yield of the weapons that destroyed the Japanese cities. At the other extreme, the practical lower limit is at yields that can be more conveniently provided by chemical explosives. The range of yield for tactical nuclear weapons is generally considered to be from kilotons to hundreds of tons of TNT. The yield selected for a particular operation is related to the hardness and area of the target and the accuracy with which the weapon can be delivered. The object would be to ensure that there is a high probability that the whole of the target lies within the lethal radius, so that the target is damaged to some minimum level.

Tactical nuclear warheads can be made of a weight and dimension small enough to be delivered by many tactical delivery systems, some of which are dual purpose—that is, they can be used to deliver conventional high-explosive or even chemical or biological warfare warheads. American weapons of this type that are available, some of which are deployed overseas, include strike aircraft; Pershing, Sergeant, and Honest John rocket launchers; 155- and 203-mm. howitzers; Nike-Hercules and surface-to-air missile launchers; and atomic demolition munitions (i.e., nuclear land mines). The latter could be used to destroy bridges, make craters in road and rail routes, create landslides into ravines, and generally provide barriers to an advance. Tactical nuclear weapons are deployed in greatest quantity in Europe, but they are also in other theaters.

DETERRENCE BY TACTICAL NUCLEAR WEAPONS

The manner and situations in which tactical nuclear weapons might be used have been the subject of prolonged and anxious debate. The first deployments of tactical nuclear weapons in Europe were made to give support to NATO forces against the more numerous Warsaw Pact forces in Europe. How realistic such a policy could be when the Soviets had intermediate- and medium-range ballistic missiles targeted on Western Europe is now academic; the possibility of using tactical nuclear weapons to neutralize the preponderance of manpower deployed by the Warsaw Pact has become a less viable policy as the Soviets have equipped their own forces with tactical nuclear weapons. When a war in Europe, with both sides deploying tactical nuclear weapons, has been studied by war-gaming techniques, the situation has quickly gotten out of control and has escalated to the use of tactical nuclear weapons and has continued to an all-out nuclear exchange. The notion that a low-level tactical nuclear war could be continued for any length of time in Europe appears to be misconceived and unduly optimistic.

Tactical nuclear weapons thus present a threat of escalation to both sides in which the cities of Europe would be devastated. There may be a degree of asymmetry in the present position, in that the United States would probably be reluctant to use tactical nuclear weapons in Europe against a conventional attack because of the possibility of escalation, since the Warsaw Pact countries would be within range of tactical weapons but the U.S. homeland could be attacked only with much larger and longer-range strategic nuclear weapons. With this inhibition in the use of tactical nuclear weapons, NATO would not be in a position to counter a conventional attack by Warsaw Pact forces unless NATO conventional forces were themselves strengthened. The problem in NATO has been to provide conventional forces when there has been reluctance in several countries to do so. While the attacker may require the well-known ratio of three to one in manpower against a defense in a battle, in an attack on a broad front this ratio would not apply, since the attacker could choose the place for attack and concentrate his forces.

Tactical nuclear weapons, whatever the inhibitions on their use on moral grounds, are a very real threat against an opponent not similarly armed. It is difficult to know if such threats have been effective, but some observers considered that the Vietcong siege of the U.S. Marine base at Khe San was lifted in April 1969 because of demands made in the U.S. press for the use of tactical nuclear weapons.

TACTICAL USE OF NUCLEAR WEAPONS

While intercontinental nuclear weapons systems have fairly well-defined roles in strategy, tactical nuclear weapons may have a number of possible uses; they vary in size and may have yields from several thousand tons down to hundreds of tons equivalent of high explosive. Larger-yield weapons could be delivered by aircraft or missiles against targets deep in the opponent's homeland, such as transport centers, attacks that it would be difficult for the victim to distinguish from strategic attacks. At the other end of the scale, low-yield nuclear warheads could be fired by artillery or carried by short-range missiles or aircraft and used instead of a barrage with conventional high-explosive warheads. The advantages of tactical nuclear warheads as compared with high explosive warheads are the following:

Only one delivery vehicle would be required to ensure at least the same area of damage as from a bombardment from a number of batteries of artillery or missile launchers or several squadrons of aircraft armed with conventional warheads; thus logistics are simplified and flexibility of response is increased

By selection of a warhead with a sufficiently large yield, the whole of a target area can be destroyed with a high degree of probability of success

For attacks on point targets (e.g., bridges) the large lethal radius from a nuclear warhead can compensate for inaccuracies of aim and target location

For attacks on hardened targets (e.g., command posts) the magnitude of nuclear weapon effects (e.g., blast) will more thoroughly ensure destruction of the target

Nuclear weapons have damaging effects in addition to blast, and these might be employed against some targets

The threat of nuclear weapons will prevent the massing of troops and vehicles for an attack

Use of one or a few tactical nuclear weapons could be a demonstration of determination to escalate the conflict unless the other side ceased its attack.

ATOMIC DEMOLITION MUNITIONS

Nuclear explosives could be used in the form of atomic demolition munitions placed in position where invasion routes could be cut—for example, by the destruction of river crossings or corniche roads, for blocking mountain defiles, damming rivers to cause flooding or bursting dams of reservoirs for the same purpose, and blowing down of masses of trees to impede vehicle movement.

Since such munitions would be used only in the invaded territory and could be embedded sufficiently deep to cause minimum fallout, they have some special attractions for defense. They would do their task with less effort and time for installation than would be required for high explosives; and at the same time they could signal a determination to escalate to nuclear weapons if further pressed, without incurring the odium of an attack on the opponent's forces or his territory.

NUCLEAR DEPTH CHARGES

Tactical nuclear weapons could have a much larger yield than conventional high explosive of the same weight. High accuracy of delivery would not be so necessary, since the volume exposed to the blast wave in water would be proportional to the yield; thus nuclear weapons would be particularly useful for attacking enemy submarines whose precise location was not certain. A long-range attack by missile or by aircraft would be necessary to avoid damage to the counterattacking vessel, but a vessel equipped with these systems could control a very large area of ocean.

ARMS CONTROL IN EUROPE

The reasons why Europe has enjoyed a particularly long period of peace, or at least freedom from war, are debatable.* However, both NATO and Soviet doctrines, after prolonged study of the military problems of Europe, agree that once the nuclear threshold has been

---

*A. Buchan and P. Windsor, Arms and Stability in Europe (London: Chatto and Windus, 1963); Denis Healey, "Thinking About the Unthinkable," The Listener (April 23, 1970).

crossed, it would be difficult, if not impossible, to restrain conflict to below the level of the strategic nuclear exchange.

A study by the Institute of Strategic Studies suggests that this situation of mutual deterrence may not persist for a number of reasons.* Three possible policies for NATO can be postulated to deal with a changing situation: strengthening of conventional forces, so that resort to nuclear weapons can be avoided or delayed; production of nuclear weapons by several of the NATO countries of Western Europe; and negotiation of a political settlement in Europe involving a significant measure of arms reduction. The latter policy could aim at reducing the risk of war through accident and, at the same time, permit economic saving and concentration on means contributing to mutual trust.

Arms control in Europe has usually been considered as relating more particularly to Central Europe, where there is greatest concentration of weapons. The flanks—that is Norway, Greece, and Turkey—present fewer difficulties and could be taken care of in a more general agreement. Arms control in Central Europe involves three types of military systems: strategic nuclear systems based outside, but targeted on, the area; tactical nuclear weapons systems deployed within the area; and conventional forces deployed within the area. Most of NATO's strategic nuclear weapons belong to and are deployed by the United States and there are, in addition, submarines armed with nuclear weapons, strike fleets, and some bombers at overseas bases. These weapons are assigned mostly to targets within Russia, but some may be allocated to special targets in Central Europe. The Soviet Unions strategic ICBM's and submarine-launched missiles are undoubtedly assigned to targets in the United States and a few overseas bases; most intermediate- and medium-range ballistic missiles and long-range bombers are probably assigned to targets in Europe; but a smaller proportion, it can be judged from their launch sites, are intended to threaten targets in the Far East an elsewhere.

There could be difficulties in obtaining an agreement on arms limitation in Central Europe unless the negotiations have been preceded by other negotiations on general strategic arms limitations or such negotiations are carried out simultaneously. Apart from technical

---

*Institute for Strategic Studies, Disarmament and European Security (London, 1963).

difficulties, it would be difficult to obtain an atmosphere of sufficient mutual trust unless negotiations on strategic arms had shown some signs of success. One of the technical difficulties would be that of defining what was to be included in, and excluded from, an agreement relating to tactical weapons. When discussing this same problem with regard to strategic nuclear systems, the idea was advanced that these could be differentiated from tactical systems by specifying the size, weight, or some other parameter of the launch vehicles. In distinguishing strategic from tactical nuclear delivery systems in this way, it should not be forgotten that in Europe many tactical nuclear systems could have strategic effects.

A number of suggestions have been made for a nuclear-free zone in Europe; detailed proposals have been made by the Polish government, known as the Rapacki, Gomulka, and Lachs plans. The first of these proposals, presented before the U.N. Assembly in 1957, was for a two-stage process of denuclearization in Central Europe and a reduction in conventional forces. The Gomulka Plan (1963) was less ambitious and called for a freeze on nuclear warheads in the same area; the Lachs Plan was even more limited and was for regional non-proliferation—that is, a ban on the transfer of control of nuclear weapons. This last has been largely overtaken by the Non-Proliferation Treaty. What has to be decided before the form of an agreement can be considered is whether a reduction in nuclear arms in Europe is desirable and, if it is, whether it should be independent of a reduction in conventional forces.

It has already been indicated that use of tactical nuclear weapons in Europe is inhibited by fear of retaliation; but so is an attack with conventional forces, since, if these are great enough to overwhelm the opposing conventional forces, nuclear weapons could be used to break up the attack. Thus a ladder of escalation is created, whereby an attack by one side is met by a counter at about the same level, forcing the attacker either to give up his objective or to scale up his attack, until eventually tactical nuclear weapons are called in, and then strategic nuclear weapons. Since neither side is prepared to go this far for limited objectives, the first step has to be avoided.

VERIFICATION IN EUROPE

Mutual deterrence as sketched above has worked in Europe over a considerable period; it will not be lightly abandoned, and any agreement must take this into account. Whatever the form of agreement, some form of verification specifically applied to nuclear warheads might be required. In principle, three kinds of inspection are possible: a perimeter inspection system with control posts at entry points to the designated area; inspection within the area, which, to be effective, might require access for perimeter inspection of dumps; and a combination of these two systems. It is most unlikely that the location of dumps would be revealed, since this would be an encouragement to preemptive attack. Thus there seems to be little point in further discussion of inspection within a zone.

A perimeter inspection system could be designed for designated areas of Central Europe. Control posts could be set at the points of entry to the area, and all consignments of goods entering the area could be checked. Instruments sensitive to the products of radioactive decay could be used to examine packages, and perhaps a proportion of packages could be X-rayed as well. If such instruments were permitted, it might be possible to examine a large proportion of all packages. The minimum physical dimensions of a warhead, the special precautions that would normally have to be taken with the movement of fissile material, and the extra packaging that might be necessary to avoid detection by instruments might make it necessary to concentrate full examination only on the larger packages, with occasional inspection of smaller packages. Control posts at the main points of entry, such as ports, border crossings, and airports, would have to be supplemented by mobile patrols between the fixed posts. The mobile patrols could be equipped with jeeps, fast patrol boats, helicopters, and light aircraft.

To alter significantly the tactical situation in Europe, a number of warheads would have to be smuggled into the zone. Having formed an estimate of what this number would be and also an estimate of the probability of detection for a single warhead (that is, the fraction of packages being thoroughly inspected), it is possible to calculate the chances for discovering one warhead before a militarily significant number had entered the zone. A numerical example may indicate the possibilities of sample inspection.

Suppose one parcel in five in a consignment contains a warhead and one in two of all parcels is being examined; then there would be a one-in-ten chance of a warhead being discovered in the first package to pass through the system. But by the time ten parcels pass through the system, there would be a two-out-of-three chance of at least one warhead being discovered. The inspection system would be alerted, all packages would then be inspected completely—not only at this control post but at all other control posts that had been warned—and efforts would be made to trace loads that had been through the posts over the past few days.

The description just given of the theory of how a control post system could work may be rather optimistic. There are many practical problems that would require some form of solution. The transfer of goods across the zone boundaries was described as being in packages; in fact goods are transferred from one country to another in many forms. How would it be possible to ensure that warheads were not hidden in liquid cargoes (oil, chemicals, etc.) and that the bulk of the cargo was not acting as a shield against detection by instruments? Would it be necessary to transship all such cargoes at the control point or for an inspector to accompany them to the point of discharge? The same problem would arise with loads of solid material, such as wheat. Some of the solid and liquid cargoes, such as foods, would have to be treated with care to avoid contamination during inspection. How would control of emergency landing fields be carried out? Would the inspectors have access to the flight control organization? Would they be permitted to have their own radars? The number of control posts required to cover even major zone crossing points would be considerable and there would be, in addition, the mobile patrols, so that the control organization would need a large number of personnel, taking shifts, rests, and leave into account. Would any nation be prepared to be host to such a large contingent of its opponent's nationals? Would the business community face with equilibrium and understanding what must be a considerable and expensive disruption of normal traffic? It might be unwise to be optimistic about the possibilities of a verification system for nuclear warheads in a zone of Europe.

The system described was by adversary inspection. Would it be possible to overcome some objections by operating self-inspection? Undoubtedly this would be much easier to organize, since it could be integrated with existing national services, such as customs, air traffic control, and so on. However, in so vital a matter the likelihood of a nation entrusting its security to its opponent is very low.

From the foregoing discussion it appears that the possibilities of a separate agreement on control of tactical nuclear weapons are very low. Would there be any possibility of an agreement on tactical nuclear delivery vehicles? Since many of these are dual-purpose, it is not likely that they could be controlled except in terms of an agreement on force levels that embraced both conventional and nuclear weapons and troops. This form of agreement will be examined in the following chapter.

CHAPTER

18

ARMS CONTROL OF TACTICAL WEAPONS

In the field of tactical weapons this book has focused on Europe because it holds the greatest concentration of military arms, equipment, and manpower and because there are constant sources of friction in its political divisions. Furthermore, events elsewhere in the world that bring the superpowers into confrontation will be reflected in increased tension in Europe. Although a train of events could start elsewhere, its culmination in Europe could lead to the most destruction and loss of life. Arms control elsewhere in the world is dependent upon political settlements between those in the area and limitation of arms supplies by the superpowers and their allies; the source of supply in many cases is European.

Another reason for concentrating on Europe is that problems of arms control and disarmament elsewhere are often mainly political, and such technical requirements as are involved can be derived from solutions that have been designed for Europe.

In recent years a number of vague—probably intentionally so—notions have been floated for the improvement of European security. There have also been doubts cast on such propositions, it being argued that, despite the unsolved problems, Europe has enjoyed a long period of peace and prosperity and that gradual transition by increasing trade, cultural, and diplomatic exchanges may be preferable to intense inter-government debate with the doubtful prospect of a successful agreement at the end.

A third point of view considers that a major settlement may be difficult to achieve and uncertain in the outcome, but that there could be positive, if limited gains from obtaining agreements on specific topics. Theo Sommer has examined the form of some limited agreements:[1]

A 25 percent reduction in force levels

A declaration on the nonuse of force or a nonaggression pact or pacts

Exchange of observers at military exercises

A "hot line" between the NATO and Warsaw Pact commands

An agreement on total force levels

Limitation of armaments and defense targets

A control and inspection system against surprise attack.

CONCEPTUAL FRAMEWORK FOR INSPECTION SYSTEMS

A basic requirement for any but the most elementary agreement must be some arrangements for inspection. The main points of definition around which an inspection system can be built are the area to be inspected, the arms or facilities to be inspected, and the form of inspection.

Table 24 lists some of the most important parameters in the design of an inspection system. Most of the terms are more or less self-explanatory. However, some are not obvious, and a word of explanation is necessary. "Self-inspection" is used to describe a situation when it is in the interest of the parties to adhere to the requirements of the agreement. For example, under the Limited Test Ban Treaty it is forbidden to carry out underground tests of nuclear weapons, the radioactivity from which can be detected beyond the national frontier; care will therefore be taken to avoid venting to the atmosphere. The intensity of inspection can be a coarse mesh, the object of which is to search for the presence of large military formations in a demilitarized zone, or more generally for a massive preparation for war. At the other end of the scale, particularly detailed inspection may be necessary to ensure that plutonium is not being diverted from the civil program to the manufacture of weapons.

ROLE OF INTELLIGENCE

It would be unrealistic to assume that an inspection system would be entirely without information from intelligence sources. Intelligence

TABLE 24

Parameters for Tactical Inspection Systems

Parameter	Type	Examples
Authority	International	IAEA
	Adversary	Potsdam teams Military attachés
	Self	Limited Test Ban Treaty
Area inspected	Global	Non-Proliferation Treaty
	Regional	Antarctica, Latin America
	Zonal	Central Europe, demilitarized zone
Extent	Whole area	Central Europe
	Graduated inspection	
Nature	Physical	Retained missiles
	Nonphysical	Budget, records
Objects	Forces	Total manpower
	Weapons	Tanks, missile launchers
	Material	Fissile material stocks
	Production facilities	
Stage of manufacture	Production	Limitation on quantities
	Nonproduction	Prohibition of weapons
	Destruction	Bomber bonfire
Access	Surveillance from satellites	
	Perimeter inspection of area	
	Perimeter inspection and at outposts	
	Perimeter inspection of fixed facilities	Manufacturing plant, vehicle parks, stores

(Continued)

Table 24 (continued)

Parameter	Type	Example
	Aerial over-flights	
	Arranged tours of inspection	
	Unannounced tours of facilities	
	Monitoring transport	
	Search of facilities	
	Participation in management of facilities	
Mobility	Fixed	Outposts, river crossings
	Mobile between fixed posts	Border patrols
	Public thorough-fares	
	Complete Mobility	
Intensity	Coarse mesh	Readiness for war
	Fine mesh	All violations, or biological agents, plu-tonium
Sampling	100%	
	Selected samples	
	Random sampling	
Relation to intelligence	Complementary	
	Duplicate	
Relationship with host	Inspections only by agreement	
	Always escorted	
	Escorted only to facility or area	
	Monitoring of re-cords	
	Personnel inter-rogation	
Transport	Public vehicles only	
	Provided by host	

Parameter	Type	Examples
	Host driver/ escort	
	Conventional mass-produced vehicles	Cars, etc.
	High-performance vehicles	Four-wheel drive
	Special vehicles	Speedboats, helicopters.
Sensitivity	Areas open to foreigners	
	Areas open to citizens	
	Industrial production facilities	
	Military facilities	Bases and launch pads
	Military communication posts	
	Military and government command centers	
Communication channels	Written messages only	
	Telephone and telegram	
	Radio to local headquarters	
	Radio direct to headquarters from area	
Communication security	Censored	
	En clair	
	Coded	
Data handling	Collation and analysis by teams	
	Clerical assistance	
	Automatic data processing	Punched cards, computers

(Continued)

Table 24 (continued)

Parameter	Type	Examples
Equipment	Recording material	Notebooks, tape-recorders
	Eyeball inspection	Maps, compasses
	Binoculars	
	Simple, unobtrusive cameras	
	Cameras with long focal length lenses	
	Fixed sensors	Use of runways, bridges, etc.
	Mobile sensors	Radioactivity, chemical analysis
	Samples for full analysis at base	
Timing	Limited annual quota	
	Arranged in advance	
	Unannounced	
	Carte blanche	

is often misunderstood: a considerable portion is the collection, collation, and analysis of public information. This part is essential to the efficient working of an inspection system, and for it to be duplicated would appear to be an unnecessary expense. As for the more convert functions of an intelligence service, it would appear to be beyond credibility that there would be no transmission of information between intelligence and inspection. In the case of national systems—that is, adversary inspection—there would be little problem from the free flow of information, providing sources could be safeguarded. In the case of international inspection systems, there would be more serious problems in using covert information obtained by national intelligence organizations.

It should not be forgotten that there is a distinction between the objectives of inspection and intelligence. Inspection is intended to discover whether an agreement is being violated—with, if possible, some supporting data of the magnitude of the violation—and to deter violations through fear of discovery. Intelligence is intended to gather as much information as possible about as many different activities as possible; and it aims to estimate the magnitude, type, quality, and future expectations of activity in a variety of fields.

SAMPLE AND PROGRESSIVE INSPECTION

"Sample inspection," in the context of arms control and disarmament, is different from the inspection of samples of material although similar in general principles. According to the model for one type of sample inspection, a country or area would be divided by the host country into, say, 100 districts of approximately equal military value—e.g., the size of the district could be related to population, military establishments, etc. Ten of these districts would be selected by the inspecting authority, it being assumed that the districts selected are representative of all the districts. If the districts are truly similar, there are mathematical methods of calculating the degree of confidence that can be placed in the total military situation in the country. But sample inspection is now considered a rather naïve concept. It is doubtful if at any time military officers and others charged with the national security would be sufficiently trusting to accept a method which relies so much upon the honesty of an opponent in allocating his resources or, it would be realistic to say, upon little-understood juggling with figures. The objections are that the sample may not be representative for a variety of reasons; inspections may not discover all of the violations in the inspected area; and, given notice, certain manufacturing plants and deployed equipment could be dispersed or disguised.

Progressive inspection can take two forms: progressive access inspection, and progressive zonal inspection; in the latter the area under inspection is increased in stages but the type of inspection does not change. Progressive access inspection is of a fixed area but with increasing severity of inspection, which could be in the following stages: external verification, military attache and visitor privileges, inspection of declared facilities, quota inspections (i.e., a fixed number per year), inspection of key transport facilities (such as ports, harbors, airfields, and rail junctions), and, eventually, "carte-blanche" inspections.

Progressive inspection and graduated inspection are similar, if not the same, concepts.

OBSERVATION POSTS

In the literature of arms control, the terms "control post" and "observation post" describe a unit in a network of such posts, set up for the purpose of watching for military activity. The posts are generally manned by a staff supplied and reporting to either the opponent or an international organization. The word "control" in English may carry the connotation that those manning the post have rights of supervision—for example, by denial of access to troops of the host country. This meaning may be even stronger in other languages and may lead to misinterpretation of intentions. In fact, these forms of supervision are so unlikely to be agreed upon (unless a victor/vanquished relationship exists) that they are rarely considered as subject to agreement. It is thus good practice to use the term "observation post."

There are a large number of variables that have to be taken into account when setting up an observation post system. The decision as to whether the system should be an international system, with personnel supplied through, and responsible to, the United Nations or some other international agency, or whether it is an "adversary inspection" system, with personnel supplied by an opponent or an alliance, will possibly be subject more to broader political attitudes than to the technical requirements. Here it will be noted that adversary inspections may have advantages in introducing a high level of expertise, a reduced possibility of the individual's being suborned, and better guarantees against dangerous technical information (e.g., of nuclear weapons) finding its way to third parties.

Changes in force levels may be detected at the point of origin, during transit, or at the destination; and the choice of which principle to inspect for determines the main characteristics of the system. Observation posts may be limited to fixed posts at major ports and other entry points to the zone subject to arms control; other posts may be sited at airfields. Limited mobile patrols between the fixed units and along the zone boundaries would increase intrusiveness; the next step would be supplementary barriers within the zone; finally, there would be freedom for the teams to move freely within the zone. A minimal deployment would involve a comparatively small number of observation posts, but a balance is likely to be proposed between mobility and numbers. Compared with a very wide mesh, a "fine mesh" system would have many posts and numerous linking patrols.

What could be agreed might depend very much more on the nature of the societies than on technical/military judgment. The contribution of the latter might be to evaluate the reliabilities of different systems and thereby to indicate the minimum system that would provide adequate and timely warning of infringement. Another factor affecting the density of observation posts is the extent of the zone covered by agreement. An agreement covering Europe alone could require different deployments from one that included the United States and the Soviet Union. The purpose of the agreement would influence the density of posts in different parts of the zone. For an agreement limited to conventional weapons but extending to include Europe, the United States, and the Soviet Union there would most likely be a high density of posts near the common frontier, with a decreasing density at greater depth into the territories. An agreement relating to the state of preparedness of strategic missiles would conceivably have control posts at launch sites and none elsewhere. It is possible that the observation post systems on either side might be different in deployment for similar effectiveness: in Western Europe there are many transport routes into Central Europe, but in Eastern Europe there are fewer and more widely spaced traffic routes. For adequate coverage some fixed posts in Western Europe might be traded for mobile posts in Eastern Europe.

Communication of information back to the headquarters organization could be by several methods. The first decision would have to be whether the information can be treated as secret to the country or alliance carrying out the observation. To permit information to be sent out in code would introduce doubts as to its being limited to that which was permitted—in other words, whether the system was being used to transmit espionage and intelligence material. To require information to be "en clair" might cause the host country to suspect that inspectors were circumventing regulations. It is possible, even likely, that members of observation teams would be targets for security surveillance; and attempts might be made to recruit them as agents. These possibilities are mentioned to indicate the variety of problems that must be faced. The actual process of despatching information might be telegram, teleprinter, radio, courier, or diplomatic pouch. Suspicion of the clandestine transmission of information other than that related to the task might lead to preference for the teleprinter, which provides permanent records of both outgoing and incoming messages.

The status of the inspector and members of his family could vary considerably; there could be full diplomatic immunities, or restriction to full rights as foreigners, or to rights as citizens.

Movement could be completely free or limited to land, sea, or air passages and by bookings available to the public. Some areas might be prohibited, or travel might be permitted only within a zone of duty. Prior notification or requests for permission for journeys might be required. The notification might have to specify a complete itinerary of routes, timing, and stopping places. As far as inspection of individual military bases, factories, warehouses, railway yards, airfields, and ports is concerned, this might be completely free but would more likely be limited; and some places—for example, laboratories—might be banned completely. Access and times of visiting might be limited. Inspection might be restricted to what could be seen from public places, such as the highway. During a visit an inspector might have certain rights in obtaining information. He might have the right to see everything, to the extent of his curiosity and endurance. Rights might include examination of records, questioning of personnel, or private interviews without the management, guide, escort, or interpreter present.

Permitted inspection equipment could be limited to "eyeball" inspections but might include maps, directories, cameras (both ordinary and advanced), tape recorders, monitors for radioactivity, and other specialized sensors. The vehicles used might be limited to public transport or could include private cars, special military vehicles, motor patrol boats, helicopters, and light aircraft.

The inspectors might have to be easily identifiable by having to wear uniforms, or it may be considered more appropriate for them to be inconspicuous and to wear civilian clothes. Similarly, vehicles belonging to the organization might have to carry insignia. Inspectors might have to be accompanied while on duty by an escort, guard, driver, interpreter, or assistant from the host country. This requirement would not be entirely restrictive, since it would facilitate journeys and activities, help in identifying military units, and mollify military police. This last feature might be particularly valuable if the inspectors had special rights—for example, in regard to counting or photographing military equipment or setting up manned or unmanned sensors—since not all security-minded individuals in the host country would be aware of the extent of these rights and attempting to enforce them might prove dangerous.

PRACTICAL EXPERIENCE: THE MILITARY LIAISON MISSIONS AND THE ARMS CONTROL AGENCY

Several inspection systems are now operating in Europe, including both adversary and self-inspection systems. The inspectors are generally serving or retired military personnel. Morris Janowitz has anticipated that one of the functions that will devolve on military personnel in the future will be participation in political and military schemes for arms control and inspection.[2] One form of inspection that has been very successful, within inevitable limitations, has been the military liaison missions. They are not well known, and this may have been a factor in ensuring a strictly professional attitude toward the tasks of the teams.

Six of these missions have been active in Germany for over twenty years. The three Western units consisted, according to a report in 1967, of 14, 18, and 31 American, French, and British personnel, respectively, all but one serving military personnel.[3] The missions are accredited to the commander-in-chief of the Group of Soviet Forces, Germany. The official headquarters of the Western missions is at Potsdam, a suburb of Berlin; and the units are often called the "Potsdam missions." The Soviet units are accredited to commanders-in-chief of the U.S. army, French forces in Germany, and British Army of the Rhine.

From the point of view of arms control, the military liaison missions are interesting. They provide governments with information on the nature and extent of each other's military activities in Germany, which are, of course, particularly important at times of crisis. Insofar as the missions have certain rights to travel and make observations, they serve as an example of mobile inspection teams and may also be a prototype for future exchanges of military missions.

Another inspection system that is operating in Europe is the Western European Union's Arms Control Agency, although only in continental Western Europe. This operates a form of self-inspection within the NATO alliance.

Advantages that could be derived from using and further deploying and widening the scope of the agency are that it exists and already has a structure, experience, and methods of operation that it would otherwise take time to develop. In addition it has its own extensive documentation available, contacts with other sources of documents, and experts in various disciplines who are experienced in devising and applying control measures. It possesses many contacts with experts and organizations in a number of countries; and these contacts are fostered by technical information visits and symposia, together with formal channels for information, advice, and assistance from member countries and other countries not covered by the agreement. An essential feature of such an organization as the Arms Control Agency is that it provides additional sources for cross-checking information tendered through official channels and can give details of steps taken to maintain and improve weapons systems that are under development or that, for other reasons, are not yet within the jurisdiction of the agency.

FIRST LOOK

The U.S. Arms Control and Disarmament Agency and the U.S. Department of Defense have jointly conducted a number of investigations and trials over a wide spectrum of possible arms control agreements. Among them have been trials of inspection procedures suitable for conventional forces. The size and scope of the trials were increased at each stage until by 1966 the next logical stage was a fairly large-scale experiment. In this the activities of a number of teams were investigated and their observations integrated with other sources of information, such as aerial surveillance. Since the earlier trials had been conducted in the United States, it was desirable that the new experiment should take place in an environment that would be foreign to the inspection organization and individual inspectors but in which the additional problem of a different language could be avoided. These considerations led the U.S. authorities to propose that field test 15 should be carried out in Great Britain. The British authorities agreed to the proposals and a joint military planning and exercise staff were assembled for Exercise First Look, conducted in the summer of 1968. Civilian scientists joined the team to provide expertise, particularly in the design of statistical experiments.

Previous work had shown that the optimum inspection team has two members, a team leader and an assistant inspector/driver. Team leaders were junior officers from all the U.S. services: Marines, Army, Navy, and Air Force. Assistant inspector/drivers were British NCO's from the Army and Air Force; it was decided that their special knowledge of unit equipment, uniforms, and insignia would fairly represent that which would have been acquired in an organization that had been operating for some time and would compensate for the necessarily limited training that could be given to the inspectors.

The target for inspection was an area of approximately 2,000 square miles in southern England containing some 40 major military units, such as Army bases, airfields, stores and depots, and many small units of various kinds. The area comprised both countryside and towns.

The main problem that the test was designed to solve was the number of two-man teams necessary to inspect the area to a satisfactory level. Other factors for which it was important to obtain data, besides the number of teams, included the degree of access permitted to military bases (i.e., were the inspectors allowed in, or could they inspect only from outside?), the equipment allowed (e.g., cameras for recording vehicle markings and numbers), use of unattended sensors (e.g., to discover if dispersed airfields were in use), availability of aerial surveillance information, whether a deliberate evasion was being practiced, and the use of data-handling equipment (e.g., computers).

The organization of the test was to have a number of inspection systems working in parallel on the same data but with each system having different facilities—for example, different access, equipment, etc. The performance of each of the different inspection systems (23 in all) was continuously observed by the test headquarters, which was kept informed of the real situation through liaison officers stationed in the target units (i.e., those under observation).

An objective criterion for performance was the estimate of aircraft, tanks, etc., as compared with the actual numbers. However, estimation of the state of readiness for war of the forces concerned—that is, order of battle—was considered more important. This is a more subjective judgment that relies on military experience. Data were collected on standard forms that were adapted for computer analysis. Where permitted, the analysis was available to the chief inspector of each group of inspection teams by the following day; for other teams a post-test analysis was carried out. The test generated a massive amount of information, all of which has not yet been analyzed in detail, although some results are well defined.

Unattended sensors were built around commercially available four-track tape recorders. Simultaneous records were made from two microphones, an infrared sensor, and a seismometer. With experience it was possible to distinguish, for example, between different types of aircraft and also the direction of movement. Although with modern techniques it would have been possible to reduce the equipment to quite small dimensions, it was decided that in order to conform to the overt nature of the test, the sensor equipment should not be so small as to arouse suspicion; and even an improved version was about the size of a suitcase. During the test a method for computer analysis of these records was developed.

Aerial surveillance was designed to be nonintrusive; missions were flown at 40,000 feet and were requested and specified in advance. However, the weather was unusually overcast, and about a third of the missions were aborted. Aerial surveillance did not increase the efficiency of inspection, but this could be explained in part by delays in processing the information and lack of experience in its interpretation. In other circumstances aerial surveillance has been shown to be effective, and it could be invaluable in rapidly setting up arms control in an area about which little is known; fortunately permanent military establishments are easily recognized from their regular arrangement, and their purpose can often be guessed—for example, earth embankments and wide spacing will indicate explosive manufacture or storage.

Perhaps the most surprising and important result was that the smallest inspection organization (one team of two in 1,000 square miles), particularly if it had access to bases, can perform efficiently; increasing the number of teams increases effectiveness only by relatively small amounts.

NATO PROPOSALS FOR BALANCED FORCE REDUCTIONS

Communiques issued by the NATO Council have spoken of studies carried out on balanced force reductions in Europe. Despite setbacks the Council has said that the studies will continue, in preparation for the time when the atmosphere for fruitful discussions is more favorable.

Few details of the studies have been released, but it is possible to speculate on some of the problems that would have to be considered. The area covered by the treaty could be all of the NATO and Warsaw Pact countries, Europe without Russia, or a more limited zone. The boundaries of the zone could be national frontiers or natural boundaries, such as rivers or mountains. As regards nationalities of troops, the agreement could apply to all troops in the zone or stationed troops only—that is, those not native to the country—or to indigenous troops. Troops will include professionals and conscripts, and these may require different treatment. Professional troops would be expected to be better trained, more suitable for redeployment, and difficult to replace once demobilized; with conscription, large numbers of trained manpower are available for call-up. Problems would arise about the amount of annual training permitted and the number of troops that can be mobilized at any one time. The establishments of units could be at peacetime or wartime levels; only forward—that is, "teeth"—units could be controlled, or rear units could also be included in the agreement. The agreement could be symmetrical—that is, the reductions on both sides could be of the same type—or asymmetrical— for example, with an exchange of tanks for strike aircraft. Troops surplus to the limits permitted by the agreement could be demobilized or redeployed out of the zone.

Reinforcement times would be important and would have to be taken into account; indeed, they might be a major factor in setting a bottom limit to permitted forces. The Soviet Union can reinforce by road and rail, whereas the United States has to deploy across the Atlantic; but this is becoming easier with the introduction of very large aircraft, such as the 747 and C-five, and (in the future) with very fast supersonic aircraft. It would, therefore, be possible to move American troops, but not heavy equipment, such as tanks, guns, and missile launchers, relatively quickly. The United States might require to stockpile equipment in Europe while having duplicate equipment at the home bases for training purposes, a system known as double basing. On the other hand, it might be argued that it would be equitable, because of better transport facilities, for the Soviet Union to have to take its surplus equipment back to Russia. When troops are demobilized, rather than redeployed, their equipment could be taken out of the area or destroyed. There are many other points that would require some attention: if forces have to be compared, is it sufficient to evaluate them man for man, or should differences, such as the quality of leadership, tactics, training, morale, reliability, intelligence, equipment, and reserves be taken into account?

Aircraft pose particular problems, for it is difficult to equate aircraft of different types; a straightforward percentage reduction of the main categories might be one way. At one time the question of ploughing up some airfields was also considered, but the introduction of V/STOL aircraft will make dispersal airfields less important in the future. The actual wording of an agreement could be simple—for example, there could be a reduction of units by the same fraction rather than by absolute numbers[4]—but all the above criteria must be considered by those designing the agreement.

INSPECTION OF PRODUCTION FACILITIES FOR CONVENTIONAL WEAPONS

Obtaining agreement for adversary or international inspection of plants that are actually manufacturing weapons would be difficult because there might be dissemination of military technology to third parties in international teams, there could be transfer of technical manufacturing know-how to the adversary, and the state of art in current weapons would be revealed to the opponent thus facilitating the manufacture of counter weapons. A problem that would arise in connection with verification of the levels of production would be the specification of those items subject to inspection. As Lefebure has pointed out, the warmaking potential of a nation is related to its total manufacturing capacity.[5] To some extent this is still true, despite the increased emphasis that must be put on forces-in-being at the beginning of a conflict.

It is very difficult to know where to draw a line between material that could be used for military purposes and that which has only a civil employment; transport aircraft, heavy trucks, bulldozers, radios, radar, even clothing and food supplies are items of normal civilian requirement which have military significance. It is better, in practical terms, to draw the line at major items that can be used only for military purposes, such as armored fighting vehicles, fighter and bomber aircraft, and naval ships. An advantage is that all of these tend to be manufactured in specialized plant and yards, thus easing the task of inspection.

It may be possible to narrow the area of inspection to some key components, such as rocket motors; however, if the remainder of the system is not subjected to some form of inspection, covert manufacture of the inspected item might be attempted. Probably the best arrangement is a vigorous inspection of the vital item and a more general inspection for other components, manufacture of which could indicate a potential for producing the armament.

NOTES

1. Theo Sommer, "A Chance for Europe," Survival (January 1969).

2. Morris Janowitz, The Professional Soldier (New York: Free Press, 1964).

3. Thomas S. Lough, "The Military Liaison Missions in Germany," Journal of Conflict Resolution (June 1967).

4. Asymmetries between NATO and the Warsaw Pact are discussed in Ivor Richards, "A European Defence Policy," Survival (March 1970).

5. Lefebure, Op. cit.

CHAPTER

19

CHEMICAL AND BIOLOGICAL WARFARE

HISTORY OF CHEMICAL AND BIOLOGICAL WARFARE

Chemical and biological agents have a long history of use in warfare: poisoning of wells, use of noxious smokes, introduction of disease among the opponent's troops, and similar unorthodox means for attacking an enemy have been employed in making war. Modern chemical weapons in the form of "war gases" were used on a large scale in World War I and were responsible for many casualties. Many of these casualties recovered from the effects of gassing; indeed, the ratio of fatalities to those affected was lower than that for more conventional weapons. This has led to some rather optimistic speculation as to the comparative "humanity" of chemical and biological agents and has been used as an argument in favor of continuing research on the way the casualty figures were obtained. Most of the quoted statistics refer to American forces, for which it apparently was a rule that all who had been exposed to gas, to whatever extent, should report for medical examination. This would have led to an inflated number of total casualties, many of whom may not have been injured in the slightest. Despite arguments in favor of chemical weapons, the great majority of the nations considered them inhumane and were in favor of banning their use in war, with the result that an international agreement, the Geneva Protocol, was signed in 1925 prohibiting their use except in retaliation.

During World War II chemical and biological agents were not used despite the advances that had been made in development of new agents and in the methods of manufacture in the chemical industry. It is not known how effective the Geneva Protocol was in preventing use of the chemical weapons that were available and in large-scale production by both sides and how much restraint was from mutual deterrence. It is likely that the Geneva Protocol provided a set of rules, the breaking of which would offend neutrals and permit the other side to retaliate, with results it would be difficult to anticipate. Certainly there were occasions when there were strong temptations to use chemical weapons. The Germans had developed particularly lethal chemical agents that they had manufactured in large quantities and that could have been used on one or other front or against cities that were within range of aircraft and even of artillery. It has been reported that gas warfare was considered by the British, but one of the factors against this was possible retaliation against the masses of troops on the Normandy beachheads. In the Pacific campaign the United States was faced with enormous losses. Conditions were particularly favorable to the use of chemical gases, in that each of the islands to be attacked was isolated, so that other land areas would not be affected by wind drift; the enemy was deeply entrenched and well protected against high explosives; and the United States had air superiority and long-range naval guns. Chemical weapons of the deliberately poisoning types were not used in the Indochina, Korean, Algerian, Vietnam, or many of the other conflicts since the end of World War II. The only known uses of chemical weapons have been on a relatively small scale. How far mutual deterrence by chemical and biological agents has been effective will be further considered later in this chapter.

CLASSIFICATION OF CHEMICAL AND BIOLOGICAL AGENTS

The U.S. Army defines chemical warfare as tactics and techniques of warfare by use of toxic chemical agents; biological warfare is employment of living organisms, toxic biological products, and chemical plant growth regulators to produce death or casualties in man, animals, or defense against such action.

A number of classifications of various value have been made of chemical and biological agents. Some classifications are on the basis of effects on the victims—for example, agents that are likely to be lethal, those which will incapacitate for a period, and those which harass. Other classifications are based on the chemical and biological nature of the agents. Table 25 reproduces the broad grouping used in the report of a group of international experts for the Secretary-General of the United Nations. This report has been an important and authoritative source of information and opinion; some of its general conclusions will be referred to in this chapter. The experts thought that it was difficult to make a division between

TABLE 25

Classification of Chemical and Biological Agents

Effective Against Man and Animals
Nerve gases
Blister gases (vesicants)
Choking agents
Blood agents
Toxins
Tear and harassing gases
Psychochemicals
Effective Against Plants
Herbicides/defoliants

Source: United Nations, "Report to the Secretary-General on Chemical and Bacteriological (Biological) Weapons and the Effects of Their Possible Use," A/7575 (July 1, 1968).

chemical and biological process, even if this is not fully understood at present. However, a simple and common-sense differentiation between chemical and biological agents that has been suggested is to call chemical warfare the technique of poisoning and biological warfare the technique of destruction by disease. In the remainder of this section it is assumed that this distinction can be made, as can one between agents of high and those of comparatively low lethality.

CHEMICAL-BIOLOGICAL WARFARE AND NUCLEAR WARFARE

The use of chemical and biological agents as weapons of mass destruction can be compared with nuclear bombardment. From the point of view of an aggressor, territory could be taken over without destroying property; and left intact, for example, would be radio and television stations, which could be used to control the population. With some agents the defenders might be only temporarily incapacitated, so that altogether there need not be widespread destruction and loss of life. All this could be achieved at lower cost than for a nuclear arsenal.[1]

In the case of war between nuclear powers, after the destruction of the opponent's nuclear retaliating capacity by a successful first strike, chemical and biological agents could be used against his cities, which could be seized virtually intact.

CHEMICAL WEAPONS

The descriptions of the various types of agents that follow are in rather general terms; details of composition and effects can be found in several of the references quoted.

Chemical warfare was defined by I. F. Watkins as the "intentional use in war of toxic chemicals to produce casualties either by incapacitation or by death."[2] Incapacitation can be caused by chemicals, which need not be lethal, that produce a wide variety of temporary and reversible effects, such as blindness, paralysis, and mental confusion. We return to this matter later.

Although chemical warfare agents are often called "poison gas," most of them are in fact liquid at ordinary temperatures, while others are solid; the agents are dispensed as mists, smokes, or sprays. The manner in which an agent can be dispersed and used depends to a great extent upon its vapor pressure. Liquids with a high vapor pressure—that is, those which evaporate rapidly—are more suitable for a surprise attack and are nonpersistent. Solids are dispensed as aerosols; that is, in a finely divided form that tends to remain suspended and drift with the wind. In this way they can also be used for a surprise attack without long-term contamination of the territory. Liquid agents with a low vapor pressure are persistent and can be used to contaminate terrain, clothing, entrenchments, vehicles, fortifications, and other military equipment.

From the above, it might be considered that some agents are more particularly suited for attack, while others are more suited for defense, in that they could be used to provide a barrier against troops moving forward. This kind of barrier would be only partly effective against troops with protective equipment but, even so, could reduce mobility and hinder reinforcement to some extent. These alternative uses of chemical agents do not appear to have been discussed in the open literature; but such a distinction is, in any case, only one of degree—a surprise counterattack could be carried out against troops massing for an assault, or persistent agents could be used to deny reinforcements to a front under attack or to protect the flanks of an attacking force.

Since World War II chemical weapons have increased in effectiveness in a number of ways. Lethality has been increased in some types of agents, while others have been developed for special purposes; and the expansion of the chemical industry has not only increased the potential for bulk manufacture but has also introduced new processes. The means for dispensing agents have been improved (the U.S. Department of the Army has listed the following delivery systems: mortar, howitzer, gun, rocket, missile, fighter aircraft, bomber aircraft, and bomblets and spray),[3] and large quantities have been stockpiled by both the United States and the Soviet Union.

Increased research during World War II was directed mainly to organophosphorus compounds ("nerve gases"), nitrogen mustards, and organic fluorine compounds. Tabun, an organophosphorus agent, was discovered in a search for improved insecticides. It is believed that more potent poisons than the nerve gases have been discovered, but some of these highly active chemicals have reversible effects—the victims recovered completely—and this discovery has led to a new concept. Some highly lethal, naturally occurring compounds that are known and have been isolated may, for various reasons, not be suitable as chemical agents; the requirements for a usable chemical agent are many and include availability of raw materials or intermediate products, ease of production, long storage life, resistance to deterioration during dispensing (which may be by explosion or a burning type of canister), and suitability for use in the field.

Little publicity has been given to the benefits from manufacture of chemical agents, yet major contributions have been made to our knowledge of airborne particulates, atmospheric turbulence and diffusion, filtration, design and testing of protective devices, safety standards for operators, and improvements in design of plant. Many of these advances have benefited the chemical industry in general and have been invaluable to the developing atomic energy industry. In addition, some of the compounds themselves and the protective chemicals have led to unanticipated advances in medicine and medical science.

BIOLOGICAL WEAPONS

Biological warfare was described above as "the technique of destruction by disease," and it has been said that the biological weapon is the only self-propagating weapon in existence.

There is no new principle in the use of disease as an agent of war; most wars have been accompanied by widespread disease among combatants and populations—indeed, war and conquest have often been the means for spreading illnesses into areas that had previously been free of them. There have also been cases when disease has been deliberately introduced among the forces and subjects of an opponent.

What is new about biological weapons is the scale on which they might be produced and disseminated, as compared with the spread of natural disease; their effectiveness as lethal or incapacitating agents; and their potential as weapons of mass destruction. This immense increase in the potential of biological agents has come about as a result of an explosion in knowledge and techniques of biological science and engineering since World War II.

Biological weapons are generally developed from naturally occurring diseases of man, animals, and crops. They can be made more virulent by selecting particular strains, possibly after artificially inducing mutations by exposure to nuclear radiation or to mutant-producing chemicals. Mixing material in solutions of counter agents of increasing strength, strains that survive can breed to provide bulk quantities of powerful agents that are resistant to countermeasures.

An essential difference between chemical and biological weapons is that chemical weapons, to be effective, must be present at least to a certain minimum concentration, while with biological agents only a few molecules (that is, a very low concentration in air) may be enough to infect. Subsequently the agent reproduces within the victim and may, with some species, become a source of infection to others. Thus the amount of a biological agent to produce an infective dose in the air at the target area could be quite small, perhaps only a few pounds of agent. The amount required to be dispensed will depend on the size of the target and the fraction of the attacked population it is intended to infect; in the case of diseases that can be transmitted, a high initial dose will increase the speed with which the epidemic will spread throughout the population and, thus, the load on the medical services attempting to cope with the outbreak. Some biological agents are specifically intended to attack crops and thus deny food to the enemy—in other words, to cause starvation.

There are some requirements that limit the suitability of biological agents. It must be possible to produce the agent in quantity, and it must have a reasonably long shelf life; dissemination must not reduce its toxicity; and the agent must be in a form that can be ingested—that is, as a gas, vapor, or aerosol. The disease must be difficult to inoculate against in advance of an attack, or to treat when contracted; and a large number of casualties of sufficient severity must result from the attack. Some chemical agents, we have seen, are not intended to be lethal but to disable the opponent temporarily; there are also biological agents that would induce a more or less severe illness but few deaths. General problems of incapacitating agents are returned to later.

UNITED NATIONS REPORT A/7575

The increasing dangers from chemical-biological warfare have been reflected in the concern shown in the United Nations; at the suggestion of the delegations meeting at the Eighteen Nations Disarmament Conference the Secretary-General of the United Nations was invited to call together a group of experts of international repute to advise him. The secretary-general's report has been published, and some of the main conclusions are the following:[4]

Gas has been used in warfare and has caused casualties, and newer gases are even more lethal

Nonlethal agents, when used in war, can enhance the effectiveness of other weapons

There is no evidence that biological agents have been used in war, and their effectiveness has yet to be estimated; nevertheless, the potential importance can be guessed from the effects of infective diseases that have accompanied wars in the past

The Geneva Protocol (1925) may have been instrumental in preventing the use of chemical agents in World War II

The outstanding characteristic of chemical and biological agents is the variability and even the unpredictability of effects; these agents are additional to, and would not replace, other weapons

It is impossible to protect populations against widespread attacks, and military units could be protected for only a short time

Large-scale biological epidemics could overwhelm existing medical services

Once chemical and biological agents had been used in war, further escalation would most certainly follow.

HARASSING AGENTS

Harassing agents could be either biological or chemical agents; but because of the slower development of symptoms with biological agents and the risks to the attacking troops, practical harassing agents are much more likely to be chemical agents.

The object of a harassing agent is to make it impossible for opposing troops either to stay in an area or to carry out their military duties, including the proper handling of their weapons. Harassing agents are not necessarily intended to be lethal; but in order to provide a sufficient concentration in the atmosphere over the entire area under attack, there may be lethal concentrations where the warheads burst. Partly to avoid this problem, but more for economy of agent, the charge may be separated into bomblets.

Because harassing agents can cause death in high concentrations, there has been a reluctance to consider lethal and normally nonlethal agents separately. This is because it is believed that it would be difficult to define the difference and because use of a nonlethal harassing agent could well lead to escalation to lethal agents. In fact, it might be relatively easy to establish a technical criterion to define a difference between the two types of agents in terms of the concentrations in air to cause deaths of healthy adults (that is, of soldiers). Lethal concentrations of harassing agents would be more difficult to build up; the heavy concentrations around the dispersing munition would not persist long enough for exposure to a lethal dose, and unprotected personnel would probably be driven from the area. Where deaths do occur from the use of harassing agents, they are much more likely to be from unexpected use—aggravated, no doubt, by battle conditions. However, harassing agents may also be used to drive troops out of cover so that they can be attacked with other weapons.

INCAPACITATING AGENTS

Incapacitating agents are intended to render the victim incapable of resistance by being made temporarily insensible or mentally deranged or by loss of some essential faculties. By this means it would be possible to reduce resistance and to effect the capture of bodies of troops.

Both chemical and biological agents could be used as incapacitating agents. Chemical agents would act more rapidly and would be more suitable against troops; biological agents, because of the period of incubation, might be suitable only for use against populations and, by impairing their health over a long period, both reduce their support for the war and put a severe strain on medical and other services, thus adversely affecting the functioning of a society.

RIOT-CONTROL AGENTS

Riot-control agents are similar to harassing agents, but those selected for use by the police and military engaged in police-type actions are of the lowest possible lethality compatible with being effective. The well-known British agent CS is widely used by police forces in many parts of the world. It is less dangerous than similar riot-control agents. Some of the casualties that have occurred from use of riot-control agents appear to have been from improper use; there have been instances reported in the press when canisters have been aimed directly at members of the crowd, rather than upwind. Other casualties have resulted when gas has been used where it cannot disperse and when the objective has been attained and the crowd has dispersed, but the public have not been informed of what to do to avoid further effects. These problems could be overcome by better training and preparation.

The use of riot gas even for police actions rouses great antipathy, but it is difficult to see any effective alternative. Water cannons are large, cumbersome, not very effective—and, of course, not always available; involving fire brigades is objectionable for several reasons; clubs and batons can result in injuries—those to the head may cause permanent brain damage—affect only the front ranks of the rioters, and expose the police to casualties and accusation of brutality; firearms, of course, can kill and injure.

HERBICIDES AND DEFOLIANTS

Chemical compounds that act upon green foliage are commonly used in agriculture for the destruction or control of weeds and for the clearing of tracts of ground in preparation for the planting of crops. These chemicals are made in quantity in technically advanced countries. For military purposes similar but more active compounds have been developed that would not be permitted to be used for civil purposes because of their toxicity to man and animals.

Herbicides and defoliants have been used on a massive scale by the Americans in Vietnam, for the clearing of cover in the field of fire of outposts and bases and from the sides of roads and trails, to reduce the possibility of ambush, and also for the destruction of food crops in enemy territory. Objections to the use of these materials are based on their poisonous effects on many species, including man; the ecological damage that might result from the destruction of vegetation; and, in the case of food crops, the reliance on starvation as a means of warfare.

Apart from the link with other chemical weapons, it is difficult to see how improving the field of fire by the use of herbicides is essentially different from felling trees and burning undergrowth, provided it is not done extravagantly. Ecological effects are related to the more general problem of contamination of the biosphere. Destruction of crops as a means of denying the enemy food is akin to blockade, an established means of warfare. Experience has shown, however, that young, fit males are the last sector of the population to be affected by shortage of food. Much more likely is starvation of the more vulnerable of the civil population—the old, the very young, and nursing mothers—which could even lead to enhancement of the determination of the troops not to give in to an inhumane enemy.

COMPARISON OF CHEMICAL AND BIOLOGICAL AGENTS

One of the possible strategies in arms control is to give special attention to biological agents. In order to see if this would be possible, two tables have been prepared in which chemical and biological agents are compared. Table 26 lists some of the main parameters of the agents; in Table 27 a large number of similarities and differences are presented. This classification is to some extent subjective, but the selections are thought to be reasonable.

TABLE 26

Comparison of Chemical and Biological Agents for Operational Criteria

Criteria	Chemical Agents	Biological Agents
Toxicity	Milligrams	Micrograms to picograms
Environment		Affected by sunlight and high temperatures
Speed of operation against men	Minutes to hours	Incubation period of few days to weeks
Against crops	Days	Weeks
Duration of effects	Kill or fairly rapid recovery	Days to months of illness, death or slow recovery
Specifity	Attacks all animal species	Can be species-specific

The purposes of these tables are to show how far these agents can be considered as in one group, and to what degree chemical and biological agents are sufficiently different to be considered as two groups.

DEFENSE AGAINST CHEMICAL AND BIOLOGICAL AGENTS

Investigation into the effects of chemical and biological agents, detection, antidotes, and protective equipment has been carried out in a number of countries. In general it said that troops could be given some protection against most chemical agents for a limited

TABLE 27

Checklist Comparing Chemical and Biological Agents

Criteria	Similar	Dissimilar
Previous history of use		x
Cost of R&D	x	
Link with civil research	x	
Cost of production		x
Raw materials and intermediates used in industry	x	x
Size of production plant	x	
Precautions in manufacture	x	
Type of manufacturing plant	x	
Experimental techniques	x	
Trial techniques	x	
Shelf life		x
Present deployment		x
Present stockpiles		x
Area affected by same weight		x
Lethal dose		x
Amounts for same target		x
Multiplication within victim		x
Delivery systems/munitions	x	x
Possibility of sabotage/covert delivery		x
Offensive/defensive use		x
Damage to structures	x	
Maximum effects on man	x	
Persistence in target areas	x	x
Protective clothing, masks	x	
Time to identify		x
Time before onset of symptoms		x
Decontamination	x	
Load on medical services		x
Risk of transmission		x
Contagious		x
Possibility of mutation		x
Effect on ecology	x	x
Effect on food chains	x	x
Effect on soil erosion	x	x
Persistent infectious disease		x
Effect on domestic animals		x
Police use		x

Note: Because of the range in properties within each of the two groups, some items are checked in both columns, indicating that there is an overlap of properties.

time, but probably at some cost in mobility and fighting effectiveness. Highly mechanized forces could be self-contained, with built-in filters, monitors, and other equipment, and would be able to evacuate the attacked area rapidly. There are, however, new compounds for which the lethal dose is minute, which would almost certainly result in many casualties if used against troops.

Defence against chemical and biological agents involves a number of stages. Detection may be relatively easy for troops in the case of many chemical and biological agents, from the types of munitions used, the effects on victims and by chemical indicators. Biological agents are more likely to be dispensed secretly, and the effects are more likely to develop slowly. As soon as the presence of an agent is detected, warnings must be issued to other possible targets and the agent must be identified for counteraction. In anticipation of an attack, troops and possibly civilians must be provided with suitable protection—which includes masks, impermeable clothing, ointments, shelters, and stocks of food and clothing. After the attack the area and victims may have to be decontaminated if a persistent agent has been employed. Medical precautions that must be taken include prophylaxis to reduce vulnerability and arrangements for the treatment of victims.

Some of these precautions could require large numbers of highly skilled personnel with costly equipment; and they would have to be provided if the opponent was known to have deployed chemical and biological agents, whether they were actually used or not.

Britain appears to be particularly vulnerable to attack with biological agents which could be released by aircraft, ship, or submarine above or in the international waters of the Channel. The prevailing winds from the southwest would carry the agent across the country.[5]

Britain has experimental establishments for investigation of means of defense against chemical and biological agents in which a variety of defensive clothing has been developed, as well as gas masks. An early warning system has been invented in which a laser beam can be trained on the wake of a suspected aircraft to investigate the nature of any airborne particulate clouds that have been released.

DETERRENCE

However well-developed defenses against chemical and biological agents may be, there seems little chance that they could be completely effective in protecting the civil population. Many countries therefore rely on deterrence rather than defense. Deterrence can be from the possibility of retaliation or from the adverse effects on world opinion.

The Geneva Protocol forbids the use of chemical and biological agents in war, but many countries have reserved their right to use these agents in retaliation if they are attacked. The object of making this reservation is to establish the possibility of retaliation as a deterrent. In order for a deterrent to be effective, it must be possible to carry out such a threat—in other words, there must be the physical means for carrying out retaliation. The capacity to prepare chemical and biological agents—that is, a large and developed chemical industry that could rapidly be converted to manufacture chemical and biological agents—is not considered enough by many of those responsible for national defense, nor is a well-developed but inevitably limited ability in defense. What is thought to be required for a deterrent is forces-in-being.

In considering the effectiveness of deterrence by chemical and biological agents, the pressures against their use (except in a few limited instances) since the Geneva Protocol was signed should be examined. Some of the evidence that has been reviewed in the literature shows that during World War II there was mutual deterrence: the German government believed that British developments were much more advanced than they were in fact, while the British government, when air superiority was established in its favor, was inhibited from using chemical weapons because retaliation could be made against the allied beachheads in Europe. Supporting this argument in favor of deterrence by chemical and biological weapons, it has been pointed out that on the three occasions since World War I when poison gas has been used (one of these is not well established), the victims did not have the immediate, or even any, possibility of retaliation in kind.

Another aspect of deterrence is that a relatively small country with a minimum manufacturing capacity could offer deterrence against a large opponent by the threat of an uncontrollable epidemic through biological agents. This view would provide an inducement for small countries to acquire such weapons—"the poor man's atom bomb"—and for rich countries to equip themselves with a counter deterrent.

PRESENT DEVELOPMENTS

In the late 1960's the United States was spending $400 million per annum on research and development of chemical and biological weapons, as compared with $10 million per annum at the end of the Korean war. Total stocks were reported in April 1969 to be about 7,000 tons,[6] as against a total usage by both sides of 12,000 tons in World War I. Chemical weapons are deployed widely, including overseas.

Much less is known publicly about production of chemical and biological agents in Russia, but NATO experts have estimated that 350,000 tons of chemical ammunition is available for immediate use. Warsaw Pact military forces are equipped and trained for operating in a nuclear, chemical, and biological weapons environment.

ARMS CONTROL AND CHEMICAL AND BIOLOGICAL AGENTS

From what has been said above, it is apparent that chemical and biological agents have a wide range of properties and effects. A blanket condemnation and prohibition is difficult to justify while other weapons that kill by blast, projectile, and fire continue to exist. Weapons like napalm are not included in any restrictions already in existence or any that have been proposed. Nevertheless, at one end of the spectrum some chemical and biological agents can be regarded as weapons of mass destruction and some way of prohibiting them at least appears to be desirable, but it is a more open question whether the ban should be extended to prevent the employment of agents that are less damaging than many existing conventional weapons. The main reason for wishing to prohibit the whole range of chemical and biological agents is the possibility of escalation from those of lesser effect up to the mass destruction agents.

Concern over the effects of chemical and biological weapons has been expressed by scientists in many countries, and a number of the nations represented at the Eighteen Nations Disarmament Conference have considered a declaration by the United Nations General Assembly regarding prohibition of the use of chemical and biological methods of warfare; such a declaration would not have the power of a treaty. The form that it could take for best effect has been studied at ENDC.[7] In addition, there are three other possible approaches to the problem of arms control of chemical and biological agents that have been discussed at ENDC:

Obtaining the adherence of all countries to the Geneva Protocol

Revision and redefinition of the Geneva Protocol to bring the interpretations in line with current knowledge

Making special provisions against biological warfare because it is possible to separate control of biological agents and strengthen prohibitions in ways not possible for chemical agents.

To these must now be added unilateral actions to destroy stocks or to accept forms of verification. Each of these approaches has something to commend it, and each has strong political overtones.

The most important nonsignatory of the Geneva Protocol has been the United States; considerable pressure has been exerted to persuade the U.S. government to sign, although it has announced that it is bound generally to the terms, with rights of retaliation reserved.

IMPROVING THE GENEVA PROTOCOL

Several nations at the Eighteen Nations Disarmament Conference have advanced the argument that the Geneva Protocol has been successful in preventing the use of chemical and biological weapons and that all that is required is that nations not at present signatories should become so. How far nations would be prepared to trust to a "piece of paper" without the alternative assurance of an ability to retaliate or a reasonably reliable verification system has not yet been put to the test.

In any case, however, the Geneva Protocol has several shortcomings in the eyes of other powers. For example, it bans the use in war of chemical and biological weapons but does not ban research and development, manufacture, and stockpiling. Furthermore, some countries have specifically reserved their rights of retaliation. This has led to the notion that a supplementary protocol could be negotiated that banned these other activities. The problem of rights of retaliation is particularly complex, since different countries have entered the protocol without reservation, reserving rights of retaliation, or reserving rights against nonsignatories. Adherence to the protocol can thus mean different things to different people.

The main purpose in attempting to bring the protocol up to date is to remove ambiguities of wording (which exist between texts in different languages) and to clarify the position on harassing agents, incapacitating agents, riot-control agents, herbicides, and rights of retaliation.

Looking at the last of these points, it should be pointed out that retaliation implies that the weapons are available and that their use is legalized in some circumstances. In Europe, where the greatest concentration of weapons exists, the presence of chemical and biological agents would not add greatly to the general lethality of a war, and it is difficult to imagine escalation taking place in chemical and biological weapons that would not at the same time be accompanied by escalation with tactical nuclear weapons. Indeed, it is difficult to imagine any warfare in Europe that did not involve nuclear weapons. Thus, as far as the confrontation in Europe is concerned, there seems to be no good case for retaining chemical and biological agents.

The most likely use of chemical and biological agents would be by a great power against an underdeveloped power or against insurgents. In this case the possibility of deterrence by retaliation would not arise, so that a complete ban appears to be justified here as well as in Europe.

SPECIFICATION OF PROHIBITIONS

An important requirement in designing an agreement is the specification of what the ban shall include or exclude. A case can be made for retaining the present somewhat imprecise terminology of the Geneva Protocol, although this view is rarely expressed; ambiguity in international agreements sometimes serves useful political purposes.

The main problems from the technical point of view with regard to specifications are whether the definition of chemical and biological agents should be worded so as to include or exclude particular types of agents and whether the agreement should relate to both chemical and biological agents, or whether it would be more effective to seek either separate agreements or a special agreement applying to biological agents only.

In the next few paragraphs the arguments are given for a comprehensive agreement to apply to both chemical and biological agents, and then the counter arguments in favor of special treatment of biological agents. Reference should also be made to Tables 26 and 27, in which chemical and biological agents are compared and contrasted in regard to a number of parameters.

COMPREHENSIVE CONTROL OF CHEMICAL AND BIOLOGICAL AGENTS

There are broadly two opposing views held about the desirability of joint control of CW- and BW-agents. The argument in favor of a comprehensive agreement is that these agents have been considered together in the past, cannot easily be differentiated and to upset well established custom would only delay agreement. The general tenor of the opposite case is outlined in Table 28.

SPECIAL CONTROL OF BIOLOGICAL (BACTERIOLOGICAL) WEAPONS

The main argument in favor of special control of biological agents is that they are at an early stage and so could more easily be inspected and an agreement reached without the difficulties attendant upon a comprehensive agreement.

The case for special control has been made by Britain in the form of support for a draft agreement for control of biological weapons presented to the Eighteen Nations Disarmament Conference.[8] Some confusion might exist as to what comprises biological weapons in terms of the agreement. Other weapons that have effects on biological systems—such as chemical agents, incendiary agents, and herbicides—are to be excluded from the agreement. In order to make this explicit, the term "microbiological" was introduced but now appears to have been abandoned in favor of the word "bacteriological" as a qualification to "biological." Some of the arguments in favor of a special agreement are presented in Table 29.

EXCLUSIONS OF TYPES OF CHEMICAL AND BIOLOGICAL AGENTS

The next problem in designing an agreement is to decide what types of weapon should be included and excluded. By convention several types of chemical munitions are not considered as chemical weapons: incendiary agents, obscuring smokes, and, of course, chemical high explosives.

Should the agreement also exclude other general types of weapons? A principal requirement would be to ban highly lethal agents, but should harassing agents be included? We have seen that at least some of the harassing agents are of low lethality but with sufficient dose, determined by the concentration multiplied by duration of exposure, there may be some deaths. A reason for including harassing agents is that their use in war could be a step in escalation to more lethal weapons. Verification would be made exceedingly complicated if some agents were permitted to be manufactured.

TABLE 28

Arguments for Joint Control of Chemical and Biological Agents

---

Chemical and biological agents have always been considered together in the past, and there are legal precedents for continuing to do so

There is widespread condemnation of this form of warfare

This condemnation, shared by scientists and others, might be capitalized upon in the verification machinery

Chemical-biological warfare could be discussed in a wide forum, whereas the next steps in the control of nuclear weapons are, by the nature of things, more likely to be discussed privately between the United States and Soviet Union

The Geneva Protocol of 1925 has a number of ambiguities that could be rectified (if this is desirable)

Considerable technical advances have been made that should be considered

The Non-Proliferation Treaty has banned nuclear weapons in many countries, with the result that there might be an incentive to turn to chemical and biological agents, if only on the assumption that the opponent might also be doing the same thing

R&D and production are similar to those carried out in industrial laboratories and manufacturing plants: unless some kind of verification and appeals machinery was instituted, it would be impossible to be sure that suspicions were not justified

Inspection would be difficult for both chemical and biological agents

Both chemical and biological agents might be developed that produce only temporary incapacity and few serious casualties

Materials similar to both chemical and biological agents are in production for everyday use in technically advanced countries

TABLE 29

Arguments for Special Control of Biological Agents

Biological (bacteriological/microbiological) warfare has not been employed

As far as is known, there has been comparatively little investment in R&D as compared with chemical, nuclear, and conventional weapons

It might be comparatively easy to verify that large-scale testing, including field trials, was being carried out

None of the great powers appears to be contemplating first use of biological weapons

Biological weapons do not appear to be very feasible as tactical weapons but only for more or less indiscriminate strategic attacks against whole populations

Spread of infection beyond the target population would be difficult to control

Strains highly resistant to prophylaxis would be difficult to control even when the attacker decided to attempt to check the outbreak

Mutations that might occur in the microorganisms (particularly if radioactivity were also present) could produce even more resistant strains and could affect even the vaccinated population of the attacker

Biological agents need be dispensed only in very small quantities and would be more suitable for long-range strategic attack, whereas the large quantities that would be required for a chemical attack could be delivered only in the tactical battle area

Biological agents appear to be more suitable for aggression, while chemical agents, because of the hindrance they would present to the crossing of terrain, might on the whole be more suitable as defensive weapons

Because of the small amounts needed, biological agents may be delivered by many delivery systems and by clandestine means and even in peacetime, so that it would be difficult to prove that an attack had been made

On the other hand it would be necessary to use such large quantities of chemical agents that it would be impossible to disguise their use

Chemical agents are chemicals that would not normally be found in the environment, while biological agents are generally derived from naturally occurring species and are more difficult to identify: an outbreak might be spontaneous and might not be the result of an attack

Detection systems are simpler and cheaper for chemical agents than for biological agents

The most feasible means of preventing attack by chemical agents is by a prohibition on munitions and delivery systems; this does not seem possible for biological agents

Airborne chemical agents are dangerous only during the passage of the cloud; the dangers from biological agents cannot be so easily estimated, and an area might become contaminated for a long time, even years

Chemical weapons are in large-scale production; because of the existence of manufacturing plants and deployed stocks, verification would be difficult and uncertain—it might take considerable time to negotiate an agreement to cover all of these points, and in the meantime development, production, and deployment of biological weapons could continue

Troops are equipped against chemical agents so that these may be used to reduce effectiveness rather than cause casualties

Biological agents require time to take effect and the diseases may last for days, weeks, and months; chemical agents, if they do not kill, may have effects of relatively short duration

(Continued)

TABLE 29 (Continued)

Chemical agents, in the amounts necessary for effective large-scale military purposes, require chemical plants of a fair degree of complexity; a fairly numerous, trained staff; development of munitions and delivery systems; extensive field trials; stockpiling and troop training—it would be difficult to do this in complete secrecy. Biological agents could be manufactured in small quantities in one of fairly numerous medical, pharmaceutical, teaching, research, and government laboratories, with less risk of the secret being betrayed

Chemical agents can be stored for long periods but some biological agents deteriorate fairly rapidly, although techniques for storage are being improved

General abhorrence and particular ethics in such bodies as the medical profession might result in individuals being prepared to report clandestine activities by their own governments that were contrary to an international agreement

A small country, or even criminal or dissident groups, could devastate a large country with biological agents

---

Some defoliation agents can be lethal in heavy doses, particularly the military types that contain arsenic. Nevertheless, it is difficult to believe in the value of attempts to broaden the definition of chemical agents to be banned to include herbicides and defoliants; this step would almost certainly serve to delay or prevent an agreement on the more lethal agents. There is a case, on the other hand, for reconsideration of the use of agents to destroy crops, particularly since the sufferers are more likely to be noncombatants, and also for concern about long-term ecological effects—although in fairness it must be pointed out that war in the past has often had serious ecological effects.

"HUMANE" WEAPONS

A considerable body of people believes that chemical and, to a less important extent, biological agents could be used as "humane" weapons, permitting war to be fought with less loss of life and damage to property. One of the dreams of military thinkers has been of weapons that would render the enemy incapable of resistance, so that loss of life could be reduced to a minimum. Support for this point of view tends to come from those who foresee themselves engaged at some time in the future in military actions against insurgents, particularly when the latter are indistinguishable from and can mingle with the civil population. Use of "humane" agents could reduce casualties among both civilians and combatants. The kind of agents that could be used for this purpose are incapacitating and harassing agents of low lethality. A ban on use of these agents would force recourse to more dangerous conventional weapons. On the other hand, there has been a considerable body of opinion against the development and use of any chemical and biological agents; and the condemnation has extended to nonlethal agents, which could be a step in the ladder of escalation to more lethal agents and which could be—and have been—used as adjuncts to increase the effectiveness of conventional weapons.

The problem will perhaps become clearer if we look at the conditions in which chemical agents are likely to be used. (Biological agents are more likely to be used covertly and for the present can be excluded from the discussion.) Nonlethal chemical agents are most likely to be employed in the following circumstances:

By a developed country engaged in war with a much less developed country, when the threat of retaliation is small

By a developed country engaged in what it interprets as a police-type action against insurgents opposing the legitimate government of an ally

In support of U.N. police-type operations

By any government against civil rioters.

In Europe, where there is the greatest deployment of chemical agents, a condition of mutual deterrence may exist and, in any case, if a general war did break out, it is likely that all constraints would be quickly abandoned and chemical agents would merely add to a general holocaust.

We now consider each of the modes of employment mentioned above. Use of highly sophisticated agents by a highly developed country against people unable to defend themselves in any way and the likely use of chemical agents, even of nonlethal types, in conjunction with other weapons raise problems of world opinion and of possible retaliation, either by chemical weapons supplied by another advanced power or in other ways—for example the killing of hostages and prisoners or poisoning of wells and food supplies. The issue is by no means clear-cut, but on balance it might be wiser to ban such use of nonlethal agents.

In the fourth situation, the use by a government of nonlethal agents against its own citizens, on practical grounds the facts would appear to be in favor of retention of the use of chemical agents by the police and the military acting in support of the civil police. Compared with other police weapons, CS gas, for example, causes far fewer permanent injuries. Even "instant banana," a slippery substance said to be under development, could lead to broken bones and concussion. A possible adjunct in these circumstances would be an evil-smelling but otherwise innocuous substance that is absorbed by the skin. Use of such material could make the rioters more easily identifiable afterward.

The second of the situations in which chemical agents are likely to be used is the engagement of a developed power in a police-type action. This situation spans the difference between the use of chemical agents in a war against an underdeveloped country and internal police use of riot-control agents. It is here that the greatest doubts would arise as to the possibility of escalation. Some of the processes of escalation from the use of nonlethal to lethal agents are the following:

A weapons system would be developed capable of disseminating a range of chemical and biological agents

The use of protective equipment by the enemy might lead to resort to more powerful weapons

The enemy may retaliate in kind or make an overproportionate response

Countries not involved in the conflict will equip themselves with similar agents

There will be an erosion of the prohibitions on the use of "gas."

If, despite the dangers of escalation and the use of nonlethal agents as adjuncts to conventional arms, it seems desirable to permit the use of nonlethal agents in either of the first two situations, then it is necessary to be able to define nonlethal weapons in such a way that they can be distinguished from lethal agents. Of course, nonlethal agents can cause death in high concentration, as can many other substances; but the concentration for lethality is much greater than the concentration for the lethal agents. It might also be possible to have nonlethal agents registered. What is certain is that governments would not give up riot-control gas for use against their own citizens. Since use of riot gas even against nationals may cause international disquiet, it might be arranged that each use be reported to the Secretary-General of the United Nations. Another reason for wishing to retain "humane" weapons is that, in the long term, U.N. forces may be engaged in operations in which nonlethal agents would seem to be appropriate.

UNILATERAL CONTROL OF CHEMICAL AND BIOLOGICAL AGENTS

There have been several valuable unilateral actions leading to control of chemical and biological agents. Pugwash scientists arranged for laboratories in a number of countries to be inspected by international teams. The British government has held open days at the two research establishments at Porton, one of which is involved in microbiological research and the other chemical research. The aim of the invitations was to demonstrate that the establishments are engaged in defensive, rather than offensive, research. It has been suggested that it would be appropriate for the Porton establishments to be transferred from the Ministry of Defense to, say, the Medical Research Council; a possible gain from this step would be to make an outstanding microbiological laboratory available for more general research. Another suggestion has been that international exchanges of information on defense measures against chemical and biological agents could be encouraged.

The most important unilateral action in the field of chemical and biological warfare was the order by the president of the United States, in November 1969, to cease work on offensive uses of biological agents.

INSPECTION AND VERIFICATION

Serious difficulties are usually thought to attend inspection and verification associated with arms control of chemical and biological agents. However, closer examination may reveal some possibilities of control.

Inspection for chemical agents resolves into two separate problems: ensuring that chemical agents are not being manufactured and witnessing the destruction of deployed stocks.

Present stocks are enormous and widely deployed. The munitions take many forms: bombs, shells, sprays. It would be difficult to ensure with any high degree of assurance that all of the munitions had been revealed and destroyed. It might be easier to control delivery systems, but it will be recalled that many systems are dual-purpose and can deliver a variety of munitions. Manufacturing plants for chemical weapons are similar to those for the manufacture of other chemicals in fairly common use, and some of the raw materials and intermediate products are the same as those for nonmilitary products. To ensure that clandestine manufacture was not taking place might require inspection visits by skilled personnel over a range of civil industry.

Control of research and development might be equally difficult for reasons similar to those given above and, in any case, limited production might be permitted for the purpose of testing defense and protective systems. It would be difficult to ensure that the same equipment was not also being used for further development or to prepare hidden stockpiles.

Restrictions on trials might be more easily verified; but in the case of agents that have already been developed, further trials may not be important or necessary.

Control of biological agents appears to many commentators to show greater promise than control of chemical agents. Because biological agents have not been manufactured or deployed in large quantities, the same problems do not appear to exist in regard to destruction of stocks. As for inspection of manufacturing plants and plants used for other purposes (which can be converted), it may be possible to arrange an inspection that could be more effective than that for chemical agents.

Some inspection by invitation has already been carried out in several countries under arrangements made by scientists of the Pugwash movement. The problem has been under study since 1964; and voluntary inspections have been carried out by international teams that have visited laboratories in Czechoslovakia, Austria, Denmark, and Sweden. In a somewhat analogous way, as mentioned above, Great Britain has had open days at the Porton laboratories.

TABLE 30

Summary of Possible Arms Control Measures for Chemical and Biological Agents

Separation of biological agents for special treatment
A decision on whether agreements should be comprehensive or limited to lethal agents only
Dependent upon this, criteria for differentiating between lethal and nonlethal agents
Limitation on the use of herbicides for clearance of fields of fire and prohibition of attacks on crops
Arrangements for inspection for manufacture of biological weapons, which could capitalize on ethics of medical and other scientists
Reporting of occasions when riot-control agents are employed

Biological agents are generally based on naturally occurring diseases, so that research and production may be carried out in any case to provide means for controlling natural epidemics. It would be difficult to differentiate by inspection between work carried out for development of biological agents and that for medical purposes. An indication of intention might be the degree of secrecy that surrounded the work. Another approach to control of biological agents is to rely upon the general abhorrence of biological warfare, and the ethics of the medical profession, to support verification. This approach may not have much appeal to the military or to physical scientists, to whom it may appear extremely naïve, but there are good reasons for believing that it would be fruitful.

For those biological agents that have a comparatively short shelf life, control of manufacture alone would be enough, for any deployed stocks would soon become unserviceable.

Table 30 summarizes some of the possible methods for arms control of chemical and biological agents.

NOTES

1. World Health Organization, Health Aspects of Chemical Biological Weapons 1970 is particularly competent. Matthew S. Meselson, "Chemical and Biological Weapons," Scientific American (May 1970) contains tables and figures of effects.

2. T. F. Watkins, J. C. Cackett, and R. G. Hall, Chemical Warfare, Pyrotechnics and the Fireworks Industry (London: Pergamon, 1968).

3. U.S. Department of the Army, Navy, and Air Force, Field Manual. Employment of Chemical and Biological Agents (March 1966).

4. United Nations, "Report to the Secretary-General on Chemical and Bacteriological (Biological) Weapons and the Effects of Their Possible Use, document A/7575 (1969).

5. John Marriott, "Chemical and Biological Warfare, International Defence Review, II (November 1969).

6. Evidence to Senate Committee on Foreign Relations (April 1969), quoted in Nature (July 5, 1969).

7. Argentina, Brazil, Bavaria, India, Mexico, Morocco, Nigeria, Pakistan, Sweden, United Arab Republic, and Yugoslavia, "Working Paper on a Prospected Declaration by the United Nations General Assembly Regarding Prohibition of the Use of Chemical and Biological Methods of Warfare," ENDC/265 (August 26, 1969).

8. United Kingdom, "Biological Warfare: Draft Convention and Accompanying Draft Security Council Resolution," ENDC/255 (July 10, 1969).

CHAPTER

20

THE FUTURE AND ARMS CONTROL

In the last few hundred years, with the expansion of science and the technology deriving from it, the attempt to predict and even control the future has become increasingly important. Mistakes made in deciding priorities and allocating resources may be difficult to rectify. Because of their knowledge of the way science is advancing and of the limitations of the physical world, scientists are becoming involved in predicting and planning for a future that is beyond the next few years—i.e., beyond the period with which traditional political management and planning is normally concerned. In addition to his unique knowledge of advanced science, the scientist shares with the economist certain analytical skills that are valuable for prediction.

Of major concern to those attempting to foresee the future are those dangers which alone or in combination could lead to worldwide disaster and even the destruction of humanity. A major nuclear war would devastate not only the superpowers but also Europe and many bases in other parts of the world, while clouds of radioactivity would drift over the whole of the northern hemisphere and spread more slowly into the southern hemisphere. The major threats to international peace and stability are the pressure of population on resources, even though the immediate threat of widespread starvation appears to have been checked by the development of high-yield strains of cereal crops; the rising levels of expectation among the masses of the underprivileged in many countries, as they become aware through mass communications of what is available to more favored populations; nationalism and political instability in some underdeveloped countries; the using up of nonreplaceable resources, such as mineral deposits, and of topsoil when injudicious means of agriculture are employed; contamination of the environment by pollution with waste products and overdosing with fertilizers, insecticides, and chemicals; and the degradation of life in the great overcrowded cities.

While these pressures could generate outbreaks of war that could then escalate and involve the superpowers, it may be that over the next half century the third world may become an overcrowded, violent slum, not offering a direct challenge to the richer nations but presenting new problems in the organization of peace-keeping.

THE ROLE OF THE MILITARY IN THE FUTURE

The use of force in international affairs has so changed in recent years that it is now more appropriate in many cases to consider military forces as "constabulary forces" that are continuously prepared to act, are committed to the minimum use of force, and that seek viable international relations rather than victory.* Interaction between military and political matters makes even less tenable a hard division between strategy and tactics, since relatively low-level operations must be carried out under close central control and with constant concern for world opinion. At the same time the difference is reduced between wartime and peacetime organization.

Arms control strategies must be based on present capabilities but must also be forward-looking, to estimate possible changes in the relationships between countries and other changes—such as in technology, economics, and internal politics—that may have an impact on the need for arms. Account must be taken of the political importance of arms and their relation to economic strength, with regard not only to other negotiating parties but also to the relative strengths of other powers not engaged in the negotiations.

Some of the major destabilizing forces mentioned above can be forecast in general terms with a great deal of confidence. What cannot be forecast is the course of isolated events, some of which might cause difficulties in apparently more settled parts of the world. The strategic posture of the larger powers has to take into account these possibilities and is designed for the "worst possible case." Suitable arms control agreements can considerably limit the worst possible case by reducing the armaments available to a possible opponent, the incentives for a preemptive or overwhelming first strike, and the suspicions that might generate conflicts.

---

*The different types of military organization are analyzed in M. R. D. Foot, "What Are Armed Forces for?" New Society (February 26, 1970).

PROBLEMS FOR THE SUPERPOWERS

Turning now to those specific strategic problems that face the superpowers, decisions will have to be made in the near future by both the United States and Soviet Union as to whether to procure major systems such as new manned bombers, new strategic missiles, and ballistic missile defenses; what strategic levels are appropriate; and what positions should be adopted regarding negotiations to end the arms race. Possible proliferation of nuclear weapons to other countries raises other important policy issues. Is it desirable to try to inhibit the spread of nuclear weapons capabilities to other countries? What price are individual nuclear powers willing to pay to prevent this from happening? What are the chances of success in preventing nuclear spread, and what should be the response to proliferation and other developments that the nuclear powers are unable to prevent?

It is slowly being recognized that the superpowers have joint interests that are not limited to prevention of nuclear war. Increased consumption and consumer influence in the Soviet Union are in the interests of both countries, and the maintenance of international peace will in most cases be in the long-term interest of both.

Wesley Posvar has attempted a projection into the 1980's of the major political situation.* He anticipates frequent insurgency and racial warfare with, at the same time, limited nuclear arms control, which will introduce problems of possible deception by many powers, more nuclear powers than at present, the threat of covert nuclear attack in many parts of the world, and increased use of international military forces. He anticipates that where direct military activity is prevented for one reason or another, including the presence of U.N. forces on the cease-fire line, resort will increasingly be made to covert attacks, often of a spectacular and publicity-seeking kind. Such activities will be difficult to prevent, since they may be carried out by groups over which governments have little or no control, or which may be in opposition to their nominal government. They may also force governments into policies they would prefer to avoid; more extreme groups will be difficult to distinguish from conspiracies and even criminal gangs. It will be claimed, of course, that the participants are only doing what they can to defend their legitimate interests;

---

*Wesley W. Posvar, "Strategy and Politics," Air Force/Space Digest (December 1966).

and in practice tactics may be similar to those of citizens who joined partisan groups in Europe during World War II. Because views on the ethics of free-ranging operations will vary, it may be difficult to rally international support for effective counteraction.

THE IMMEDIATE FUTURE IN EUROPE

In Europe there is a good chance that the political situation will gradually improve and that limited and local arms control will be introduced. In Table 31 some possible future strategic relationships in Europe are presented. Some of these situations are, by the very nature of political realities, very unlikely; and others present more desirable states than now exist. The problems will be in persuading others to follow similar objectives and in devising the appropriate policies to achieve these ends.

A factor that may favor peace in Europe is the growth of international trade and business, with the development of the European Economic Community and the rise of multinational companies. Although most of the growth in international business has been within Western Europe, more contacts are being made with agencies in Eastern Europe.

The existence of powerful groups in each country interested in promoting trade and contacts with similar groups in other countries could act to promote stability.

ADVANCES IN MILITARY TECHNOLOGY

It is, of course, impossible to foresee exactly what advances will be made in the future in military weapons and systems. It is possible, however, to forecast continued advance in directions already charted, in the continued application of electronics and mechanization.

In space the number of military surveillance satellites will no doubt increase, and their equipment will become more sophisticated. Satellites in geostationary orbits will keep permanent watch on important areas and will provide relay stations between satellites in low orbit and their ground stations. By this means it will be possible to provide real-time data from a variety of sensors, including television, infrared, and other radiation detectors. Satellites with some maneuverability in space, equipped with remote handling equipment, will be available. Manned and unmanned craft of this type will be

TABLE 31

Possible Future Strategic Situations in Europe

Relationship Between United States and Western Europe	Relationship Between United States and Soviet Union: Competition	Arms Control	Disarmament
U.S. Hegemony			
U.S. Leadership		Approximate	
Atlantic Alliance		Present	
Western European Alliance		Position	
National Independence			
European Defense Community			

required to supplement the work of astronauts in assembling space stations, but it should also become quite possible to use these manipulators to carry out inspections of opponent's space craft and so reduce the chances of any nation clandestinely breaching the present space treaty.

Manned space stations in orbit for long periods, with arrangements for crew relief, will provide military platforms with a variety of sensors combined with the flexibility and versatility of human observers. Stations on the moon will also provide similar facilities at longer range.

Missiles sited on the moon could provide an invulnerable second-strike force that would have several days warning that an attack has been launched; but this advantage will be eroded with the advent of antiballistic missile defenses, which should be able to cope with the small number of missiles that could be installed on the moon. Unless an agreement, formal or tacit, is reached, an arms race between ABM and offensive nuclear strategic missiles could accelerate, or gradually decrease, in tempo. ABM are likely to be deployed by the superpowers, but how widely will depend on the nature of any agreements, the state of art, and the political situation. Considerable effort will be put into the development of lasers for attacking missiles. Lasers in ground installations or in satellites have great potential advantages, in that the pulse of energy travels with the speed of light, so that the time lag between locating and tracking the target and counter-attacking is much less than for ABM and hence accuracy should be improved. On the other hand, a direct hit must be achieved. Lasers also have great potential as message channels in space, for range-finding and fixing positions; they may also have potential for observation of objects on the ground.

There will be improvements in air-launched missiles for attacking radars, defensive aircraft with early-warning radars, and intercepter aircraft. Air defense missiles and bombers equipped with similar missiles will be able to attack their targets from long range. However, as air defenses against bombers continue to improve and with the high cost of large aircraft and difficulties of deployment, there appears to be little likelihood of renewed interest in large deployments of multi-engine bombers. Development of military combat aircraft will tend to concentrate on tactical aircraft, particularly on vertical and short takeoff and landing types that can be widely dispersed and are less vulnerable to a preemptive strike. Similar aircraft will also be used for supporting police-type operations in remote areas.

Field armies will continue to be heavily armored and will rely more on mechanization. This is likely to be most apparent in the logistic elements: supply trains will be made up of a number of powered vehicles designed with cross-river capabilities and connected so that only one driver and mate are necessary. It will be possible to unhitch individual vehicles and direct their movements by radio. Eventually this facility may extend to armored fighting vehicles. In order to make the automated battlefield possible, it will be necessary to improve information collection and handling. One form of collection will be unmanned aircraft equipped with a variety of sensors and eventually with television, capable of supplying real-time data: other sensors will be sown over a wide area to report proximity of troops or vehicles; such devices would transmit only in short bursts when triggered, so that they would be difficult to locate and nullify. Data from a variety of sources will be integrated through computers and presented as visual displays, much as is now familiar in command and control of aircraft. Ground troops will be integrated with fixed-wing aircraft and helicopters that will be used for mobility and supply and in close support by attacking targets. Strategic movement of land forces will be enhanced by the coming into service of very large transport aircraft and by supersonic transports, which, although smaller than large subsonic aircraft, will permit a high rate of initial reaction and many round trips. Ships carrying helicopter and V/STOL and preloaded transports will increase the rate of response with heavy reinforcements.

Large ships will still be vulnerable to missile attack. Defense will be provided by search aircraft, long-range missiles, radars, and antimissile missiles, coordinated by computers. A range of high-speed short-range craft will be produced; some of these will be on hovercraft and hydrofoil principles, and they will have capabilities for coastal defense against surface ships and submarines. Large surface ships will be further jeopardized by satellite reconnaissance; and the large ocean-going nuclear-powered submarine, still relatively invulnerable to detection, will contineu to be the capital ship of the great powers. While improvements in detection and counterattack by antisubmarine warfare will be made, it is difficult to see a major threat that could eliminate a whole fleet of these vessels before a second strike could be launched.

A most important factor in the future will be continuing improvement in quality and timeliness of data collection by sensors and processing and interpretation by computers. It is difficult to see how it would be possible for either of the superpowers to prepare and launch an overwhelming first strike without giving sufficient warning to alert the defenses and second-strike forces, and perhaps even incite a preemptive strike by his opponent. With nuclear war becoming more irrational, it seems that the alternative to drift is a policy of arms control. Organizing such a policy will require integration of a broad range of skills by participants of high quality. Compared with the efforts put into devising weapons systems and the plans for their operational use, the effort put into arms control so far has been small; but as the costs and dangers of the arms race continue to increase, and as it becomes more appreciated that the only function of strategic forces is largely to deter action by other strategic forces, alternative ways for achieving international stability and freedom from fear of aggression will be sought. This is not to suggest that arms control can solve all problems; but with less reliance on force to provide instant but impermanent solutions, attention could be directed to study and solve the more fundamental problems that face mankind.

APPENDIXES

APPENDIX

POSSIBLE FORMS OF ARMS CONTROL AGREEMENTS

Ban or control of specified research
Ban or control of specified developments
Ban or control or testing of specified types of weapons
Inspection of civilian industry, academic and government research centers, etc. (e.g., for nuclear and biological activities)
Ban on production of specified types of weapons
Ban on production of "offensive" weapons
Ban on production of specified "defensive" weapons (e.g., ABM, anti-submarine warfare, etc)
Total ban on deployment of specified weapons
Ban on deployment beyond specified areas
Ban on deployment within specified areas
Limitation on numbers
Limitation on size (e.g., battleships)
Limitation on range
Limitation on caliber
Limitation on yield of individual weapons
Limitation on total yield in deployment and stocks
Ban on the use except in retaliation (deterrence)
Witnessed destruction of specified weapons
Inspection of remainders
Limitation on replacement by type
Limitation on replacement by numbers
Limitation on rounds fired in troop training
Ban on the introduction of new types of weapons
Agreement upon and respect for sanctuaries, thresholds, and limits
Agreements on demilitarized areas
Agreement on no armaments in specified areas
Agreement on no nuclear arms in specified areas

Ensuring against accidental discharge of weapons
Exchange of information on techniques of safeguarding and control
Ban or limitation on exports and import of weapons, technology, materials
Limitation on the number of troops with colors [forces-in-being]
Limitation on total military manpower, including civilian auxiliaries
Limitation on total number of reservists
Limitation on the training of reservists
Witness of military maneuvers and parades
Inspection of military field activities
Observers at military command and control centers
Communication links between opposing political and military commands

APPENDIX

B

A CHRONOLOGY OF ARMS CONTROL

1945	August 6	Atomic bomb exploded at Hiroshima
1946	January 24	U.N. Atomic Energy Commission created
	June 14	Baruch Plan submitted by United States
1947	February 13	U.N. Commission for Conventional Armaments created
1949	September 23	First Soviet nuclear weapons explosion
1952	January 11	U.N. Disarmament Commission created
	October 3	First British nuclear weapon explosion
	November 1	First U.S. hydrogen bomb explosion
1953	August 21	First Soviet hydrogen bomb explosion
	December 8	U.S. "Atoms for Peace" program presented
1956	October 26	Statute of the International Atomic Energy Agency approved by the United Nations
1957	May 15	First British hydrogen bomb explosion
	July 29	IAEA established
	December 14	Western European Union Arms Control Agency convention signed
1958	January 1	Euratom treaty came into force
1959	December 1	Antarctic treaty signed
1960	February 13	First French atomic bomb explosion
1961	January 31	United States commenced reconnaissance by unmanned satellite
	September 20	U.S./Soviet joint statement on principles of disarmament
1962	March 14	Opening of first session of Eighteen Nations Disarmament Conference
	March 16	Soviet Union commenced reconnaissance by unmanned satellite
1963	June 20	U.S./Soviet memorandum on the "hot line"

	August 5	Partial Test Ban Treaty signed
1964	April 20	Cutback in production of fissile material announced by United States, Soviet Union, and Great Britain
	October 16	First Chinese atomic bomb explosion
1965	November 19	U.N. resolution on nonproliferation
1967	January 27	U.N. resolution on outer space
	February 14	Latin America treaty signed
	June 17	First Chinese hydrogen bomb explosion
	October 1	Experts' report on nuclear weapons presented to United Nations
1968	March 11	U.S./Soviet joint draft of Non-Proliferation Treaty submitted to ENDC
	March 14	Revised U.S./Soviet draft of Non-Proliferation Treaty submitted
	August 6	British draft of prohibition on microbiological warfare submitted to ENDC
	November 27	Great Britain ratifies Non-Proliferation Treaty—first nuclear power to do so
1969	March 18	Inauguration of hot line between Washington and Moscow
	July 2	Experts' report on chemical and biological warfare presented to United Nations
	July 10	British draft prohibition of biological warfare
	October 7	U.S./Soviet joint draft seabed treaty
	November 17	Opening of first round of SALT
	November 24	U.S. and Soviet ratification of Non-Proliferation Treaty
	November 25	U.S. renunciation of biological warfare and first use of chemical warfare
	December 15	U.N. resolution on seabed
	December 16	U.N. resolution on chemical and biological warfare
1970	February 14	Non-Proliferation Treaty came into force
	December 7	U.N. General Assembly asked Secretary-General to appoint committee of experts to report on economic and social consequences of arms race
1971	February 11	Seabed treaty signed
	March 30	Soviet Union tabled draft agreement to ban biological agents
	April 3	United States announced intention to begin destruction of biological agents
	April 18	U.S. Senate ratified Latin America treaty
	April 20	IAEA board of governors approved safeguards agreement for Non-Proliferation Treaty

	May 20	United States and Soviet Union announced intention to work out agreement for ABM limitation
	June 11	Soviet proposal for conference of nuclear powers and for control of naval forces in distant waters
	September 11	U.S./Soviet agreement for consultation in event of nuclear accident
	September 17	Satellite hot line between United States and Soviet Union for exchange of data on Mars exploration put into operation
1972	April 10	Convention on Biological Weapons signed

BIBLIOGRAPHY

BOOKS

Aron, Raymond. On War: Atomic Weapons and Global Diplomacy. London: Secker and Warburg, 1958.

Bader, William B. The United States and the Spread of Nuclear Weapons. New York: Pegasus, 1968.

Bailey, F. G. Strategems and Spoils: A Social Anthropology of Politics. Oxford: Blackwell and Mott, 1969.

Barnaby, C. F., ed. Preventing the Spread of Nuclear Weapons. London: Souvenir Press, 1969.

Beaton, Leonard. The Struggle for Peace. London: Allen and Unwin, 1966.

________ and John Maddox. The Spread of Nuclear Weapons. London: Chatto and Windus, 1962.

Beaufré, André. Deterrence and Strategy. London: Faber and Faber, 1965.

Bell, Coral. Negotiation from Strength. London: Chatto and Windus, 1962.

Blackett, P. M. S. Studies of War: Nuclear and Conventional. Edinburgh: Oliver and Boyd, 1962.

Brennan, D. G., L. W. Johnson, J. B. Wiesner, and G. S. McGovern. Anti-Ballistic Missile: Yes or No? A special report from the Center for the Study of Democratic Institutions. New York: Hill and Wang, 1969.

________, ed. Arms Control, Disarmament and National Security. London: American Academy of Arts and Sciences, 1961.

Brodie, Bernard. Strategy in the Missile Age. London: Oxford University Press, 1959.

Brown, Frederick J. Chemical Warfare: Study in Restraints. Princeton: Princeton University Press, 1968.

Brown, Neville. Nuclear War: The Impending Strategic Deadlock. New York: Praeger, 1964.

________. Arms Without Empire: British Defence in the Modern World. Harmondsworth: Penguin, 1967.

Buchan, Alistair, and Philip Windsor. Arms and Stability in Europe: A British-French-German Enquiry. London: Chatto and Windus for the Institute of Strategic Studies, 1963.

Bull, Hedley. The Control of the Arms Race. London: Weidenfeld and Nicolson for the Institute of Strategic Studies, 1961.

Burton, J.W. Systems, States, Diplomacy and Rules. Cambridge: Cambridge University Press, 1968.

Calder, Nigel, ed. Unless Peace Comes. New York: Viking Press, 1968.

Chayes, Abram, and Jerome B. Wiesner, eds. ABM: The Evaluation of the Decision to Deploy an Anti-Ballistic Missile System. London: Macdonald, 1969.

Clarke, Robin. We All Fall Down: The Prospects of Biological Warfare. Harmondsworth: Penquin, 1968.

Coddington, Alan. Theories of the Bargaining Process. London: Allen and Unwin, 1968.

Cookson, John, and Judith Nuttingham. A Survey of Chemical and Biological Warfare. London: Sheed and Ward, 1969.

Dougherty, J. E., and J. F. Lehman eds. Arms Control for the Late-Sixties. New York: Van Nostrand, 1967.

Duscha, Julius. Arms, Money and Politics. New York: Washburn, 1964.

Forward, Nigel. The Field of Nations. London: Macmillan, 1971.

Garthoff, Raymond L. Soviet Military Policy. London: Faber and Faber. 1966.

Griffin, Sidney F. The Crisis Game. New York: Doubleday, 1965.

Gullion, Edmund A., ed. Uses of the Seas. New York: Prentice-Hall, 1968.

Havard, W. E. and J. Baar. Spacecraft and Missiles of the World. New York: Harcourt, Brace, 1966.

Hersh, Seymour. Chemical and Biological Warfare: America's Hidden Arsenal. Indianapolis: Bobbs Merrill, 1968.

Hitch, C. J. Decision-Making for Defense. Berkeley: University of California Press, 1965.

Holst, J. J., and W. Schneider. Why ABM? London: Pergamon, 1969.

Howard, W. E., and J. Baar. Spacecraft and Missiles of the World. Harcourt, Brace. New York. 1966.

Hunt, K. The Requirements of Military Technology in the 1970s. London: Pergamon Press for the Institute for Strategic Studies, 1967.

Jacobson, Harold K., and E. Stein. Diplomats, Scientists and Policitians: The United States and the Nuclear Test Ban Negotiations. Ann Arbor: University of Michigan Press, 1966.

Janowitz, Morris. The Professional Soldier. New York: Free Press, 1964.

Jensen, Neils. Optical and Photographic Reconnaissance Systems. New York: John Wiley, 1968.

Jungk, Robert. Brighter than a Thousand Suns. Harmondsworth: Penguin, 1958.

Kahn, Herman, and Anthony Wiener. The Year 2000. London: Macmillan, 1967.

Kaplan, Morton A. System and Process in International Politics. Second edition. New York: John Wiley, 1967.

Knorr, Klaus, and Thorton Read. Limited Strategic War. London: Pall Mall Press, 1962.

Larus, Joel. Nuclear Weapons Safety and the Common Defense. Columbus: Ohio State University Press, 1967.

Lefebure, Victor. Scientific Disarmament. London: Mundanus, 1931.

Lefever, E. W. Arms Control. London: Thames and Hudson, 1962.

Lewin, Leonard. Report from Iron Mountain on the Possibilities and Desirability of Peace. Harmondsworth: Penguin, 1968.

McNamara, Robert. The Essence of Security: Reflections in Office. London: Hodder and Stoughton, 1968.

Martin, T. L., and D. C. Latham. The Strategy of Survival. Tucson: University of Arizona Press, 1963.

Morgenthau. Hans J. Scientific Man versus Power Politics. New York: Phoenix, 1965.

Moss, Norman. Men Who Play God. London: Gollancz, 1968.

Perkins, Dwight. China and Arms Control. New York: Praeger, 1965.

Platt, Washington. Strategic Intelligence Production. New York: Praeger, 1957.

Ransom, Harry Howe. The Intelligence Establishment. Cambridge: Harvard University Press, 1970.

Rathjens, George W. The Future of the Strategic Arms Race. Options for the 1970s. New York: Carnegie Endowment for International Peace, 1969.

Richardson, Lewis F. Statistics of Deadly Quarrels. London: Stevens, 1960.

________. Arms and Insecurity. London: Stevens, 1960.

Rose, Steven, ed. CBW, Chemical and Biological Warfare. London: Harrap, 1968.

Rotblat, Joseph. Pugwash: The First Ten Years. London: Heinemann, 1969.

Rothschild, J. H. Tomorrow's Weapons: Chemical and Biological. New York: McGraw-Hill, 1964.

Saaty, Thomas L. Mathematical Models of Arms Control and Disarmament. New York: John Wiley, 1968.

Scheinmann, Lawrence. Atomic Energy Policy in France Under the Fourth Republic. Princeton: Princeton University Press, 1965.

Schelling, Thomas. Arms and Influence. New Haven: Yale University Press, 1966.

Schwarz, U., and R. Hadrik. Strategic Terminology. London: Pall Mall Press, 1966.

Stone, Jeremy J. Strategic Persuasion: Arms Limitation Through Dialogue. New York: Columbia University Press, 1967.

Stonier, Tom. Nuclear Disaster. Harmondsworth: Penguin, 1964.

Strong, Kenneth. Men of Intelligence. London: Gollancz, 1970.

Taylor, Gordon Rattray. The Biological Time Bomb. London: Thames and Hudson, 1968.

Teller, Edward, Wilson K. Talley, Gary H. Higgins, and Gerald W. Johnson. The Constructive Uses of Nuclear Explosives. New York: McGraw-Hill, 1968.

Twitchett, Kenneth J., ed. International Security: Reflections on Survival and Stability. London: Royal United Services Institute and Oxford University Press, 1971.

Wainhouse, David W. International Peace Observation. London: Oxford University Press, 1966.

________. Arms Control Agreements, Designs for Verification and Organisation. London: Oxford University Press, 1969.

Watkins, T. F., J. C. Cackett, and R. G. Hall. Chemical Warfare, Pyrotechnics and the Fireworks Industry. London: Pergamon, 1968.

Wiesner, Jerome B. Where Science and Politics Meet. New York: McGraw-Hill, 1965.

Willot, Albert. Desarmement: Les postes d'observation. Brussels: Universite Libre de Bruxelles, 1968.

Wilson, Andrew. The Bomb and the Computer. London: Cresset Press, 1968.

Young, Wayland. Existing Mechanisms of Arms Control. London: Pergamon, 1966.

ARTICLES, PAPERS AND DOCUMENTS

Ailleret, Charles. "Directed Defence," Survival, February 1968.

Albonetti, Achille. "The NPT Draft Under Scrutiny," Survival, July 1967.

Alexander, A. S. "The Cost of World Armaments," Scientific American, October 1969.

Anderson, J. Edward. Letter on limitation of strategic arms in Scientific American, May 1970.

Anglin, F. M. "Discrimination of Earthquakes and Explosions using Short Period Seismic Array Data," letter in Nature, September 3, 1971.

Archer, Robert D. "The Soviet Bombers," Space/Aeronautics, April 1969.

Ball, Ian. "US Hints at New Methods of Spying by Satellite," Daily Telegraph, June 13, 1969.

Barber, Stephen. "US Freeze on Nuclear Arms Urged," Daily Telegraph, April 9, 1970.

Barnaby, C. F. "Consequences of ABM Deployment," letter in Nature, April 19, 1968.

________. "The Gas Centrifuge Project," Science Journal, August 1969.

________. "Limits on the Nuclear Club," New Scientist, March 12, 1970.

________. "SIPRI's Verdict on CBW," New Scientist, June 4, 1970.

________. "False Promise of Disarmament," New Scientist, August 6, 1970.

________. "Technology and the Myth of Deterrence," New Scientist, September 24, 1970.

________. "The Centrifuge and the Main Threat," New Scientist, May 13, 1971.

________. Alan Lee Williams, and Geoffrey Lee Williams. The Nuclear Future Fabian Tract, 394. London, June 1969.

________, et al. The Supreme Folly: Chemical and Biological Weapons. Geneva: Women's International League for Peace and Freedom, 1970.

Barton, John. "A Reconsideration of the Criteria for Deterrence," Bulletin of the Atomic Scientists, December 1967.

Beaton, Leonard. "Safeguards on Plutonium," Nature, December 31, 1966.

________. "Nuclear Fuel for All," Survival, September 1967.

________. "Nuclear Proliferation," Science Journal, December 1967.

________. "Controlling the Atom Menace," Survival, March 1969.

________. "Dangers of a New Warhead," Times, July 16, 1969.

________. "Who Is Responsible ?" book review in Nature, September 20, 1969.

________. "A Ban on Germs," Survival, January 1970.

Beaufré, André. "Some Reflections on the Problem of Arms Control," Arms Control and Disarmament, I (1968).

Bell, Coral. "A Game of Jeopardy," New Society, June 25, 1970.

Bellany, Ian. "MIRVS and the Strategic Balance," Nature, May 2, 1970.

Bethe, Hans A. "Hard Point vs City Defense," Bulletin of the Atomic Scientists, June 1969.

Bhagavantam, S. "Multiplying H-Bombs," Guardian, August 4, 1969.

Biddle, W. F. "Plutonium—Properties and Potential Uses in Power Reactors," Metal Industry, October 4 and 11, 1957.

Binder, L. James. "Truly a Weapon for All Seasons," Army, May 1969.

Birnbaum, Karl E. "Ways Towards European Security," Survival, June 1968.

Bode, H. L. Nuclear Explosions in Cavities. RM-3727. Santa Monica, California: Rand Corporation, 1965.

Bothwell, Frank E. "Is the ICBM Obsolete?" Bulletin of the Atomic Scientists, October 1969.

Boulding, Kenneth E. "Accomplishments and Prospects of the Peace Research Movement," Arms Control and Disarmament, I (1968).

________. "Research for Peace," Science Journal, October 1969.

________. "The Scientific Revolution," Bulletin of the Atomic Scientists, September 1970.

Brainard, R. W. "Visual Search: Capabilities and Methods of Enhancement," paper of the Battelle Memorial Institute, May 1967.

Brennan, D. G. "New Thoughts on Missile Defence," Bulletin of the Atomic Scientists, June 1967.

________. "The Case for Missile Defence," Foreign Affairs, April 1969.

________, and Johan J. Holst. Ballistic Missile Defence: Two Views. Adelphi paper. (London: Institute of Strategic Studies, 1967).

Brody, Richard A. "Some Systematic Effects of the Spread of Nuclear Weapons Technology: A S udy Through Simulation of a Multi-nuclear Future," Journal of Conflict Resolution, III, 4 (December 1963).

Brown, David A. "SRAM Production Expected in Mid-1970," Aviation Week and Space Technology, December 1, 1969.

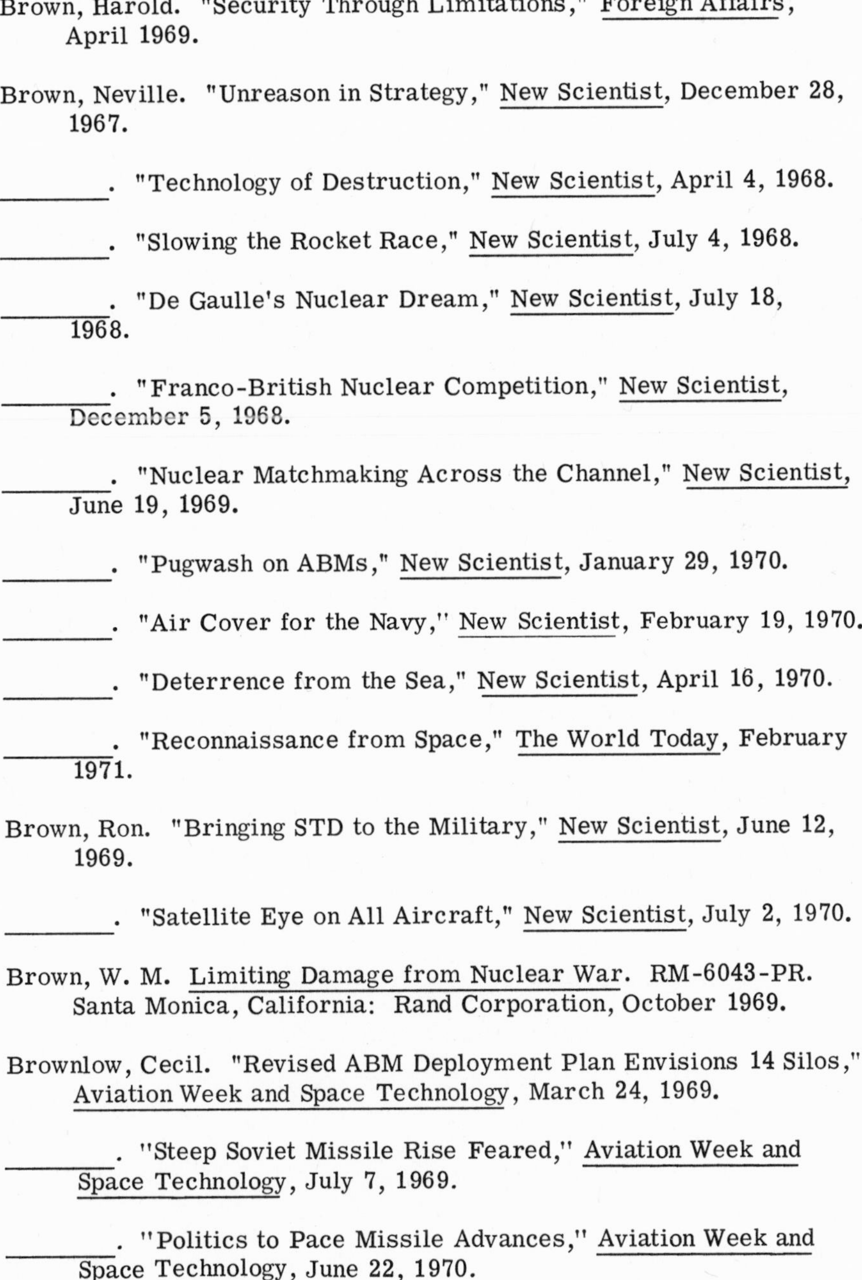

Brown, Harold. "Security Through Limitations," Foreign Affairs, April 1969.

Brown, Neville. "Unreason in Strategy," New Scientist, December 28, 1967.

________. "Technology of Destruction," New Scientist, April 4, 1968.

________. "Slowing the Rocket Race," New Scientist, July 4, 1968.

________. "De Gaulle's Nuclear Dream," New Scientist, July 18, 1968.

________. "Franco-British Nuclear Competition," New Scientist, December 5, 1968.

________. "Nuclear Matchmaking Across the Channel," New Scientist, June 19, 1969.

________. "Pugwash on ABMs," New Scientist, January 29, 1970.

________. "Air Cover for the Navy," New Scientist, February 19, 1970.

________. "Deterrence from the Sea," New Scientist, April 16, 1970.

________. "Reconnaissance from Space," The World Today, February 1971.

Brown, Ron. "Bringing STD to the Military," New Scientist, June 12, 1969.

________. "Satellite Eye on All Aircraft," New Scientist, July 2, 1970.

Brown, W. M. Limiting Damage from Nuclear War. RM-6043-PR. Santa Monica, California: Rand Corporation, October 1969.

Brownlow, Cecil. "Revised ABM Deployment Plan Envisions 14 Silos," Aviation Week and Space Technology, March 24, 1969.

________. "Steep Soviet Missile Rise Feared," Aviation Week and Space Technology, July 7, 1969.

________. "Politics to Pace Missile Advances," Aviation Week and Space Technology, June 22, 1970.

Brzezinski, Zbigniew. "Peace and Power," Encounter, November 1968.

Bull, Hedley. "The Scope for Super-Power Agreement," Arms Control and National Security. New York: Hudson Institute, 1969).

________. "Chemical and Biological Weapons: The Prospects for Arms Control," Australian Outlook, XXIV, 2 (August 1970).

Bullard, Sir Edward. "The Detection of Underground Explosions," Scientific American, July 1966.

________. "Detecting Underground Explosions," Survival, February 1967.

Bundy, McGeorge. "The Nuclear Arms Race," Survival, September 1969.

Burch, R. F. A Comparison of the Short Period Seismic Noise at the Four United Kingdom Atomic Energy Authority Type Arrays and an Estimate of Their Detection Capabilities. London: H.M.S.O., January 1969.

Bureau of Naval Personnel, United States Department of the Navy. Principles of Guided Missiles and Nuclear Weapons. NAYPERS 10784=A. Washington, D.C., 1966.

Burnett, A. Doak. "A Nuclear China," Survival, July 1970.

Buzzard, Sir Anthony. "Defence Policy," letter in Daily Telegraph, July 23, 1968.

Cade, C. Maxwell. "Wavelengths of Life and Death," New Scientist, September 19, 1968.

Cade, J. A. "A New Look at Space Spin-off," Spaceflight, July 1970.

Calleo, David. "Changing US Mood Could Force Defence Review," Times, July 29, 1969.

CCD (Conference of the Committee on Disarmament). "Union of Soviet Socialist Republics and United States of America: Draft Treaty on the Prohibition of the Emplacement of Nuclear Weapons and Other Weapons of Mass Destruction on the Seabed and the Ocean Floor and in the Subsoil Thereof." Paper 269. October 7, 1969

Chomsky, Noam. "The Welfare/Warfare Intellectuals," New Society, July 3, 1969.

Clarke, Robin. "Non-Proliferation: An Outbreak of Sanity," Science Journal, January 1969.

________. "The Softwave of Peace," Science Journal, December 1969.

________. "US Renounces All Biological Weapons," Science Journal, January 1970.

Clemens, Walter C. "Outer Space: Strategy and Arms Control," Bulletin of the Atomic Scientists, November 1967.

________. "The Ecology of Weaponry," Bulletin of the Atomic Scientists, September 1970.

Clifford, Clark M. "A Viet-Nam Re-appraisal," Foreign Affairs, July 1969.

Coates, Joseph F. "Safe Police Weapons," Science and Technology, May 1968.

Cockcroft, Sir John. "Control of Atomic Energy," Survival, November 1967.

Codding, George A., Jr. "Changes in International Organisation: A Review," Journal of Conflict Resolution, XIII, 2 (June 1969).

Coffey, S. I. "The Anti-Ballistic Missile Debate," Foreign Affairs, April 1967.

Cohen, N. D. "The Quick Count System: A User's Manual." RM-4006-PR. Santa Monica, California: Rand Corporation, 1964.

Colvin, C. A. Opportunity for Survival—A Look at Nuclear Material Safeguards. ARH-1709. Atlantic Richfield Hanford Company, May 19, 1970.

Converse, Elizabeth. "The War of All Against All," Journal of Conflict Resolution, special review issue, 1968.

Cookson, John. "CBW Review," letter in New Scientist, January 29, 1970.

Corbishley, D. J. Some seismic results of the US Gasbuggy and Rulison underground nuclear explosions. London: H.M.S.O., 1970.

Crawford, Eric W. "Withdraw Missile Submarines ?" Bulletin of the Atomic Scientists, November 1967.

Crosby, H. Ashton. "The Case for Anti-Ballistic Missiles," U.S. Navy Institute Proceedings, July 1967.

Daniels, J. T. "Criticality Inspection by the Authority." AHSB(S) R-150. Health and Safety Branch, U.K. Atomic Energy Authority, 1968.

Davies, D. "A Comprehensive Test Ban," Science Journal, November 1968.

________. Rapporteur. Progress Report of the Seismic Study Group. Stockholm: International Peace Research Institute, February 1970.

Denney, S. H. "A Review of Literature on the Theory of Hit and Kill Probabilities." M.Sc. thesis. Monterey, California: U.S. Navy Postgraduate School, September 1970.

Dentler, R. A., and P. Cutwright. "Social Effects of Nuclear War," Nuclear Science Abstracts, XVII, 20 (July 1963), 1-10.

Denton, Frank H., and Warren Phillips. "Some Patterns in the History of Violence," Journal of Conflict Resolution, XII, 2 (June 1968).

De Volpi, Alexander. "Expectations from SALT," Bulletin of the Atomic Scientists, April 1970.

Dixon, Bernard. "Pestilence to Order," New Society, July 18, 1968.

Doty, Paul. "A Freeze on Strategic Delivery Systems," Bulletin of The Atomic Scientists, February 1965.

Dougherty, J. E. Arms Control and Disarmament; the Critical Issues. Washington, D.C.: Georgetown University, Center for Strategic Studies, 1966.

Dresher, Melvin. A Sampling Inspection Problem in Arms Control Agreements: A Game-theoretic Analysis. RM-2972-ARPA. Santa Monica, California: Rand Corporation, February 1962.

Dyson, Freeman. "The Case for Missile Defense," Bulletin of the Atomic Scientists, April 1969.

Edelson, Edward. "Nuclear Digging on Trial," New Scientist, October 26, 1969.

Eighteen Nations Disarmament Conference. "United Kingdom: The Technical Possibility of International Control of Fissile Material Production." Paper 60. August 31, 1962.

________. "Sweden: Memorandum on the Control of an Underground Test Ban Treaty." Paper 191. July 19, 1967.

________. "United Kingdom: Working Paper on Microbiological Warfare." Paper 231. July 6, 1968.

________. "United Kingdom: Working Paper on the Comprehensive Test Ban Treaty." Paper 232. August 20, 1968.

________. "Union of Soviet Socialist Republics: Draft Treaty on Prohibition of the Use for Military Purposes of the Sea-bed and the Ocean Floor and the Subsoil Thereof." Paper 240. March 24, 1969.

________. "Sweden: Working Paper with Suggestions as to the Possible Provisions of a Treaty Banning Underground Nuclear Weapons Tests." Paper 242. April 6, 1969.

________. "Nigeria: Working Paper on the Comprehensive Test Ban Treaty." Paper 246. May 15, 1969.

________. "Canada: Working Paper Listing Recent Canadian Scientific Papers on Seismological Research with Abstracts now Available." Paper 248. May 21, 1969.

________. "United States of America: Draft Treaty Prohibiting the Emplacement of Nuclear Weapons and other Weapons of Mass Destruction on the Sea-bed and Ocean Floor." Paper 249. May 22, 1969.

________. "Canada: Working Paper on the Comprehensive Test Ban." Paper 251. May 23, 1969.

________. "United States of America: Working Paper on Seismic Investigation Proposal." Paper 252. May 23, 1969.

________. "United Kingdom: Biological Warfare: Draft Convention and Accompanying Draft Security Council Resolution." Paper 255. July 10, 1969.

________. "Poland: Working Paper Concerning the Report of the Secretary-General of 1 July 1969 on Chemical and Bacteriological (Biological) Weapons and the Effects of Their Possible Use (A/7575)." Paper 256. July 22, 1969.

________. "Sweden: Working Paper Describing the Hagfors Seismological Observatory in Sweden." Paper 257. August 14, 1969.

________. "United Kingdom: Further Note on United Kingdom Research on Techniques for Distinguishing Between Earthquakes and Underground Explosions." Paper 258. August 14, 1969.

________. "Canada: Remarks by G. Ignatroff, Representative of Canada, at Informal Meeting on CTB." Paper 259. August 14, 1969.

________. "Brazil: Working Paper on the Control Provisions for a Treaty on the Non-armament of the Sea-bed and Ocean Floor." Paper 264. August 21, 1969.

________. "Argentina, Brazil, Burma, Ethiopia, India, Mexico, Morocco, Nigeria, Pakistan, Sweden, United Arab Republic and Yugoslavia: Working Paper on a Proposed Declaration by the United Nations General Assembly Regarding Prohibition of the Use of Chemical and Biological Methods of Warfare." Paper 265. August 26, 1969.

________. "Canada: Chemical and Bacteriological (Biological) Warfare: Draft United Nations General Assembly Resolution." Paper 266. August 26, 1969.

________. "Announcement by U.K. Representative of Intention to Place Bradwell Nuclear Power Station Under Safeguard." PV 266. June 21, 1966.

________. "Joint U.S./U.S.S.R. Communiqué on Discussions on Peaceful Uses of Nuclear Explosions." PV 412. May 20, 1969.

Elson, Benjamin M. "SAC Evaluates Onboard Data Processing," Aviation Week and Space Technology, July 21, 1969.

Erickson, John. "Soviet BMD," Survival, May 1967.

________. "The Military Use of Space by the Russians," The Listener, February 20, 1969.

Fairhall, David. "Britain's Share in the Secrets War," Guardian, July 4, 1969.

________. "Playing the Germ War Game," Guardian, August 6, 1969.

Feld, Bernard T. "The Sorry History of Arms Control," Bulletin of the Atomic Scientists, September 1970.

________. "Scientists' Role in Arms Control," Bulletin of the Atomic Scientists, January 1970.

________, T. Greenwood, G. W. Rathjens, and S. Weinberg, eds. Impact of New Technologies on the Arms Race. A Pugwash monograph. Cambridge, Massachusetts: Massachusetts Institute of Technology, 1971.

Fishlock, David. "Nuclear Earthworks for Sale," Financial Times, January 17, 1968.

Foot, M. R. D. "What Are Armed Forces for?" New Society, February 26, 1970.

Foster, John S. "Options for Strategic Systems," Astronautics and Aeronautics, August 1970.

Fourquet, M. "French Strategic Concepts: The Role of the Forces," Survival, July 1969.

Frank, Lewis A. "Nuclear Weapons Development in China," Bulletin of the Atomic Scientists, January 1966.

Frisch, David H. "Scientists and the Decision to Bomb Japan," Bulletin of the Atomic Scientists, January 1970.

Fulbright, J. W. "Foreign Policy Implications of the ABM Debate," Bulletin of the Atomic Scientists, June 1969.

Gailar, Joanne L. "Seven Warning Signals: A Review of Soviet Civil Defence," Bulletin of the Atomic Scientists, December 1969.

Galston, Arthur W. "Military Uses of Herbicides in Viet-Nam," New Scientist, June 13, 1968.

Galtung, Johan. "Conflict as a Way of Life," New Society, October 16, 1969.

Garwin, Richard L., and Hans A. Bethe. "Anti-ballistic Missile Systems," Scientific American, March 1968.

Gatland, Kenneth W. "Espionage from Orbit," Flight, April 10 and 17, 1969.

Getler, Michael. "Chinese Missile Shot Forcing NIKE Choice," Technology Week, November 7, 1966.

Giacconi, Riccardo, and Bernard Harris. "Comments on Remote Sensing," Institute of Electrical and Electronic Engineers, Transactions on Geoseismic Electronics, October 1969.

Giddings, Ralph L. "Arms Control: No Simple Answers," U.S. Naval Institute Proceedings, February 1970.

Glasstone, Samuel. The Effects of Nuclear Weapons. Washington, D.C.: U.S. Atomic Energy Commission, 1964.

Goen, L. L., et al. "Critical Factors Affecting National Survival." Paper of the Stanford Research Institute, March 1969.

Goldman, J. E. "The Second Industrial Revolution," Science Journal, November 1969.

Gorere, Stephen. "Inspection and Control in Euratom," Bulletin of the Atomic Scientists, March 1967.

Gumston, W. T. "The Controversial ABM," Science Journal, July 1969.

Haines, R. G. "Eyes and Ears on the Nuclear Patrol," New Scientist, August 28, 1969.

Healey, Denis. "Thinking About the Unthinkable—the Secretary of State Talking to Professor Laurence Martin," The Listener, April 23, 1970.

Helms, Richard. "Spying and a Free Society—CIA Chief Speaks Out," US News and World Report, April 26, 1971.

Herzfeld, C. M. "Ballistic Missile Defence—This Time for Real," Nature, September 28, 1969.

Hibbs, A. R. "ABM and the Algebra of Uncertainty," Bulletin of the Atomic Scientists, March 1968.

Hill, Roger J. "Mutual and Balanced Force Reductions: The State of Alliance Policy," NATO Review, September/October 1971.

Hillaby, John. "Danger: Man at Work," New Scientist, September 19, 1968.

Himmel, Nieson S. "Advanced Space Station Concepts Crystallising," Aviation Week and Space Technology, September 22, 1969.

Hobsbawn, E. J. "The Rules of Violence," New Society, July 24, 1969.

Howard, Michael. "Strategy of CBW," Nature, December 21, 1968.

Hughes, Bernard. "Which Way Across Panama?" New Scientist, November 21, 1968.

Humphrey, J. H. "Initiative Against Chemical and Biological Warfare," New Scientist, September 29, 1966.

Ikle, F. C. The Violation of Arms Control Agreements: Deterrence vs Detection. RM-2609-ARPA. Santa Monica, California: Rand Corporation, 1960.

Imai, Rynkichi. "The Non-proliferation Treaty and Japan," Bulletin of Atomic Scientists, May 1969.

Inglis, David R. "Conservative Judgement and Missile Madness," Bulletin of the Atomic Scientists, May 1968.

Inglis, David R. "Nuclear Threats, ABM Systems and Proliferation," Bulletin of the Atomic Scientists, June 1968.

________. "Outlook for Nuclear Explosives," New Scientist, April 4, 1969.

________, and Carl L. Sandler. "A Special Report on Plowshare," Bulletin of the Atomic Scientists, December 1967.

Institute for Strategic Studies. "Disarmament in Europe," Survival, June, 1964.

International Atomic Energy Agency. Planning for the Handling of Radiation Accidents. Vienna, 1969.

Jackson, Henry M. "In the ABM Debate, Who Are the Real Hawks ?" Air Force/Space Digest, June 1969.

Johnson, Arthur W. "Weather Satellites II," Scientific American, January 1969.

Johnson, D. H. M. "Who Owns the Sea-bed ?" New Scientist, February 20, 1969.

Johnson, Douglas. "ABM: The High Cost of Living," U.S. Naval Institute Proceedings, October 1967.

Johnson, E. G. "Kistemaker's Great Adventure," (Elsevier's Weekblad), U.K. Atomic Energy Authority, Capenhurst, Translation no. 209, April 12, 1969.

Jonas, Anne M. "Penetrating the ABM Labyrinth," Air Force/Space Digest, June 1969.

Jones, Robert N. "A Closer Look at CS Gas," New Society, June 18, 1970.

Junnosuke, Kishida. "Chinese Nuclear Development," Survival, September 1967.

Kahn, Herman, and Anthony Wiener. "Technological Innovation and the Future of Strategic Warfare," Astronautics and Aeronautics, December 1967.

________, William Pfaff, and Edmund Stillman. "War Termination Issues and Concepts." Hudson Institute, HI-921/3-PR. June 1, 1968.

Karzas, W. J., and B. Latter. Electromagnetic Radiation from a Nuclear Explosion in Space. RM-2849-AFT. Santa Monica, California: Rand Corporation, October 1961.

Kaye, G. D. "Arms Control and the Strategic Balance," Department of National Defense of Canada, Defense Research Armament Establishment Memo M.21. April 1970.

________, and G. R. Lindsey. "Letter: MIRVs and the Strategic Balance," Nature, August 15, 1970.

Kaysen, Carl. "The Strategic Balance," Survival, September 1968.

Kent, Glenn A. On the Interaction of Opposing Forces Under Possible Arms Agreements. Cambridge, Massachusetts: Harvard University Center for International Affairs, March 1963.

Kerr, T. H. "Air Defence, the Problem," Flight International, April 17, 1969.

Kissinger, Henry H. "Arms Control, Inspection and Surprise Attack," Foreign Affairs, July 1960.

Klass, Philip J. "Cosmos Flights Seen as ICBM Aids," Aviation Week and Space Technology, October 16, 1967.

________. "Soviets Resume ABM Work at Moscow," Aviation Week and Space Technology, June 23, 1969.

________. "Military Satellites Gain Vital Data," Aviation Week and Space Technology, September 15, 1969.

________. "NASA Considers Satellite Network," Aviation Week and Space Technology, October 13, 1969.

Klineberg, Rosemary, James Lyon, and Bruce Russett. Studyfair, Volume I: Studies of Information and Arms Control. Institute of Defense Analysis, October 1963.

Kock, F. H. C. "Problems of Comparing Force Levels," NATO Review, March/April 1971.

Kolodziej, Edward A. "French Strategy Emergent," World Politics, April 1967.

Kowarski, Lew. "The Spreading Nuclear Wave," New Scientist, August 6, 1970.

Kramish, Arnold. "The Watched and Unwatched: Inspection in the Non-proliferation Treaty." Adelphi paper No. 36. Institute of Strategic Studies, June 1967.

Lall, Betty Goetz. "Arms Reduction Impact," Bulletin of Atomic Scientists, September 1966.

Langer, Elinor. "CBW: Weapons and Policies," Survival, May 1967.

Latham, Gary. "Lunar Seismology: The Beginning," New Scientist, July 17, 1969.

Latter, A. L., and E. A. Martinelli. Active and Passive Defense. P-3165. Santa Monica, California: Rand Corporation, August 1965.

Lawes, Glen. "Centrifuge Enrichment in Europe," New Scientist, March 20, 1969.

Leary, Frank. "Arms Control—How Real?" Space/Aeronautics, September 1968.

________. "Who's Winning the Underseas War?" Space/Aeronautics, February 1969.

________. "Anti-satellite Defence," Space/Aeronautics, June 1969.

________. "Man in Space: Stations and Bases," Space/Aeronautics, September 1969.

Lederberg, Joshua. "A Freeze on Missile Testing," Bulletin of the Atomic Scientists, March 1971.

Leitemberg, Milton. "Misconceptions on MIRVs," letter in Nature, December 26, 1970.

Lewis, Richard S. "SALT in Vienna: The Waltz of the Powers," Bulletin of the Atomic Scientists, September 1970.

Lindsey, G. R. "The Strategy and Economics of Missile Defence," Department of National Defense, Canada, Operational Research Division Informal Paper No.66/P.23. Undated.

Lindsey, Robert. "Project Mobile Fallout: Sea-going Tracking Stations," Aerospace Technology, May 6, 1968.

Loftas, Tony. "Ocean Law in Deep Waters," New Scientist, March 12, 1970.

________. "Decade for Ocean Escalation," New Scientist, July 2, 1970.

London, Michael P. "Advanced Strategic Missiles," Space/Aeronautics, June 1968.

________. "USX: Sub-hunting from the Air," Space/Aeronautics, April 1969.

________. "Bl—the Last Bomber?" Space/Aeronautics, April 1970.

Longuet-Higgins, Christopher, and Stephen Isard. "The Monkey's Paw," New Scientist, September 3, 1970.

Lough, Thomas C. "The Military Liaison Missions in Germany," Journal of Conflict Resolution, XI, 2 (June 1967).

Low, Ian. "Science and Weaponry," New Scientist, February 29, 1968.

Lowehhar, Herman. "Hardened Electronics," Space/Aeronautics, August 1969.

McCracken, Daniel D. "Anti-ABM Essay Contest Announced," Computer and Automation, March 1971.

Maddox, John. "The Nuclear Club," The Listener, June 5, 1969.

Mannella, G. G. "Aerospace Sensor Systems," Astronautics and Aeronautics, December 1968.

Marriott, John. "Chemical and Biological Warfare," International Defence Review, II (November 1969).

________. "NATO's Anti-Submarine Warfare Potential," International Defence Review, III, (March 1970).

________. "Detecting the Lone Submarine," New Scientist, June 1971.

________. "The United Kingdom Warning and Monitoring Organisation," International Defence Review, IV (1969).

Martin, L. W. "Strategic Implications of Ballistic Missile Defence," Survival, July 1967.

Marwick, Charles. "Death in Skull Valley," New Scientist, April 25, 1968.

________. "Nuclear Digging Comes Clean," New Scientist, May 23, 1968.

May, Michael M. A Public Corporation for Plowshare. Monograph of University of California, Lawrence Radiation Laboratories, 1969.

Mendl, Wolf. "French Attitudes on Disarmament," Survival, December 1967.

Meselson, Matthew S. "Behind the Nixon Policy for Chemical and Biological Warfare," Bulletin of the Atomic Scientists, January 1970.

________. "Chemical and Biological Weapons," Scientific America, May 1970.

________, and Julian Perry-Robinson. "Escalation of Chemical Warfare," New Scientist, August 14, 1969.

Miller, Barry. "Avionics: Special Report, Electronic Warfare: ECM Gaining Greater Aircraft Role," Aviation Week and Space Technology, August 25, 1969.

________. "Hostile Radar Location Gear Pushed," Aviation Week and Space Technology, September 1, 1969.

________. "Advanced ECM Devices Designed," Aviation Week and Space Technology, September 8, 1969.

________. "Air Force Using Line-scan Camera," Aviation Week and Space Technology, January 26, 1970.

________. "New Roles for Electro-optics," Aviation Week and Space Technology, June 22, 1970.

Miller, Martin J. "Soviet Nuclear Tactics," Ordnance, May-June 1970.

Morgan, Karl Z. "Tainted Radiation," Science and Technology, June 1969.

Mulley, Fred. "Prospects for the Comprehensive Test Ban," Science Journal, November 1968.

National Planning Association. Strengthening the Government For arms Control. A Special Committee Report. Planning pamphlet N.109. Washington, D.C., July 1960.

Nixon, Richard. Official text of the statement on 26 November 1969, Survival, January 1970.

Norman, Lloyd. "Nike-A," Army, March 1967.

Normyle, William J. "Future Goals of NASA Described," Aviation Week and Space Technology, October 13, 1969.

Pally, A. "The Consequences of Ionization of the Atmosphere," translated in Technology and Armament (Tekhnika i Voorazheniy,) no. 4 (1968).

Pardo, Arvid. "Who Will Control the Sea-bed?" Foreign Affairs, October 1968.

Pardoe, G. K. C. "Earth Resource Satellites," Science Journal, June 1969.

Parker, Kenneth. "Engineering with Nuclear Explosives," New Scientist, April 2, 1970.

Pauling, Linus. "Genetic and Somatic Effects of High-Energy Radiation," Bulletin of the Atomic Scientists, September 1970.

Pavlov, G. I. "Symposium on Planning Measures for Uses of Radiation Emergencies," Atominaye Energiya, No. 5 (1969).

Pay, Rex. "U.S. ABM Would Imperil Test Ban Treaty," Technology Week, March 20, 1967.

Perle, Richard. "Arms Control Criteria," U.S. Military Review, October 1970.

Perry, G. E. "Orbital Interceptor," Spaceflight, July 1970.

Peters, Duncan. "Britain Must Win Race to Develop the Gas Centrifuge," The Engineer, January 22, 1970.

Plattner, C. M. "Advanced ASW Gear," Aviation Week and Space Technology, September 15, 1969.

Posvar, Wesley W. "Strategy and Politics," Air Force/Space Digest, December 1966.

Pugh, G. E. "Restraint, Strategy and Arms Control," Orbis, 1963.

Quade, E. S. Military Systems Analysis. RM-3452-PR. Santa Monica, California: Rand Corporation, 1963.

Quester, George H. "Israel and the Nuclear Non-proliferation Treaty," Bulletin of the Atomic Scientists, June 1969.

Rankin, M. B. F. "Launching into Inner Space," New Scientist, February 20, 1969.

Raser, John R. "Weapons Design and Arms Control: The Polaris Example," Journal of Conflict Resolution, IX, 4 (December 1965).

Rathjens, George W. "The Dynamics of Arms Control," Scientific American, April 1969.

________. "Is Safeguard Worth the Risk?" Bulletin of the Atomic Scientists, June 1969.

________, and G. B. Kistiakowsky. Letter on limitation of strategic arms, Scientific American, May 1970.

Rich, Alexander, and John R. Platt. "How to Keep the Peace in a Disarmed World," Bulletin of the Atomic Scientists, April 1966.

Richards, Ivor. "A European Defence Policy," Survival, March 1970.

Robertson, Roland. "Strategic Relations Between National Societies: A Sociological Analysis," Journal of Conflict Resolution, XII, 1 (March 1968).

Robinson, David. "Learning to Live with Nuclear Spread," Air Force Magazine, August 1966.

Robinson, J. P. Perry. Letter on CS overstatement, New Scientist, October 2, 1969.

Rodberg, Leonard S. "Limiting Strategic Technology," Bulletin of the Atomic Scientists, November 1969.

Rose, Hilary, and Russell Stetler. "What Gas Did in Derry," New Society, September 25, 1969.

Rose, Steven. "A, B and C of the Arms Race," Science Journal, July 1968.

________. "CBW in Edinburgh," New Scientist, January 30, 1969.

________. "Proliferation Treaty Controls and the IAEA," Journal of Conflict Resolution, XI, 2 (June 1967).

________, and Robert Smith. "CS—a Cause for Concern," New Society, September 4, 1969.

Rosenhead, Jonathan. "No War Without Death," New Society, October 24, 1968.

Rotblat, Joseph, and C.F. Barnaby. "Controlling the Bomb," New Scientist, June 20, 1968.

Royal United Services Institution. The Soviet Union in Europe and the Near East: Her Capabilities and Intentions. Proceedings of a seminar. London, 1970.

Ruina, J. R. "The Nuclear Arms Race: Diagnosis and Treatment," Bulletin of the Atomic Scientists, October 1968.

Safronov, Y.P., I. N. Tikhomirov, and G. I. Ul'yanov. Recognition Devices. Translation no. 52554. Arlington, Virginia: Joint Publications Research Service, 1971.

Sagan, Leonard. "A Reply to Sternglass," New Scientist, October 2, 1969.

________, Edward S. Weiss, and Dorothy J. Worth. "Infant Mortality Controversy," Bulletin of the Atomic Scientists, October 1969.

Sartori, Leo. "The Myth of MIRV," Survival, December 1969.

Schwartz, Charles. "The Atomic Scientists in Politics," Bulletin of the Atomic Scientists, June 1969.

Scoville, Herbert, Jr. "Verification of Nuclear Arms Limitation; an Analysis," Bulletin of the Atomic Scientists, October 1970.

________. "The Limitation of Offensive Weapons," Scientific American, January 1971.

Seaborg, Glen. "Nuclear Power: Two Years After Geneva," Journal of the British Nuclear Energy Society, October 24, 1966.

Seitz, Frederick. "We Can't Afford a Pearl Harbour in the Space Age," Air Force/Space Digest, June 1969.

Shapley, Deborah. "Plutonium: Reactor Proliferation Threatens a Nuclear Black Market," Science April 9, 1971.

Shaw, Milton, and Merrill Whitman. "Nuclear Power Suddenly Here," Science and Technology, March 1968.

Shubik, Martin. "On the Study of Disarmament and Escalation," Journal of Conflict Resolution, XII, 2 (March 1968).

Simons, Howard. "World Arms Bill," New Scientist, September 22, 1966.

Sternglass, Ernest J. "Infant Mortality and Nuclear Tests," Bulletin of the Atomic Scientists, July 1969.

________. "A Reply" (on effects of fallout), Bulletin of the Atomic Scientists, December 1969.

Stewart, Alice. "The Pitfalls of Extrapolation," New Scientist, July 24, 1969.

Stone, Jeremy J. "ABM—the Next MLF?" Bulletin of the Atomic Scientists, September 1966.

Stubbs, Peter. "How to Light a Mini H-bomb," New Scientist, November, 21, 1968.

Talensky, M. "Anti-missile Systems and Disarmament," Bulletin of the Atomic Scientists, February 1965.

Tamplin, Arthur R. "Foetal and Infant Mortality and the Environment," Bulletin of the Atomic Scientists, December 1969.

________, and J. W. Gofman. "The Radiation Effects Controversy," Bulletin of the Atomic Scientists, September 1970.

Taylor, Fred. "Probing the Atmosphere from Orbit," New Scientist, June 12, 1969.

Teller, Edward. "The Dormant Nuclear Revolution," Technology Week, January 23, 1967.

________. "Can a Progressive Be a Conservationist?" New Scientist February 19, 1970.

Thirlaway, H. I. S. "Diagnosing Underground Explosions and Earthquakes," Contemporary Physics, January 1968.

Thompson, T. S., and W. R. Bibb. "Response to Gofman and Tamplin: The AEC Position," Bulletin of the Atomic Scientists, September 1970.

Tucker, D. G. "Sonar: Sharper Senses in the Depths," New Scientist, February 20, 1969.

U.K. Atomic Energy Authority. The Detection and Recognition of Underground Explosions. London: H.M.S.O., 1965.

U.K. Atomic Weapons Research Establishment. Data Processing Facilities and Data Available at the UKAEA Data Analysis Centre for Seismology. Pamphlet no. 2. July 1967.

U.K. Foreign and Commonwealth Office. "Treaty Banning Nuclear Weapons Tests in the Atmosphere, in Outer Space and Under Water." (Moscow, August 5, 1963). Cmnd 2245. London, 1964.

________. "Declaration of the Conference of Non-nuclear Weapons States, Held in Geneva from 29 August to 28 September 1968." Arms Control and Disarmament, Notes on Current Developments, no. 5. London, January 31, 1969.

________. "Treaty on the Non-proliferation of Nuclear Weapons." Cmnd 4474. London, November 1970.

United Nations. "Geneva Convention on the Continental Shelf." April 29, 1958.

________. "Antarctic Treaty." December 1, 1959.

________. "International Repertory of Institutions Specialising in Research for Peace and Disarmament." Reports and Papers in the Social Sciences, no. 23. 1966.

________. "The Military Uses of the Sea-bed and the Ocean Floor Beyond the Limits of Present National Jurisdiction." Working paper prepared by Secretariat, A/AC 135/28. July 10, 1968.

United Nations General Assembly. "Report to the Secretary-General on Chemical and Bacteriological (Biological) Weapons and the Effects of Their Possible Use." A/7575. July 1, 1968.

________. "Report of the Conference of Experts to Study the Possibilities of Detecting Violations of a Possible Agreement on the Suspension of Nuclear Tests." A/3897. August 28, 1958.

________. "Report to the Secretary-General on the Effects of the Possible Use of Nuclear Weapons and on the Security and Economic Implications for States of the Acquisition and

Further Development of These Weapons." A/6858. October 10, 1967.

U.S. Air Force. "Second Quarterly Technical Report: Montana Large Aperture Seismic Array." Air Force Systems Command, Directorate of Planning and Technology. ARPA Order no. 800. November 1968.

U.S. Arms Control and Disarmament Agency. "Field Test Program, Preliminary Report, Field Test 15/Exercise First Look Inspection and Observation of Retained Levels of Ground and General Purpose Air Forces in a Specified Area (UK)." January 1969.

U.S. Atomic Energy Commission. "Selected Background Information on Uranium Enriching." ORD-668. March 1969.

________. "Radiological Emergency Procedures for the Non-specialist." PB-187 267. June 1969.

U.S. Department of the Army, Navy and Air Force. Employment of Chemical and Biological Agents. Field Manual FM 3-10. March 1966.

U.S. Office of Civil Defense. Post-Attack Recovery from Nuclear War. Proceedings of a symposium, National Research Council, National Academy of Sciences, November 6-9, 1967.

Valery, Nicolas. "The Billion Dollar Enrichment Business," New Scientist, September 16, 1971

Van Voorhis, S. N. "Statement by D. S. Semyonov, Head of Soviet Delegates," letter in Survival, February 1970.

Vercuèse, Dominique. "Detection of Underground Explosions," Disarmament (Paris: World Veterans' Federation), September 1967.

Viney, D. E. "Constraining Chemical-Biological Warfare," Disarmament (Paris: World Veterans' Federation), September 1967.

Watson, William W. "Nuclear Weapons for UN?" Bulletin of the Atomic Scientists, March 1970.

Wedge, Bryant, and Cyril Muromcew. "Psychological Factors in Soviet Disarmament Negotiations," Journal of Conflict Resolution, IX, 1 (March 1965).

Wegner, L. H. Quick Count: A General War Casualty Estimation Model. RM-3811-PR. Santa Monica, California: Rand Corporation, September 1963.

Weimer, K. L. A. "The Ultra-centrifuge Project." Chemisch Weekblad, March 28, 1969.

Weinber, Alvin M. "Let Us Prepare for Peace," Bulletin of the Atomic Scientists, September 1968.

Wetmore, Warren C. "Apollo Tests Four-Camera Terrain Study," Aviation Week and Space Technology, May 26, 1969.

White, Clayton S. "The Nature of the Problems Involved in Estimating the Immediate Casualties from Nuclear Explosions." LF-1242-1. Albuquerque, Lovelace Foundation for Medical Education and Research, 1968.

Wick, Gerald L. "Is There a Safe Radiation Limit?" New Scientist, August 6, 1970.

Wiesner, Jerome B. "The ABM Debate Continues," Bulletin of the Atomic Scientists, June 1967.

________. "Hope for GCD," Bulletin of the Atomic Scientists, January 1968.

________. "Arms Control: Current Prospects and Problems," Bulletin of the Atomic Scientists, May 1970.

________, and Herbert F. York. "National Security and the Nuclear Test Ban," Scientific American, October 1964.

Wigner, Eugene. "Civil Defense: Project Harbour," Bulletin of the Atomic Scientists, February 1966.

Wilde, Max. "CBW and the Community," New Scientist, January 29, 1970.

Williams, Cecily D. "Proliferation Problems and War," Proceedings of the Medical Association for the Prevention of War, February 1966.

Willrich, Mason. "International Control of Civil Nuclear Power," Bulletin of the Atomic Scientists, March 1967.

Wilson, A. J. "Some Principles for Peace-keeping Operations—a Guide for Senior Officers." Mimeograph no. 2. Paris: International Information Centre on Peace-Keeping Operations, 1967.

Wiltshire, Dennis A. "Spin-off from Space," Spaceflight, October 1969.

Winston, Donald C. "ABM Plans Utilize Deception, Redundancy," Aviation Week and Space Technology, December 1, 1969.

________. "Soviet Power Cited to Aid Military Budget," Aviation Week and Space Technology, May 4, 1970.

Witze, Claude. "The ABM; Voices For and Against," Air Force/Space Digest, June 1969.

Wohlstetter, Albert. "ABM; a Prudent Response to a Continuing Threat," Air Force/Space Digest, June 1969.

Wolfe, Thomas W. "Soviet Military Policy," Survival, January 1968.

Wood, Derek. "A New Element in Warfare; the Arrival of V/STOL on the Battlefield," International Defence Review, no. 1 (1968).

Woodman, Dill. "Hurrah for CS!" letter in New Scientist, September 25, 1969.

World Health Organization. Health Aspects of Chemical Biological Weapons. Geneva, 1970.

Wright, R. H. "Researching into Peace," New Scientist, January 16, 1969.

York, Herbert F. "The Arms Race and the Fallacy of the Next Move," Bulletin of the Atomic Scientists, June 1969.

________. "A Personal View of the Arms Race," Bulletin of the Atomic Scientists, March 1970.

Young, Elizabeth. "ABM Deployment," letter in New Scientist, October 16, 1969.

Young, Oran R. "The Political Consequences of Active Defence," Bulletin of the Atomic Scientists, February 1968.

________, et al. "The ABM Debate," Bulletin of the Atomic Scientists, May 1967.

Yuan Tzu-neng, Te Yuan-li, and Ho Ying-yung. Principles and Applications of Atomic Energy. Translated for U.S. Air Force under Contract, reference AF 33(657)-16409.

Yuter, S. C. "The Role of World Law in Arms Control," Bulletin of the Atomic Scientists, October 1969.

Zoppo, Ciro E. The Issue of Nuclear Test Cessation at the London Disarmament Conference of 1957: A Study in East-West Negotiations. RM-2821-ARPA. Santa Monica, California: Rand Corporation, September 1961.

Zuckermann, Sir Solly. The Control of Proliferation: Three Views. Adelphi paper no. 29. London: Institute of Strategic Studies, 1966.

ABOUT THE AUTHOR

For much of his career, W. F. BIDDLE has been involved in some aspect or other of weapons technology. Beginning with inspection and testing of aircraft engines, he had a period of research in the steel industry. In 1949 he joined the Metallurgy Division of the Atomic Energy Research Establishment at Harwell and worked subsequently at the Springfields Laboratories and the Atomic Weapons Research Establishment at Aldermaston. For most of his time in the U.K. Atomic Energy Authority he was involved in research into the properties of uranium and plutonium and in the development of fuel elements for nuclear reactors. He has published in the technical press on these subjects.

In 1960 Mr. Biddle was appointed a Senior Inspector in the newly formed Inspectorate of Nuclear Installations; he contributed to the safety assessment and inspection of nuclear power stations and associated plants. In 1966 he went to the Ministry of Defense and engaged in studies on a variety of topics, including arms control. He was associated with the Anglo-American arms control exercise First Look and has acted as adviser to delegations to NATO.

Mr. Biddle has a B. Sc. in metallurgy, an M. Sc. in nuclear engineering, and a postgraduate diploma in public administration from the University of London. This book is based on a study presented as a Ph.D. thesis. Mr. Biddle is a part-time tutor in the Open University.